GUIDE TO FOOD STORAGE

Follow this guide for food storage, and you can be sure that what's is fresh-tasting and ready to use in recipes.

pantry

In the Freezer (at -10° to 0° F)

Dairy and Eggs

Cheese, hard	6 months
Cheese, soft	6 months
Egg substitute, unopened	1 year
Egg whites	1 year
Egg yolks	1 year
Ice cream, sherbet	1 month

Fruits and Vegetables

Commercially frozen fruits	1 year
Commercially frozen vegetables	8 to 12 months

Meats, Poultry, and Seafood
Beef, Lamb, Pork, and Veal

Chops, uncooked	4 to 6 months
Ground and stew meat, uncooked	3 to 4 months
Ham, fully cooked, half	1 to 2 months
Roasts, uncooked	4 to 12 months
Steaks, uncooked	6 to 12 months

Poultry

All cuts, cooked	4 months
Boneless or bone-in pieces, uncooked	9 months

Seafood

Fish, fatty, uncooked	2 to 3 months
Fish, lean, uncooked	6 months

In the Refrigerator (at 34° to 40° F)

Dairy and Eggs

Butter	1 to 3 months
Buttermilk	1 to 2 weeks
Cheese, hard, wedge, opened	6 months
Cheese, semihard, block, opened	3 to 4 weeks
Cream cheese, fat-free, light, and 1/3-less-fat	2 weeks
Egg substitute, opened	3 days
Fresh eggs in shell	3 to 5 weeks

Meats, Poultry, and Seafood
Beef, Lamb, Pork, and Veal

Ground and stew meat, uncooked	1 to 2 days
Roasts, uncooked	3 to 5 days
Steaks and chops, uncooked	3 to 5 days

Chicken, Turkey, and Seafood

All cuts, uncooked	1 to 2 days

Fruits and Vegetables

Apples, beets, cabbage, carrots, celery, citrus fruits, eggplant, and parsnips	2 to 3 weeks
Apricots, asparagus, berries, cauliflower, cucumbers, mushrooms, okra, peaches, pears, peas, peppers, plums, salad greens, and summer squash	2 to 4 days
Corn, husked	1 day

In the Pantry (keep these at room temperature for 6 to 12 months)

Baking and Cooking Staples

- Baking powder
- Biscuit and baking mixes
- Broth, canned
- Cooking spray
- Honey
- Mayonnaise, fat-free, low-fat, and light (unopened)
- Milk, canned evaporated fat-free
- Milk, nonfat dry powder
- Mustard, prepared (unopened)
- Oils, olive and vegetable
- Pasta, dried
- Peanut butter
- Rice, instant and regular
- Salad dressings, bottled (unopened)
- Seasoning sauces, bottled
- Tuna, canned

Fruits, Legumes, and Vegetables

- Fruits, canned
- Legumes (beans, lentils, peas), dried or canned
- Tomato products, canned
- Vegetables, canned

ISBN-13: 978-0-8487-3482-4
ISBN-10: 0-8487-3482-3
ISSN: 1526-1565

Printed in the United States of America
First Printing 2011

Be sure to check with your health-care provider before making any changes to your diet. *Weight Watchers* and **PointsPlus**™ are the registered trademarks of Weight Watchers International, Inc., and are used with permission by Time Home Entertainment Inc. Printed in the United States of America. All rights reserved.

OXMOOR HOUSE

VP, Publishing Director: Jim Childs
Editorial Director: Susan Payne Dobbs
Creative Director: Felicity Keane
Brand Manager: Victoria Alfonso
Senior Editor: Heather Averett
Managing Editor: Laurie S. Herr

WEIGHT WATCHERS® ANNUAL RECIPES FOR SUCCESS 2012

Editor: Rachel Quinlivan West, R.D.
Project Editors: Emily Chappell, Sarah H. Doss
Assistant Designer: Allison Sperando Potter
Director, Test Kitchens: Elizabeth Tyler Austin
Assistant Directors, Test Kitchens: Julie Christopher, Julie Gunter
Test Kitchens Professionals: Wendy Ball, R.D.; Allison E. Cox; Victoria E. Cox; Margaret Monroe Dickey; Alyson Moreland Haynes; Stefanie Maloney; Callie Nash; Catherine Crowell Steele; Ashley T. Strickland; Leah Van Deren
Photography Director: Jim Bathie
Senior Photo Stylist: Kay E. Clarke
Associate Photo Stylist: Katherine Eckert Coyne
Assistant Photo Stylist: Mary Louise Menendez
Production Managers: Theresa Beste-Farley, Tamara Nall Wilder

CONTRIBUTORS

Copy Editor: Dolores Hydock
Proofreader: Norma Butterworth-McKittrick
Indexer: Mary Ann Laurens
Menu Planner Editor: Carolyn Land Williams, M.Ed., R.D.
Nutritional Analysis: Caroline Glagola, Kate Grigsby
Interns: Erin Bishop, Maribeth Browning, Laura Hoxworth, Alison Loughman, Lindsay A. Rozier, Caitlin Watzke
Test Kitchens Professional: Kathleen Royal Phillips
Photographer: Mary Britton Senseney

TIME HOME ENTERTAINMENT INC.

Publisher: Richard Fraiman
VP, Strategy & Business Development: Steven Sandonato
Executive Director, Marketing Services: Carol Pittard
Executive Director, Retail & Special Sales: Tom Mifsud
Executive Director, New Product Development: Peter Harper
Director, Bookazine Development & Marketing: Laura Adam
Publishing Director: Joy Butts
Finance Director: Glenn Buonocore
Assistant General Counsel: Helen Wan

Cover: Pan-Seared Steaks with Warm Tomatoes and Feta, page 90

WeightWatchers®

ANNUAL RECIPES *for* SUCCESS
2012

Oxmoor
House®

WeightWatchers®
ANNUAL RECIPES *for* SUCCESS
2012

contents

Weight Watchers®

At Weight Watchers, weight management is a partnership that combines our knowledge with your efforts. We help you on your weight-loss journey to make positive behavioral changes in your life, inspiring you with our belief in your power to succeed and motivating you every step of the way.

WEIGHT WATCHERS INTERNATIONAL BACKGROUND

SINCE ITS FOUNDING IN 1963, Weight Watchers has helped millions achieve healthy, sustainable weight loss. Weight Watchers International, Inc., is the world's leading provider of weight-management services, operating globally through a network of company-owned and franchise operations. Weight Watchers holds more than 45,000 weekly meetings where members receive group support and learn about healthy eating patterns, behavior modification, and physical activity. **WeightWatchers.com** provides innovative subscription weight-management products over the Internet and is the leading Internet-based weight-management provider in the world. In addition, Weight Watchers offers a wide range of products, publications, and programs for those interested in weight loss and weight control.

For more information about the Weight Watchers program and a meeting near you, call 1-800-651-6000 or visit **weightwatchers.com**

THE WEIGHT WATCHERS COMMITMENT TO SCIENCE

Weight Watchers backs up its weight-management plans with a strong commitment to the science of weight loss. The research and conclusions of experts and health organizations worldwide, including the World Health Organization and the National Institutes of Health, are incorporated into the Weight Watchers offerings. Weight Watchers also conducts its own research on weight-loss methods. As scientific findings change, the Weight Watchers plans evolve.

Weight Watchers®
ANNUAL RECIPES FOR SUCCESS 2012

This new cookbook empowers you to make the right food choices every day. There's never been a better time to make a positive change in your health, and you can do it while still enjoying the foods you love. Here's how:

- Over 275 great-tasting recipes that bring pleasure back to mealtime
- A **PointsPlus**® value per serving for every recipe
- Nutritional analysis with every recipe (see "About Our Recipes" on page 16)
- More than 40 color photographs of delicious recipes
- Step-by-step recipe instructions, prep and cook times, and secrets from our Test Kitchens
- Five seasonal menus, each with a Game Plan to help make preparing the meal a cinch
- Four weeks of 7-Day Menu Planners that incorporate many recipes from the cookbook plus some new ones, too

OUR FAVORITE RECIPES

All of our recipes are rigorously tested to ensure ease of preparation and excellent taste. But some are a cut above the rest. Here are our favorites from this year. We hope you enjoy them just as much as we did.

▶ **GRILLED CORN, TOMATILLO, AND AVOCADO SALSA**

PointsPlus value per serving: 3

The slightly charred corn and tomatillos are a delicious contrast to the creamy avocado and fresh tomato in this salsa. (page 18)

▼ **CHEESE AND CHIVES DROP BISCUITS**

PointsPlus value per serving: 3

These easy biscuits rely on baking mix to keep them quick and extrasharp cheddar cheese for a punch of flavor. Butter-flavored cooking spray adds buttery flavor without the calories or saturated fat. (page 30)

9

OUR FAVORITE RECIPES

▶ CHEWY CHOCOLATE-ALMOND SANDWICH COOKIES

PointsPlus value per serving: 6

The richness of these sandwich cookies makes them a satisfying sweet finish to a meal or afternoon snack. (page 47)

▶▶ DOUBLE BROWNIE CHEESECAKE TORTE

PointsPlus value per serving: 8

This dessert is a showstopper with two chocolaty brownie layers and two rich cheesecake layers, and it tastes just as fantastic as it looks. (page 38)

▶▶▶ KIWI SORBET

PointsPlus value per serving: 2

This sorbet relies on the soft, almost creamy flesh of fresh kiwifruit for its luscious flavor. This little fruit also packs a hefty dose of vitamin C. (page 42)

▼ VIETNAMESE-STYLE CATFISH

PointsPlus value per serving: 8

This Asian-inspired, highly seasoned dish takes catfish to a whole new level. Crunchy bean sprouts, fresh cilantro, green onions, and lime wedges complete it. (page 66)

OUR FAVORITE RECIPES

▶ JAPANESE TERIYAKI CHICKEN CAKES

PointsPlus value per serving: 6

These small cakes glazed with teriyaki sauce are packed with flavor. Sprinkling them with cornstarch helps them brown and crisp while cooking. (page 106)

▼ CHICKEN CUTLETS WITH WARM LEMON-ARTICHOKE RELISH

PointsPlus value per serving: 4

These chicken cutlets get a burst of bright flavor from the artichokes and lemon topping. Using canned artichoke hearts keeps the prep and cook time short. (page 102)

▲ SMOKED BBQ TOFU PIZZA
PointsPlus value per serving: 7

Smoked tofu is a key ingredient in this tasty pizza. The texture is very firm so it doesn't make the crust soggy, and it adds deep, smoky flavor to this pizza while the barbecue sauce adds some zing. (page 82)

◄ PAN-SEARED STEAKS WITH WARM TOMATOES AND FETA
PointsPlus value per serving: 8

Colorful tomatoes and feta cheese are perfect pairs for the tender steaks. Cook the steaks to the degree of doneness that you prefer. (page 90)

OUR FAVORITE RECIPES

▶ FRUIT AND NUT TOSSED SALAD

PointsPlus value per serving: 5

Crisp salad greens, crunchy nuts, and fresh apple are paired with creamy feta cheese, sweet dried cranberries, and golden raisins for a salad that's sure to please. (page 114)

▼ THAI PORK BURGERS WITH MANGO-MINT MAYO

PointsPlus value per serving: 10

Lemongrass paste, fresh herbs, fish sauce, and crushed red pepper amp up the flavor and heat of these pork burgers, while the mango-mint mayo provides a fresh, cool contrast. (page 122)

▲ ROASTED BRUSSELS SPROUTS WITH BROWNED BUTTER WALNUTS

PointsPlus value per serving: 3

The rich browned butter in this side dish is worth the extra effort—it transforms roasted Brussels sprouts into something extraordinary. (page 148)

◄ ROPA VIEJA

PointsPlus value per serving: 3

We took a shortcut by using a fully cooked roast and a vegetable blend, but those time-savers didn't affect the flavor of this hearty Cuban stew. (page 161)

ABOUT OUR RECIPES

Weight Watchers® Annual Recipes for Success 2012
gives you the nutrition facts you need to stay on track. Every recipe in this book includes a ***PointsPlus®*** value per serving. For more information on Weight Watchers, see page 7.

Each recipe has a list of nutrients—including fat, carbohydrates, fiber, and protein. You'll also find calories, saturated fat, monounsaturated fat, polyunsaturated fat, cholesterol, iron, sodium, and calcium as well as a serving size and the number of servings. Measurements are abbreviated g (grams) and mg (milligrams). Nutritional values used in our calculations either come from The Food Processor, Version 8.9 (ESHA Research), or are provided by food manufacturers.

NUTRITIONAL ANALYSIS IS BASED ON THESE ASSUMPTIONS:

- Unless otherwise indicated, meat, poultry, and fish always refer to skinned, boned, and cooked servings.

- When we give a range for an ingredient (3 to 3½ cups flour, for instance), we calculate using the lesser amount.

- Some alcohol calories evaporate during heating; the analysis reflects this.

- Only the amount of marinade absorbed by the food is used in calculations.

- Garnishes and optional ingredients are not included in an analysis.

Safety Note: Cooking spray should never be used near direct heat. Always remove a pan from heat before spraying it with cooking spray.

A NOTE ON USE FOR DIABETICS:

Almost all of our recipes can be incorporated into a diabetic diet by using the carbohydrate amount in the nutrient analysis and incorporating that into the carbohydrate amount recommended by your physician.

appetizers & beverages

Grilled Corn, Tomatillo, and Avocado Salsa, *page 18*

GRILLED CORN, TOMATILLO, AND AVOCADO SALSA

PointsPlus value per serving: 3   *pictured on page 49*

PREP: 17 minutes ▪ COOK: 8 minutes

Serve this colorful salsa with baked tortilla chips or with grilled chicken or flank steak.

    3 tomatillos
    3 ears shucked corn
    Cooking spray
    1 large diced peeled avocado
    1 cup grape tomatoes, quartered
    ¼ cup chopped red onion
    2 tablespoons chopped fresh cilantro
    2 tablespoons fresh lime juice
    ½ teaspoon salt
    ¼ teaspoon freshly ground black pepper

1. Preheat grill to high heat.
2. Discard husks and stems from tomatillos. Place tomatillos and corn on grill rack coated with cooking spray; grill 8 to 10 minutes or until tender, turning frequently.
3. While vegetables grill, combine avocado and next 6 ingredients in a medium bowl. Cut kernels from ears of corn and chop tomatillos; add to avocado mixture. Serve immediately, or cover and chill until ready to serve. YIELD: 10 SERVINGS (SERVING SIZE: ¼ CUP).

PER SERVING: Calories 65; Fat 3.5g (sat 0.5g, mono 2.1g, poly 0.6g); Protein 1.6g; Carb 8.7g; Fiber 2.5g; Chol 0mg; Iron 0.4mg; Sodium 125mg; Calc 7mg

❋ Tomatillos
Identified by their green flesh and parchmentlike husk, this tart, herbal "little tomato," as its name translates from Spanish, adds flavor to Mexican and Tex-Mex dishes like guacamole and salsas. Be sure to purchase tomatillos with dry, tight-fitting husks for the longest shelf life.

SPINACH NUTRITION

Spinach is a nutritional powerhouse. It contains magnesium, which lowers blood pressure and protects against heart disease; vitamins C and A, which prevent cholesterol from oxidizing in the body; vitamin K, which maintains bone health; and vitamin E, which acts as an antioxidant and promotes wound healing.

LEMON-SPINACH DIP WITH WALNUTS

PointsPlus value per serving: 3

PREP: 6 minutes ▪ COOK: 2 minutes

This cold spinach dip is a refreshing twist on the traditional baked version. Serve with pita chips or vegetable chips.

    1 (10-ounce) package frozen chopped spinach, thawed,
        drained, and squeezed dry
    ¾ cup plain 2% reduced-fat Greek yogurt
    1 teaspoon freshly ground black pepper
    1 teaspoon bottled minced garlic
    1 teaspoon grated lemon rind
    ½ teaspoon salt
    ¼ cup chopped walnuts, toasted

1. Combine first 6 ingredients in a medium bowl. Cover and chill until ready to serve. Sprinkle with walnuts just before serving. YIELD: 4 SERVINGS (SERVING SIZE: ⅓ CUP).

PER SERVING: Calories 107; Fat 6.3g (sat 1.2g, mono 0.7g, poly 3.5g); Protein 8g; Carb 6.7g; Fiber 2.7g; Chol 3mg; Iron 1.6mg; Sodium 364mg; Calc 146mg

LIGHT CHEESE WAFERS

PointsPlus value per serving: 1

PREP: 15 minutes ■ COOK: 15 minutes
■ OTHER: 30 minutes

Keep a log of this dough in the freezer up to 3 months. Slice and bake as many wafers as you need when the occasion arises.

> 2 cups (8 ounces) reduced-fat shredded extrasharp
>   cheddar cheese
> ¾ cup light butter, softened
> 9 ounces all-purpose flour (about 2 cups)
> ½ teaspoon salt
> ½ teaspoon ground red pepper
> ¼ teaspoon dry mustard
> ¼ teaspoon smoked paprika

1. Beat cheese and butter with a mixer at medium speed until blended. Weigh or lightly spoon flour into dry measuring cups; level with a knife. Combine flour and next 4 ingredients, stirring until blended. Gradually add flour mixture to butter mixture, beating until blended.
2. Shape dough into 2 (8-inch) logs; wrap in wax paper, and freeze 30 minutes or until firm enough to slice.
3. Preheat oven to 350°. Cut logs into ¼-inch slices, and place on ungreased baking sheets. Bake at 350° for 15 minutes or until lightly browned. Remove from baking sheets; cool completely on wire racks. Store in an airtight container up to 1 week. YIELD: 48 SERVINGS (SERVING SIZE: 1 WAFER).

PER SERVING: Calories 52; Fat 3g (sat 1.9g, mono 0.9g, poly 0.1g); Protein 1.9g; Carb 4.2g; Fiber 0.2g; Chol 7mg; Iron 0.3mg; Sodium 81mg; Calc 36mg

GOAT CHEESE TRUFFLES

PointsPlus value per serving: 1

PREP: 5 minutes ■ OTHER: 1 hour

These savory bites are delicious served with red grapes and multigrain pita chips, or smear one on a ham or turkey sandwich for a flavor boost.

> 1 (8-ounce) block ⅓-less-fat cream cheese, softened
> ½ cup (4 ounces) goat cheese
> 1 tablespoon minced fresh rosemary
> 1 teaspoon grated orange rind
> 1 teaspoon bottled minced roasted garlic
> ½ teaspoon freshly ground black pepper
> ½ cup minced fresh flat-leaf parsley

1. Place first 6 ingredients in a large bowl; beat with a mixer at medium speed until blended and smooth. Cover and freeze 30 minutes or just until mixture is firm enough to roll into balls.
2. Shape cheese mixture into ¾-inch balls; roll balls lightly in parsley. Cover and chill at least 30 minutes before serving. Store in refrigerator up to 1 week. YIELD: 20 SERVINGS (SERVING SIZE: 1 TRUFFLE).

PER SERVING: Calories 45; Fat 3.7g (sat 2.5g, mono 0.9g, poly 0.1g); Protein 1.9g; Carb 1.1g; Fiber 0.1g; Chol 11mg; Iron 0.2mg; Sodium 66mg; Calc 19mg

PESTO AND SUN-DRIED TOMATO–CHEESE TORTA

PointsPlus value per serving: 3

PREP: 19 minutes ■ COOK: 2 minutes ■ OTHER: 1 hour

> 3 garlic cloves
> 1 cup packed fresh basil leaves
> 2 tablespoons pine nuts, toasted
> 2 tablespoons olive oil
> ¼ cup julienne-cut sun-dried tomatoes, packed without oil,
>   chopped
> 1 (8-ounce) block ⅓-less-fat cream cheese
> 3 tablespoons unsalted butter, softened
> 2 tablespoons grated fresh Parmesan cheese
> 32 water crackers

1. Drop garlic through food chute with food processor on; process until minced. Add basil and pine nuts; process until finely minced. With food processor on, slowly pour oil through food chute; process until well blended, scraping sides of bowl occasionally. Remove lid and knife blade; stir in tomato.
2. Stir cream cheese in a medium bowl until smooth. Add butter, stirring until smooth. Stir in Parmesan cheese.
3. Line a small bowl with plastic wrap, allowing plastic wrap to extend over edge of bowl. Spread one-third of cheese mixture in bottom of bowl; top with half of pesto mixture. Repeat procedure, ending with cheese mixture. Fold edges of plastic wrap over cheese mixture; chill at least 1 hour or until firm.
4. Invert bowl onto a platter; remove plastic wrap. Serve with water crackers. YIELD: 16 SERVINGS (SERVING SIZE: ABOUT 2 TABLESPOONS TORTA AND 2 CRACKERS).

PER SERVING: Calories 111; Fat 8.4g (sat 4g, mono 2.8g, poly 0.8g); Protein 2.5g; Carb 7.1g; Fiber 0.5g; Chol 16mg; Iron 0.2mg; Sodium 124mg; Calc 25mg

SMOKED ALMOND CHICKEN SALAD BITES

PointsPlus value per serving: 1

PREP: 13 minutes

For best flavor, make the chicken salad ahead, and give it some time to chill.

> 1½ cups finely chopped skinless, boneless rotisserie chicken breast
> ¼ cup chopped green onions
> 2 tablespoons chopped smoked almonds
> 2 tablespoons plain fat-free yogurt
> 2 tablespoons light mayonnaise
> 1½ teaspoons chopped fresh rosemary
> ½ teaspoon Dijon mustard
> ⅛ teaspoon freshly ground black pepper
> ½ cup seedless red grapes, divided
> 25 baked pita crackers

1. Combine first 8 ingredients, stirring well. Chop ¼ cup grapes; stir into chicken mixture. Spoon 1 heaping tablespoon chicken salad mixture onto each cracker. Halve remaining ¼ cup grapes, and top each cracker with a grape half. YIELD: 25 SERVINGS (SERVING SIZE: 1 TABLESPOON CHICKEN MIXTURE AND 1 CRACKER).

PER SERVING: Calories 42; Fat 1.7g (sat 0.2g, mono 0.8g, poly 0.4g); Protein 3.4g; Carb 3.2g; Fiber 0.3g; Chol 8mg; Iron 0.3mg; Sodium 49mg; Calc 9mg

ASPARAGUS–SUN-DRIED TOMATO CROSTINI

PointsPlus value per serving: 2

PREP: 10 minutes ■ COOK: 4 minutes

For best results, look for thin asparagus spears, and trim only 3 inches from the top of each spear.

> 24 (¼-inch-thick) slices diagonally cut French bread baguette
> Olive oil–flavored cooking spray
> 2 cups (1-inch) diagonally cut asparagus
> 1 tablespoon water
> ½ cup sun-dried tomato pesto (such as Classico)
> ¼ teaspoon freshly ground black pepper
> ½ cup (2 ounces) shredded sharp provolone cheese

1. Preheat broiler.
2. Place baguette slices on a large baking sheet; coat bread with cooking spray. Broil 2 minutes or just until lightly browned.
3. While bread toasts, place asparagus and 1 tablespoon water in a small bowl. Cover with plastic wrap. Microwave at HIGH 2 minutes or just until asparagus is crisp-tender; drain.
4. Spread 1 teaspoon pesto on each toasted baguette slice; top each with 5 to 6 asparagus pieces, and sprinkle evenly with pepper. Sprinkle baguette slices evenly with cheese. Broil 2 minutes or until cheese melts.
YIELD: 24 SERVINGS (SERVING SIZE: 1 CROSTINI).

PER SERVING: Calories 68; Fat 1.1g (sat 0.5g, mono 0.3g, poly 0.2g); Protein 2.8g; Carb 12.4g; Fiber 0.7g; Chol 2mg; Iron 0.9mg; Sodium 196mg; Calc 21mg

APPLE-CHEDDAR TRIANGLES

PointsPlus value per serving: 3

PREP: 8 minutes ■ COOK: 5 minutes

Traditional partners apple and cheddar cheese get a flavor boost from rosemary in these snack-sized toasted cheese sandwiches.

> 4 (1.8-ounce) slices white-wheat bread
> Butter-flavored cooking spray
> ¼ cup apple jelly
> ½ teaspoon chopped fresh rosemary
> ½ Granny Smith apple, cut into 16 thin slices
> 4 (0.7-ounce) slices reduced-fat sharp cheddar cheese, each cut into 4 triangles

1. Preheat oven to 450°.
2. Trim crusts from bread. Cut each slice into 4 triangles. Coat both sides of bread with cooking spray. Bake at 450° for 3 minutes or until toasted.
3. Combine jelly and rosemary in a small bowl; spread jelly mixture onto 1 side of each triangle. Top each with an apple slice and triangle of cheese.
4. Bake at 450° for 2 minutes or until cheese melts.
YIELD: 8 SERVINGS (SERVING SIZE: 2 TRIANGLES).

PER SERVING: Calories 117; Fat 1.7g (sat 0.6g, mono 0.4g, poly 0.4g); Protein 4.4g; Carb 21.2g; Fiber 0.9g; Chol 2mg; Iron 1mg; Sodium 234mg; Calc 80mg

GRILLED EGGPLANT AND WHITE BEAN BITES

PointsPlus value per serving: 1

PREP: 6 minutes ■ COOK: 10 minutes

This protein-rich, low-fat appetizer combines the smokiness of grilled eggplant with the nutlike flavor of cannellini beans, plus a dash of Sriracha for heat seekers.

1 (1-pound) eggplant, cut crosswise into ⅓-inch-thick slices
Olive oil–flavored cooking spray
1 (15.5-ounce) can cannellini beans, rinsed and drained
⅓ cup bottled roasted red bell peppers, finely chopped
1 tablespoon fresh lemon juice
1 teaspoon Sriracha (hot chile sauce, such as Huy Fong)
¼ teaspoon salt
¼ teaspoon black pepper
40 baked pita crackers

1. Preheat grill to medium–high heat.
2. Coat eggplant slices with cooking spray. Place eggplant on grill rack coated with cooking spray; cover and grill 5 minutes on each side or until eggplant is tender.
3. Place beans in a medium bowl; mash with a fork. Coarsely chop eggplant; add to bowl. Add red bell pepper and next 4 ingredients, stirring well. Spoon 1 tablespoon eggplant mixture onto each cracker. Serve immediately. YIELD: 20 SERVINGS (SERVING SIZE: 2 TABLESPOONS EGGPLANT MIXTURE AND 2 CRACKERS).

PER SERVING: Calories 45; Fat 0.8g (sat 0g, mono 0.3g, poly 0.2g); Protein 2g; Carb 7.9; Fiber 1.7g; Chol 0mg; Iron 0.7mg; Sodium 115mg; Calc 13mg

Sriracha

This hot sauce made with Thai red chiles adds full-bodied flavor that's rounded with sweetness and deepened with garlic. It adds a kick to dips and sauces and also serves as a table condiment in place of ketchup, livening up dishes like scrambled eggs or French fries.

MINI TWICE-BAKED POTATOES

PointsPlus value per serving: 2

PREP: 15 minutes ■ COOK: 35 minutes
■ OTHER: 30 minutes

These are a nice make-ahead option for a party. Bake the potatoes, and prepare the filling ahead; stuff the potato shells just before baking.

1 pound very small Yukon Gold potatoes (about 20)
½ cup reduced-fat sour cream
1 tablespoon chopped fresh chives
½ teaspoon freshly ground black pepper
¼ teaspoon salt
½ cup (2 ounces) reduced-fat shredded sharp cheddar cheese
4 center-cut bacon slices, cooked and crumbled

1. Preheat oven to 400°.
2. Place potatoes on a rimmed baking sheet; bake at 400° for 30 minutes or until tender. Cool 30 minutes. Cut each potato in half lengthwise; scoop out pulp with a small spoon, leaving a thin shell. Combine potato pulp, sour cream, and next 3 ingredients.
3. Spoon potato mixture into shells; top with cheese and bacon. Place on a baking sheet lined with foil. Bake at 400° for 5 minutes or until cheese melts. Serve immediately. YIELD: 10 SERVINGS (SERVING SIZE: 4 POTATO HALVES).

PER SERVING: Calories 76; Fat 3.2g (sat 1.9g, mono 1g, poly 0.2g); Protein 3.5g; Carb 8.7g; Fiber 1g; Chol 11mg; Iron 0.4mg; Sodium 138mg; Calc 69mg

TOASTED RAVIOLI WITH GRILLED PESTO SHRIMP

PointsPlus value per serving: 1

PREP: 25 minutes ■ **COOK:** 18 minutes

Garnish these ravioli bites with a bit of marinara sauce. If you'd like, use ½ cup egg substitute in place of the egg whites.

- ½ (9-ounce) package refrigerated four-cheese ravioli (such as Buitoni)
- 18 unpeeled medium shrimp (about ¾ pound)
- 2 tablespoons refrigerated reduced-fat pesto with basil (such as Buitoni)
- Cooking spray
- 4 large egg whites, lightly beaten
- ½ cup panko (Japanese breadcrumbs)

1. Preheat grill to medium–high heat. Preheat broiler.
2. Cook ravioli according to package directions; drain.
3. While ravioli cook, peel and, if desired, devein shrimp. Combine shrimp and pesto in a bowl; toss. Thread shrimp onto 3 (12-inch) skewers.
4. Place skewers on grill rack coated with cooking spray; cover and grill 2½ minutes on each side or until shrimp are done. Cover and keep warm.
5. Dip ravioli in egg whites; dredge in panko, shaking off excess. Arrange breaded ravioli on a baking sheet coated with cooking spray. Lightly coat ravioli with cooking spray. Broil 2 to 3 minutes or until browned.
6. Top each ravioli with 1 shrimp. Serve warm. **YIELD:** 18 SERVINGS (SERVING SIZE: 1 RAVIOLI AND 1 SHRIMP).

PER SERVING: Calories 58; Fat 1.5g (sat 0.4g, mono 0.4g, poly 0.5g); Protein 6.1g; Carb 4.6g; Fiber 0.3g; Chol 32mg; Iron 0.7mg; Sodium 92mg; Calc 27mg

CRAB RANGOON BITES

PointsPlus value per serving: 1

PREP: 10 minutes ■ **COOK:** 15 minutes

Two tablespoons of sweet and sour sauce have a *PointsPlus* value per serving of 1.

- 24 wonton wrappers
- Cooking spray
- ½ cup lump crabmeat, drained and shell pieces removed
- 1 (8-ounce) tub light cream cheese with chive and onion
- ⅓ cup chopped green onions
- Sweet and sour sauce (optional)

1. Preheat oven to 400°.
2. Coat both sides of wonton wrappers with cooking spray. Fit 1 wonton wrapper into each of 24 miniature muffin cups coated with cooking spray, pressing wrappers into sides of cups. Bake at 400° for 9 minutes or until lightly browned.
3. Combine crabmeat, cream cheese, and onions. Spoon about ½ tablespoon crabmeat mixture into each wonton cup. Bake at 400° for 6 minutes or until thoroughly heated. Remove wontons from muffin cups. Serve immediately with sweet and sour sauce, if desired.
YIELD: 24 SERVINGS (SERVING SIZE: 1 WONTON).

PER SERVING: Calories 48; Fat 1.7g (sat 1.1g, mono 0g, poly 0.1g); Protein 2g; Carb 5.4g; Fiber 0.2g; Chol 9mg; Iron 0.3mg; Sodium 108mg; Calc 8mg

MUSHROOM PIZZA STICKS

PointsPlus value per serving: 3

PREP: 7 minutes ■ **COOK:** 10 minutes

- 1 (8.8-ounce) package whole-wheat naan flatbreads (such as Fabulous Flats), cut into 1½-inch strips
- Cooking spray
- ½ cup pizza sauce
- ½ (8-ounce) package cremini mushrooms, chopped
- 1 cup (4 ounces) shredded part-skim mozzarella cheese

1. Preheat oven to 450°.
2. Place naan strips on a baking sheet coated with cooking spray. Spread sauce evenly over strips; sprinkle with mushrooms, and top with cheese.
3. Bake at 450° for 10 minutes or until golden brown and bubbly. **YIELD:** 10 SERVINGS (SERVING SIZE: 1 PIZZA STICK).

PER SERVING: Calories 112; Fat 3.2g (sat 0.6g, mono 0.8g, poly 0.6g); Protein 6.2g; Carb 14.3g; Fiber 2.7g; Chol 0mg; Iron 1mg; Sodium 192mg; Calc 12mg

POLENTA ROUNDS WITH FIG PRESERVES, GOAT CHEESE, AND BACON

PointsPlus value per serving: 2

PREP: 6 minutes ■ COOK: 7 minutes

Olive oil–flavored cooking spray
1 (18-ounce) tube of polenta, cut into 12 slices
¼ teaspoon salt
¼ cup fig preserves
½ cup (2 ounces) crumbled goat cheese with garlic and
   fines herbes
4 center-cut bacon slices, cooked and crumbled

1. Heat a large grill pan over medium-high heat. Coat pan with cooking spray. Coat polenta rounds with cooking spray, and sprinkle with salt. Grill polenta rounds 3 minutes on each side or until browned.
2. Spread 1 teaspoon preserves on each round. Sprinkle each with 2 teaspoons goat cheese; top with bacon. YIELD: 12 SERVINGS (SERVING SIZE: 1 POLENTA ROUND).

PER SERVING: Calories 64; Fat 1.5g (sat 0.8g, mono 0.4g, poly 0.1g); Protein 2.1g; Carb 9.9g; Fiber 0.8g; Chol 3mg; Iron 0.3mg; Sodium 175mg; Calc 4mg

OPEN-FACED NAAN QUESADILLAS

PointsPlus value per serving: 4   *pictured on page 51*

PREP: 7 minutes ■ COOK: 4 minutes

1½ cups shredded rotisserie chicken
⅓ cup chopped green onions
2 tablespoons fresh lime juice
1 tablespoon light mayonnaise
1 teaspoon curry powder
½ teaspoon crushed red pepper
½ (8.8-ounce) package naan flatbreads
Cooking spray
1 cup (4 ounces) shredded part-skim mozzarella cheese

1. Preheat broiler.
2. Combine first 6 ingredients in a bowl.
3. Coat naan with cooking spray; place on a baking sheet. Top naan with chicken mixture, and sprinkle with cheese.
4. Broil 4 minutes or until quesadilla is crisp and cheese melts. Cut quesadilla into 8 wedges. YIELD: 8 SERVINGS (SERVING SIZE: 1 WEDGE).

PER SERVING: Calories 141; Fat 5.4g (sat 2.4g, mono 1.5g, poly 1g); Protein 13.5g; Carb 9.2g; Fiber 1.1g; Chol 31mg; Iron 0.9mg; Sodium 180mg; Calc 117mg

COOKING BACON

Bacon lends smoky flavor to any dish. When cooking bacon, start with a pan that's at room temperature—don't be tempted to preheat your pan. Starting with a cooler pan and cooking the bacon over medium heat will help minimize curling.

WAFFLE FRY–CHEESE NACHOS

PointsPlus value per serving: 5

PREP: 2 minutes ■ COOK: 27 minutes

You'd never guess these nachos, which are often called Irish nachos, could qualify as a light snack.

1 (22-ounce) package frozen waffle-cut French fries
   (such as Ore-Ida)
1 (15.5-ounce) can black beans, rinsed and drained
1 cup (4 ounces) preshredded reduced-fat 4-cheese
   Mexican blend cheese
⅓ cup chopped pickled jalapeño pepper
¼ cup chopped fresh cilantro
½ cup fresh salsa
½ cup reduced-fat sour cream
2 tablespoons water

1. Preheat oven to 450°.
2. Arrange fries on a foil-lined large rimmed baking sheet. Bake at 450° for 25 minutes or until crisp. Remove from oven; spoon beans over fries, and sprinkle with cheese. Bake an additional 2 minutes or until cheese melts.
3. Top with jalapeño and cilantro; spoon salsa down center of nachos. Combine sour cream and 2 tablespoons water; drizzle over nachos. YIELD: 10 SERVINGS (SERVING SIZE: ¹⁄₁₀ OF NACHOS).

PER SERVING: Calories 191; Fat 7.9g (sat 3.2g, mono 2.8g, poly 1.1g); Protein 6.9g; Carb 22.4; Fiber 3.4g; Chol 9mg; Iron 0.9mg; Sodium 518mg; Calc 106mg

CRISPY SPICED CHICKPEAS

PointsPlus value per serving: 3

PREP: 5 minutes ■ **COOK:** 45 minutes
■ **OTHER:** 20 minutes

This Middle Eastern–inspired snack is a great alternative to nuts. It offers the satisfying crunch of nuts without as much fat.

> 1 (15-ounce) can no-salt-added garbanzo beans, rinsed and drained
> 1 tablespoon olive oil
> ¼ teaspoon salt
> ¼ teaspoon ground cumin
> ¼ teaspoon ground coriander
> ⅛ teaspoon ground cardamom
> ⅛ teaspoon ground red pepper

1. Preheat oven to 425°.
2. Combine all ingredients in a medium bowl, tossing well to coat. Spoon beans onto a jelly-roll pan. Bake at 425° for 45 minutes or until crisp and dry, stirring every 15 minutes. Let cool 20 minutes before serving.
YIELD: 4 SERVINGS (SERVING SIZE: 3 TABLESPOONS).

PER SERVING: Calories 102; Fat 4g (sat 0.5g, mono 2.6g, poly 0.6g); Protein 3.9g; Carb 12.7g; Fiber 2.8g; Chol 0mg; Iron 0.8mg; Sodium 164mg; Calc 29mg

SMOKY HERBED SNACK MIX

PointsPlus value per serving: 4

PREP: 10 minutes ■ **COOK:** 45 minutes ■ **OTHER:** 1 hour

This quick snack mix is much more flavorful than prepackaged mixes.

> 4 cups crisscross of corn and rice cereal (such as Crispix)
> 1 cup small salted pretzel sticks, broken
> ½ cup bite-sized reduced-fat cheddar cheese crackers (such as Cheez-It)
> ½ cup whole natural almonds, coarsely chopped
> 3 tablespoons light butter, melted
> 1 tablespoon chopped fresh rosemary
> 1 teaspoon smoked paprika
> ½ teaspoon salt
> Cooking spray
> 1 cup dried apricots, coarsely chopped

1. Preheat oven to 250°.
2. Combine first 4 ingredients in a bowl. Combine butter and next 3 ingredients; drizzle over cereal mixture, tossing to coat.

3. Spread mixture into a jelly-roll pan coated with cooking spray. Bake at 250° for 45 minutes or until crisp, stirring twice. Place pan on a wire rack; gently stir in apricots. Cool completely on wire rack. Store snack mix in an airtight container up to 1 week.
YIELD: 14 SERVINGS (SERVING SIZE: ½ CUP).

PER SERVING: Calories 140; Fat 6.5g (sat 1.4g, mono 3.4g, poly 1.2g); Protein 3.2g; Carb 18.7g; Fiber 1.9g; Chol 3mg; Iron 3.9mg; Sodium 239mg; Calc 34mg

AVOCADO SMOOTHIE

PointsPlus value per serving: 4

PREP: 5 minutes ■ **COOK:** 2 minutes

Avocado adds luscious creaminess and loads of nutrients to this cool, refreshing Vietnamese specialty. It's best served icy cold, straight from the blender.

> 1 avocado
> 2 cups sweetened almond milk (such as Blue Diamond Almond Breeze Original)
> 1 cup crushed ice
> ¼ cup fat-free sweetened condensed milk
> 2 tablespoons fresh lime juice
> 1 tablespoon chopped slivered almonds, toasted

1. Cut avocado in half lengthwise; discard pit. Scoop pulp from avocado halves into blender. Add almond milk and next 3 ingredients; process until smooth. Top each serving with toasted almonds. Serve immediately.
YIELD: 5 SERVINGS (SERVING SIZE: ABOUT ¾ CUP SMOOTHIE AND ½ TEASPOON ALMONDS).

PER SERVING: Calories 142; Fat 7.6g (sat 0.9g, mono 4.4g, poly 0.9g); Protein 2.7g; Carb 17g; Fiber 3.3g; Chol 2mg; Iron 0.4mg; Sodium 79mg; Calc 129mg

✳ Almond Milk
Made from ground almonds, almond milk is a plant-based, lactose-free alternative to milk that's rich in vitamins and minerals. You'll find it in a variety of flavors—sweetened, unsweetened, chocolate, and vanilla—in both shelf-stable cartons and in the refrigerated dairy section.

FRESH BASIL GRAPEFRUITADE

PointsPlus value per serving: 3

PREP: 4 minutes ■ COOK: 7 minutes ■ OTHER: 1 hour

1 cup packed fresh basil leaves
3 cups water, divided
⅓ cup sugar
1½ cups fresh red grapefruit juice
Fresh basil leaves (optional)
Grapefruit rind twists (optional)

1. Combine 1 cup basil, 1 cup water, and sugar in a medium saucepan. Bring mixture to a boil over medium-high heat; cook 5 minutes or until sugar dissolves. Pour into a large pitcher.
2. Add remaining 2 cups water and grapefruit juice to basil syrup in pitcher, stirring well. Cover and chill at least 1 hour. Strain mixture before serving; discard basil. Serve over ice. Garnish with fresh basil leaves and grapefruit twists, if desired. YIELD: 4 SERVINGS (SERVING SIZE: ABOUT 1 CUP).

PER SERVING: Calories 103; Fat 0.2g (sat 0g, mono 0g, poly 0.1g); Protein 0.8g; Carb 25.6g; Fiber 0.2g; Chol 0mg; Iron 0.5mg; Sodium 1mg; Calc 26mg

BLUSH LEMONADE

PointsPlus value per serving: 2

PREP: 5 minutes

Serve this "lightly pink" lemonade for a children's party, or dress up a pitcher of it with fresh lemon slices and frozen cranberries for a grown-up party.

5 cups water
2 cups fresh lemon juice
1 cup no-sugar-added cranberry juice
½ cup calorie-free stevia plant sweetener (such as Truvia)
¼ cup sugar

1. Combine all ingredients in a pitcher, stirring until sweetener and sugar dissolve. Serve over ice. YIELD: 8 SERVINGS (SERVING SIZE: 1 CUP).

PER SERVING: Calories 60; Fat 0g (sat 0g, mono 0g, poly 0g); Protein 0.4g; Carb 16.9g; Fiber 0.3g; Chol 0mg; Iron 0.1mg; Sodium 1mg; Calc 7mg

HOW TO EASILY CHOP A WATERMELON

Always rinse a melon before slicing it. Watermelons are grown in the dirt and frequently handled. So even though the skin might look clean, it can harbor bacteria that may be transferred to the melon during cutting.

1. Place washed melon on a cutting board, and use a sharp, heavy knife to slice about 1 inch from the stem end to make a stable cutting surface.
2. Stand the melon up, cut side down, and vertically slice the melon in half.
3. Place halves, cut sides down, on a flat surface, and cut melon into slices. Carefully cut the melon from the rind, and cut into cubes.

WATERMELON-MINT AGUA FRESCA

PointsPlus value per serving: 2

PREP: 8 minutes ■ COOK: 4 minutes ■ OTHER: 2 hours

4 cups water
½ cup fresh mint leaves
⅓ cup sugar
5 cups cubed seeded watermelon
¼ cup fresh lime juice
Mint sprigs (optional)

1. Combine first 3 ingredients in a medium saucepan; bring to a boil. Remove from heat; cool to room temperature. Strain mint syrup in a sieve over a bowl; discard solids.
2. Place strained syrup, watermelon, and lime juice in a blender; process until very smooth. Strain mixture through a sieve over a pitcher; discard solids. Cover and chill at least 2 hours. Serve over ice. Garnish with mint sprigs, if desired. YIELD: 6 SERVINGS (SERVING SIZE: ABOUT 1 CUP).

PER SERVING: Calories 85; Fat 0.2g (sat 0g, mono 0.1g, poly 0.1g); Protein 0.9g; Carb 21.9g; Fiber 0.7g; Chol 0mg; Iron 0.4mg; Sodium 2mg; Calc 16mg

FRESH PEACH ICED TEA

PointsPlus value per serving: 2

PREP: 2 minutes ■ **COOK:** 3 minutes ■ **OTHER:** 3 hours

Peach nectar gives this tea its sweet, refreshing peach flavor. Find nectar on the juice or ethnic aisle at the grocery store.

> 4 cups water, divided
> ¼ cup sugar
> 4 peach-flavored black tea bags (such as Stash)
> 2 cups peach nectar
> 1 ripe peeled peach, sliced

1. Bring 1 cup water and sugar to a boil in a small saucepan, stirring until sugar dissolves. Remove pan from heat; add tea bags, and steep 5 minutes. Remove tea bags with a slotted spoon (do not squeeze). Cool tea to room temperature.

2. Combine cooled tea, remaining 3 cups water, and peach nectar in a pitcher; cover and chill. Serve over ice, and top with peach slices. **YIELD: 6 SERVINGS (SERVING SIZE: ABOUT 1 CUP).**

PER SERVING: Calories 86; Fat 0g (sat 0g, mono 0g, poly 0g); Protein 0.4g; Carb 22.1g; Fiber 0.9g; Chol 0mg; Iron 0.2mg; Sodium 6mg; Calc 4mg

RASPBERRY PRESS

PointsPlus value per serving: 4

PREP: 5 minutes

A "press" is a cocktail made with vodka and fresh fruit. The fruit is pressed against the glass to release its flavor. Traditional presses are topped with club soda, but we used a lemon-lime soda to add a touch of sweetness.

> ½ cup fresh raspberries
> 1 lime, quartered
> ¾ cup raspberry-flavored vodka
> 1 cup diet lemon-lime soda

1. Divide raspberries among 4 (8-ounce) glasses. Squeeze 1 lime wedge into each glass; add lime wedge. Press raspberries and lime with the back of a spoon until crushed. Fill each glass with ice. Add 3 tablespoons vodka and ¼ cup soda to each glass. Stir well, and serve immediately. **YIELD: 4 SERVINGS (SERVING SIZE: ½ CUP).**

PER SERVING: Calories 107; Fat 0.1g (sat 0g, mono 0g, poly 0.1g); Protein 0.2g; Carb 2.5g; Fiber 1g; Chol 0mg; Iron 0.1mg; Sodium 1mg; Calc 5mg

PROSECCO AND BERRIES

PointsPlus value per serving: 4   *pictured on page 50*

PREP: 5 minutes

Prosecco is a light, crisp, and affordable sparkling wine. Fresh berries add the perfect complement to this attractive aperitif.

> 1½ cups pomegranate juice, chilled
> ½ cup diet citrus soda, chilled
> ½ cup raspberries
> ½ cup blueberries
> 1 (750-milliliter) bottle prosecco or other sparkling white wine, chilled
> Mint sprigs (optional)

1. Combine first 5 ingredients in a pitcher. Pour about ¾ cup wine mixture into each of 8 glasses. Garnish with mint sprigs, if desired. **YIELD: 8 SERVINGS (SERVING SIZE: ¾ CUP).**

PER SERVING: Calories 103; Fat 0.1g (sat 0g, mono 0g, poly 0g); Protein 0.4g; Carb 10.4g; Fiber 0.7g; Chol 0mg; Iron 0.2mg; Sodium 6mg; Calc 10mg

CAMPARI SPRITZERS WITH FRESH THYME

PointsPlus value per serving: 4

PREP: 5 minutes ■ **COOK:** 1 minute ■ **OTHER:** 1 hour

Campari is a dark red aperitif infused with herbs and fruit.

> ½ cup sugar
> ½ cup water
> 8 thyme sprigs
> 3 cups diet citrus soda
> 1 cup vodka
> ⅓ cup Campari
> Thyme sprigs (optional)

1. Combine first 3 ingredients in a 2-cup glass measure. Microwave at HIGH 1 minute or until very hot; stir until sugar dissolves. Cover and chill thoroughly. Remove and discard thyme.

2. Combine thyme syrup, soda, vodka, and Campari in a large pitcher. Serve over ice. Garnish with thyme sprigs, if desired. **YIELD: 10 SERVINGS (SERVING SIZE: ½ CUP).**

PER SERVING: Calories 100; Fat 0g (sat 0g, mono 0g, poly 0g); Protein 0g; Carb 10g; Fiber 0g; Chol 0mg; Iron 0.1mg; Sodium 1mg; Calc 1mg

breads

Apple Fritter Pancakes, *page 28*

APPLE FRITTER PANCAKES

PointsPlus value per serving: 6   *pictured on page 52*

PREP: 9 minutes ▪ **COOK:** 12 minutes

These pancakes have bits of apple in every bite. Drizzle with syrup, if you'd like—2 tablespoons of sugar-free maple syrup have a *PointsPlus* value per serving of 1.

> 5.6 ounces all-purpose flour (about 1¼ cups)
> 2 tablespoons sugar
> 1½ teaspoons baking powder
> 1 teaspoon apple pie spice
> ½ teaspoon baking soda
> ½ teaspoon salt
> 1 cup finely chopped Fuji apple
> 1 cup low-fat buttermilk
> 2 tablespoons butter, melted
> 1 large egg, lightly beaten

1. Weigh or lightly spoon flour into dry measuring cups; level with a knife. Combine flour and next 5 ingredients in a large bowl. Stir apple into flour mixture. Combine buttermilk, butter, and egg, whisking until blended. Add to flour mixture, stirring just until moist.

2. Pour about ¼ cup batter per pancake onto a hot nonstick griddle or nonstick skillet. Cook 3 minutes or until tops are covered with bubbles and edges look cooked. Carefully turn pancakes over; cook 2 minutes or until bottoms are lightly browned. **YIELD: 5 SERVINGS (SERVING SIZE: 2 PANCAKES).**

PER SERVING: Calories 223; Fat 6.4g (sat 3.6g, mono 1.7g, poly 0.5g); Protein 6.2g; Carb 35.1g; Fiber 1.6g; Chol 57mg; Iron 1.7mg; Sodium 581mg; Calc 145mg

HOW TO CHOP AN APPLE

When buying apples, look for vibrantly colored ones, free of bruises and firm to the touch. The skins should be bright and smooth.

1. Using an apple corer, cut through the center of the apple, and rotate to fully separate and remove the core. Use a paring knife to slice the apple in half vertically.
2. Place the apple halves, cut sides down, on a cutting board. Slice through the skin, cutting wedges or slices.
3. Chop the wedges into pieces with a paring knife.

MEASURING FLOUR AND BAKING MIX

Properly measuring flour and baking mix is an important factor in baking. Too much (or too little) can affect the outcome of the baked product. Weighing flour and baking mix is the most accurate method to use. But if you don't have a kitchen scale, fluff the flour or baking mix with a fork, and then spoon into a dry measuring cup. Do not scoop the flour or baking mix out of the canister or package with a measuring cup because this will compact the flour or baking mix, and you'll end up with too much. Level the top with a straight edge to get an even cup.

CHOCOLATE DESSERT WAFFLES

PointsPlus value per serving: 4

PREP: 12 minutes ▪ **COOK:** 15 minutes

Top these waffles with coffee ice cream and fat-free hot fudge topping for a decadent dessert.

> 6.75 ounces all-purpose flour (about 1½ cups)
> 2.38 ounces whole-wheat flour (about ½ cup)
> ½ cup unsweetened dark cocoa (such as Hershey's Special Dark)
> 3 tablespoons sugar
> 1½ teaspoons baking powder
> ½ teaspoon baking soda
> ½ teaspoon salt
> 2 cups low-fat buttermilk
> ¾ cup egg substitute
> 2 tablespoons butter, melted
> Cooking spray
> 2 tablespoons powdered sugar (optional)

1. Weigh or lightly spoon flours into dry measuring cups; level with a knife. Combine flours, cocoa, and next 4 ingredients in a large bowl, stirring with a whisk. Combine buttermilk, egg substitute, and butter, stirring well with a whisk; add to flour mixture, stirring just until moist.

2. Preheat a nonstick waffle iron. Coat waffle iron with cooking spray. Spoon about ¼ cup batter per 4-inch waffle onto hot waffle iron, spreading batter to edges. Cook 5 minutes or until steaming stops; repeat procedure with remaining batter. Sprinkle waffles evenly with powdered sugar, if desired. **YIELD: 12 SERVINGS (SERVING SIZE: 1 WAFFLE).**

PER SERVING: Calories 145; Fat 3.6g (sat 1.9g, mono 0.9g, poly 0.5g); Protein 6.4g; Carb 23.5g; Fiber 2.3g; Chol 7mg; Iron 1.8mg; Sodium 286mg; Calc 95mg

BANANA WALNUT MUFFINS

PointsPlus value per serving: 4

PREP: 9 minutes ■ **COOK:** 15 minutes
■ **OTHER:** 2 minutes

Served warm, these quick muffins have a subtle banana flavor, but the banana flavor intensifies as these muffins cool.

1 (7-ounce) package bran muffin mix with dates
    (such as Jiffy)
½ cup mashed ripe banana
¼ cup fat-free milk
1 large egg
½ cup chopped walnuts, toasted
Cooking spray

1. Preheat oven to 400°.
2. Combine first 4 ingredients in a medium bowl, stirring just until combined (batter will be lumpy). Fold in walnuts. Spoon batter into 8 muffin cups coated with cooking spray, filling three-fourths full.
3. Bake at 400° for 15 minutes or until muffins spring back when touched lightly in center. Cool 2 minutes in pan on a wire rack; remove muffins from pan. **YIELD:** 8 SERVINGS (SERVING SIZE: 1 MUFFIN).

PER SERVING: Calories 148; Fat 6.1g (sat 0.7g, mono 0.9g, poly 3.6g); Protein 4.5g; Carb 18.7g; Fiber 3g; Chol 27mg; Iron 1.1mg; Sodium 185mg; Calc 42mg

MONKEY MUFFINS

PointsPlus value per serving: 5

PREP: 13 minutes ■ **COOK:** 15 minutes

Traditional monkey bread is a sweet pull-apart bread that's high in calories. We made a lightened version in the form of pull-apart muffins that still has a sweet, gooey glaze reminiscent of the traditional recipe.

2 (7.5-ounce) cans refrigerated buttermilk biscuit dough
1 teaspoon ground cinnamon
5 tablespoons light butter, melted
¼ cup unpacked light brown sugar
Cooking spray
2 tablespoons chopped pecans, toasted (optional)

1. Preheat oven to 375°.
2. Cut each biscuit in half; shape each half into a ball. Place dough balls in a medium bowl; add cinnamon, and toss to coat. Combine butter and brown sugar in a large bowl. Add dough balls to butter mixture, and toss to coat.
3. Place 4 dough balls in each of 10 muffin cups coated with cooking spray. Pour any remaining butter mixture evenly over dough balls. Sprinkle evenly with pecans, if desired. Bake at 375° for 15 to 17 minutes or until golden brown. **YIELD:** 10 SERVINGS (SERVING SIZE: 1 MUFFIN).

PER SERVING: Calories 181; Fat 9.6g (sat 3.7g, mono 4.2g, poly 1g); Protein 2.8g; Carb 21.3g; Fiber 0.7g; Chol 7mg; Iron 1mg; Sodium 483mg; Calc 9mg

ULTIMATE CHOCOLATE BRAN MUFFINS

PointsPlus value per serving: 3

PREP: 12 minutes ■ **COOK:** 15 minutes
■ **OTHER:** 10 minutes

These dense, dark chocolate muffins are great served cold out of the refrigerator with a glass of milk nearby.

1½ cups shreds of wheat bran cereal (such as All-Bran)
1 cup water
1 (13.7-ounce) package fat-free brownie mix (such as
    No Pudge!)
1 (6-ounce) carton vanilla low-fat yogurt
2 teaspoons baking powder
2 teaspoons vanilla extract
Cooking spray

1. Preheat oven to 350°.
2. Soak cereal in 1 cup water in a large bowl 5 minutes. Stir in brownie mix and next 3 ingredients until blended.
3. Spoon batter into 18 muffin cups coated with cooking spray. Bake at 350° for 15 to 18 minutes or until a wooden pick inserted in center comes out almost clean. Remove muffins from pans; cool at least 5 minutes on a wire rack. Serve warm, at room temperature, or chilled. **YIELD:** 18 SERVINGS (SERVING SIZE: 1 MUFFIN).

PER SERVING: Calories 101; Fat 0.4g (sat 0.1g, mono 0.1g, poly 0.1g); Protein 2.9g; Carb 23.5g; Fiber 1.5g; Chol 1mg; Iron 1.9mg; Sodium 151mg; Calc 101mg

SAUSAGE AND CHEESE BREAKFAST MUFFINS

PointsPlus value per serving: 3

PREP: 15 minutes ■ COOK: 26 minutes
■ OTHER: 2 minutes

Grab one of these muffins on your way out the door to help start your busy day the right way.

Cooking spray
6 ounces turkey breakfast sausage
½ cup finely chopped onion
3.4 ounces all-purpose flour (about ¾ cup)
½ cup yellow cornmeal
1 teaspoon baking soda
¼ teaspoon salt
1 cup nonfat buttermilk
1 large egg
¾ cup (3 ounces) shredded reduced-fat extrasharp
    cheddar cheese

1. Preheat oven to 400°.
2. Heat a medium nonstick skillet over medium-high heat. Coat pan with cooking spray. Add sausage and onion; cook over medium-high heat 8 minutes or until sausage is browned, stirring to crumble. Drain on paper towels.
3. While sausage mixture cooks, weigh or lightly spoon flour into dry measuring cups; level with a knife. Combine flour and next 3 ingredients in a large bowl; stir with a whisk. Make a well in center of mixture. Combine buttermilk and egg in a medium bowl; stir with a whisk. Stir in sausage mixture and cheese. Add sausage mixture to dry ingredients; stir just until moist. Spoon batter evenly into 12 muffin cups coated with cooking spray.
4. Bake at 400° for 18 minutes or until muffins spring back when touched lightly in center. Cool in pans 2 minutes on a wire rack. Remove muffins from pans; place on a wire rack. Serve warm. YIELD: 12 SERVINGS (SERVING SIZE: 1 MUFFIN).

PER SERVING: Calories 112; Fat 3.2g (sat 1.3g, mono 0.5g, poly 0.4g); Protein 7g; Carb 13.4g; Fiber 0.5g; Chol 34mg; Iron 0.8mg; Sodium 322mg; Calc 134mg

HERB BUTTERMILK BISCUITS

PointsPlus value per serving: 2

PREP: 8 minutes ■ COOK: 18 minutes

These are tasty with any fresh herb. We like the combination of rosemary, thyme, and parsley.

9 ounces all-purpose flour (about 2 cups)
2½ teaspoons baking powder
½ teaspoon salt
5 tablespoons chilled butter, cut into small pieces
¼ cup chopped fresh herbs
1 cup nonfat buttermilk
Cooking spray

1. Preheat oven to 400°.
2. Weigh or lightly spoon flour into dry measuring cups; level with a knife. Combine flour, baking powder, and salt in a large bowl. Cut in butter with a pastry blender or 2 knives until mixture resembles coarse meal. Stir in herbs. Add buttermilk; stir just until moist.
3. Turn dough out onto a lightly floured surface; knead lightly 4 times. Roll dough to ¾-inch thickness; cut with a 1¾-inch biscuit cutter. Place biscuits on a baking sheet coated with cooking spray. Bake at 400° for 18 minutes or until golden. YIELD: 21 SERVINGS (SERVING SIZE: 1 BISCUIT).

PER SERVING: Calories 73; Fat 2.9g (sat 1.8g, mono 0.7g, poly 0.2g); Protein 1.7g; Carb 10g; Fiber 0.4g; Chol 7mg; Iron 0.7mg; Sodium 146mg; Calc 50mg

CHEESE AND CHIVES DROP BISCUITS

PointsPlus value per serving: 3   *pictured on page 51*

PREP: 8 minutes ■ COOK: 10 minutes

There's no rolling involved in these superfast biscuits. Coating the biscuits with butter-flavored cooking spray adds more buttery flavor to each biscuit. When dropping the dough onto the baking sheet, use shallow ¼-cup scoops of batter.

8.8 ounces low-fat baking mix (about 2¼ cups)
⅓ cup (1.3 ounces) reduced-fat shredded extrasharp
    cheddar cheese
2 tablespoons chopped fresh chives
¼ teaspoon garlic powder
⅔ cup 1% low-fat milk
Butter-flavored cooking spray

1. Preheat oven to 425°.

2. Weigh or lightly spoon baking mix into dry measuring cups; level with a knife. Combine baking mix and next 3 ingredients in a medium bowl. Make a well in center of mixture. Add milk, stirring just until moist. Drop dough by about ¼-cupfuls onto a baking sheet coated with cooking spray; coat biscuits with cooking spray. Bake at 425° for 10 minutes or until golden brown. Coat biscuits with cooking spray before serving. YIELD: 12 SERVINGS (SERVING SIZE: 1 BISCUIT).

PER SERVING: Calories 109; Fat 3.1g (sat 1.1g, mono 1.4g, poly 0.4g); Protein 4g; Carb 16.3g; Fiber 0.6g; Chol 6mg; Iron 0.8mg; Sodium 311mg; Calc 181mg

HOW TO CHOP FRESH HERBS

Prepping and chopping herbs can be tricky, as the proper technique varies according to the herb that you are using. Here are a few helpful tips when it comes to chopping herbs:

1. No need to stem cilantro, dill, or parsley; their stems are tender and can be chopped and used with the leaves. Simply place the bunch on a cutting board, and chop with a sharp knife.

2. Strip rosemary and thyme leaves from their tough, inedible stems by holding the top of a stem in one hand, and then pulling in the opposite direction of the way the leaves grow.

3. The stems of mint, oregano, tarragon, and sage are also unusable, but the leaves are large enough that they can be easily pinched off one at a time.

OPEN-FACED BLT BISCUITS

PointsPlus value per serving: 4

PREP: 8 minutes ■ COOK: 14 minutes

Stop here for a complete breakfast. This loaded biscuit won't disappoint.

1 (17.3-ounce) can refrigerated reduced-fat homestyle golden wheat biscuits (such as Pillsbury Grands!)
¼ cup finely chopped tomato
¼ cup light mayonnaise
Cooking spray
2 large eggs, lightly beaten
1 cup mixed salad greens
4 center-cut bacon slices, cooked and cut in half
¼ teaspoon freshly ground black pepper

1. Preheat oven to 375°.

2. Bake biscuits according to package directions. While biscuits bake, combine tomato and mayonnaise in a small bowl.

3. Heat a small nonstick skillet over medium heat. Coat pan with cooking spray. Add egg to pan; cook without stirring until egg sets on bottom. Draw a spatula across bottom of pan to form curds. Continue cooking until egg is thick, but still moist; do not stir constantly. Remove from heat. Break up scrambled egg into 8 portions.

4. Split each biscuit open; reserve biscuit tops for another use. Top each biscuit bottom with about 1 tablespoon tomato-mayonnaise mixture, 2 tablespoons greens, about 1 tablespoon egg, and 1 half-slice of bacon; sprinkle evenly with pepper. Serve immediately. YIELD: 8 SERVINGS (SERVING SIZE: 1 BISCUIT).

PER SERVING: Calories 149; Fat 8.1g (sat 2g, mono 1.1g, poly 1.5g); Protein 5g; Carb 14.9g; Fiber 1.3g; Chol 58mg; Iron 1.3mg; Sodium 440mg; Calc 28mg

GRUYÈRE SCONES

PointsPlus value per serving: 5   *pictured on page 53*

PREP: 6 minutes ■ **COOK:** 20 minutes

Whole-wheat flour adds fiber to this scone and also complements the nutty flavor of Gruyère cheese.

> **4.5 ounces all-purpose flour (about 1 cup)**
> **4.5 ounces whole-wheat pastry flour (about 1 cup)**
> **1½ teaspoons baking powder**
> **¼ teaspoon salt**
> **3 tablespoons chilled butter, cut into small pieces**
> **1 cup (4 ounces) shredded Gruyère cheese**
> **1 cup low-fat buttermilk**
> **Cooking spray**

1. Preheat oven to 450°.
2. Weigh or lightly spoon flours into dry measuring cups; level with a knife. Combine flours, baking powder, and salt in a large bowl, stirring well with a whisk. Cut in butter with a pastry blender or 2 knives until mixture resembles coarse meal. Stir in cheese. Add buttermilk; stir just until moist.
3. Turn dough out onto a lightly floured surface; knead lightly 4 times with floured hands. Pat dough into an 8-inch circle on a baking sheet lined with parchment paper. Cut dough into 10 wedges, cutting into but not through dough. Coat top of dough lightly with cooking spray. Bake at 450° for 20 minutes or until lightly browned. **YIELD: 10 SERVINGS (SERVING SIZE: 1 WEDGE).**

PER SERVING: Calories 177; Fat 7.7g (sat 4.5g, mono 2.1g, poly 0.4g); Protein 6.7g; Carb 20.2g; Fiber 1.9g; Chol 23mg; Iron 1.3mg; Sodium 221mg; Calc 195mg

✳ Gruyère Cheese

A product of Switzerland, Gruyère cheese is pale yellow on its interior and subtly browned around the edges. Its texture is smooth yet pliable, and it has both nutty and sweet flavors.

CINNAMON SUGAR POPOVERS

PointsPlus value per serving: 4

PREP: 4 minutes ■ **COOK:** 50 minutes

If you don't have a popover tin, you can use 6 (6-ounce) custard cups. Be sure not to open the oven door during the first 35 minutes of baking or the popovers might not rise properly.

> **4.5 ounces all-purpose flour (about 1 cup)**
> **1 cup 2% reduced-fat milk**
> **2 large eggs**
> **2½ tablespoons sugar, divided**
> **1¼ teaspoons ground cinnamon, divided**
> **½ teaspoon salt**
> **Butter-flavored cooking spray**
> **2 tablespoons yogurt-based spread (such as Brummel & Brown)**

1. Preheat oven to 400°.
2. Weigh or lightly spoon flour into a dry measuring cup; level with a knife. Combine milk and eggs in a medium bowl. Add flour, 2 tablespoons sugar, 1 teaspoon cinnamon, and salt, stirring well with a whisk. In a separate bowl, combine remaining 1½ teaspoons sugar and remaining ¼ teaspoon cinnamon.
3. Place a popover tin in oven for 3 minutes. Remove tin from oven; lightly coat popover cups with cooking spray. Spoon about ⅓ cup batter into each cup; sprinkle cinnamon-sugar mixture evenly over batter. Bake at 400° for 20 minutes. Reduce oven temperature to 350° (do not remove pan from oven); bake an additional 15 minutes. Pierce each popover with the tip of a knife to let out steam. Return popovers to oven for an additional 15 minutes to crisp. Remove popovers from pan; serve warm with yogurt spread. **YIELD: 6 SERVINGS (SERVING SIZE: 1 POPOVER AND 1 TEASPOON YOGURT SPREAD).**

PER SERVING: Calories 158; Fat 4.5g (sat 1.4g, mono 1.4g, poly 1.2g); Protein 5.6g; Carb 23.6g; Fiber 0.9g; Chol 74mg; Iron 1.3mg; Sodium 264mg; Calc 65mg

POPOVERS

These miniature "bread balloons," leavened with steam and eggs rather than baking soda or baking powder, should be golden and crispy on the outside and have a hollow interior that is soft and moist. Undercooked ones are pale on the outside and gummy on the inside. Popovers deflate quickly, so serve them immediately.

PARMESAN-GARLIC PULL-APART BREAD

PointsPlus value per serving: 2

PREP: 9 minutes ■ COOK: 10 minutes

This bread is satisfying and fun to eat, pulling off each bite piece by piece.

1 (7.5-ounce) can refrigerated buttermilk biscuit
    dough
2 tablespoons light butter, melted
1 teaspoon olive oil
½ teaspoon dried Italian seasoning
1 garlic clove, minced
Olive oil–flavored cooking spray
2 tablespoons grated Parmesan cheese

1. Preheat oven to 425°.
2. Cut each biscuit into quarters. Combine butter and next 3 ingredients in a 9-inch pie plate, spreading to cover bottom of dish. Arrange dough pieces in pie plate (do not stir); lightly coat dough with cooking spray. Sprinkle cheese evenly over dough pieces.
3. Bake at 425° for 10 to 11 minutes or until biscuits are golden brown. Invert onto a platter; serve warm. YIELD: 8 SERVINGS (SERVING SIZE: 5 PIECES).

PER SERVING: Calories 87; Fat 3.4g (sat 1.2g, mono 1.5g, poly 0.3g); Protein 2.2g; Carb 12.5g; Fiber 0.5g; Chol 5mg; Iron 0.6mg; Sodium 280mg; Calc 16mg

KALAMATA OLIVE ROLLS

PointsPlus value per serving: 3

PREP: 8 minutes ■ COOK: 22 minutes

Try these rolls instead of French bread the next time spaghetti or lasagna is on your menu.

Cooking spray
½ cup chopped onion
1 (8-ounce) can reduced-fat refrigerated crescent dinner
    roll dough
¼ cup chopped pitted kalamata olives
1 tablespoon chopped fresh oregano

1. Preheat oven to 350°.
2. Heat a small nonstick skillet over medium-high heat. Coat pan with cooking spray. Add onion; sauté 5 minutes or until tender.

3. Unroll crescent roll dough; press perforations to seal, forming 1 large square. Top dough with sautéed onion, olives, and oregano. Roll up, jelly-roll fashion, starting at long end. Cut dough into 8 equal pieces. Place rolls, filling side up, 1 inch apart on a baking sheet lightly coated with cooking spray. Bake at 350° for 17 minutes or until lightly browned. YIELD: 8 SERVINGS (SERVING SIZE: 1 ROLL).

PER SERVING: Calories 109; Fat 5.9g (sat 2.2g, mono 2.5g, poly 0.7g); Protein 2.2g; Carb 13.5g; Fiber 0.2g; Chol 0mg; Iron 0.8mg; Sodium 295mg; Calc 6mg

✳ Kalamata Olives

These deep-purple Greek olives are plump and juicy with a rich flavor and bright acidity. They're also loaded with heart-healthy fats.

MANCHEGO AND SUN-DRIED TOMATO CRESCENTS

PointsPlus value per serving: 4

PREP: 11 minutes ■ COOK: 15 minutes

Manchego is a golden, semihard to hard Spanish cheese with a full buttery flavor. Substitute Monterey Jack if you can't find Manchego.

1 (8-ounce) can reduced-fat refrigerated crescent dinner
    roll dough
½ cup (2 ounces) shredded Manchego cheese
½ cup chopped sun-dried tomatoes, packed without oil
8 basil leaves

1. Preheat oven to 350°.
2. Unroll crescent roll dough, and separate into 8 triangles. Top each triangle with 1 tablespoon cheese, 1 tablespoon tomatoes, and 1 basil leaf; roll into crescent shape, starting with the longer end. Place triangles 1 inch apart on an ungreased baking sheet. Bake at 350° for 15 minutes or until golden brown. YIELD: 8 SERVINGS (SERVING SIZE: 1 CRESCENT).

PER SERVING: Calories 130; Fat 7.2g (sat 3.8g, mono 2.1g, poly 0.6g); Protein 4.3g; Carb 14g; Fiber 0.4g; Chol 8mg; Iron 1.1mg; Sodium 337mg; Calc 96mg

SEEDED BREADSTICKS

PointsPlus value per serving: 0

PREP: 8 minutes ■ **COOK:** 18 minutes

These breadsticks are a fun alternative to ordinary crackers and add savory crunch to soup or salad. Puff pastry is a light, flaky pastry made from layers of pastry dough. As it bakes, the layers separate, causing it to puff. You can find premade puff pastry in the freezer section of your grocery store. If you're not a fan of fennel, substitute poppy seeds. Two breadsticks have a *PointsPlus* value per serving of 1.

> 1 sheet frozen puff pastry dough, thawed
> Cooking spray
> 2 teaspoons fennel seeds
> 2 teaspoons sesame seeds
> 1 teaspoon coarse sea salt
> ½ teaspoon cracked black pepper

1. Preheat oven to 375°.
2. Unfold puff pastry dough; place on a lightly floured surface. Coat dough lightly with cooking spray. Sprinkle dough with fennel seeds and remaining ingredients. Cut dough into ½-inch-wide strips using a pizza cutter. Transfer strips to a baking sheet lined with parchment paper.
3. Bake at 375° for 18 minutes or until lightly browned.
YIELD: 15 SERVINGS (SERVING SIZE: 1 BREADSTICK).

PER SERVING: Calories 15; Fat 1g (sat 0.2g, mono 0.4g, poly 0.1g); Protein 0.3g; Carb 1.2g; Fiber 0.2g; Chol 0mg; Iron 0.2mg; Sodium 43mg; Calc 7mg

ZUCCHINI AND CHERRY TOMATO FLATBREAD

PointsPlus value per serving: 4

PREP: 5 minutes ■ **COOK:** 15 minutes

The simple flavors of olive oil, fresh veggies, salt, and pepper make this the perfect appetizer or accompaniment to soup or salad. Add chopped cooked chicken breast and Parmesan cheese to transform it into a main-dish pizza.

> 1 pound pizza dough, thawed
> Cooking spray
> 1 tablespoon extra-virgin olive oil
> 1 small zucchini, halved lengthwise and thinly sliced
> 1 cup cherry tomatoes, quartered
> ½ teaspoon freshly ground black pepper
> ¼ teaspoon kosher salt

1. Preheat oven to 450°.
2. Roll dough into a 12-inch circle on a baking sheet coated with cooking spray. Brush dough with olive oil; pierce dough with a fork. Bake at 450° for 5 minutes. Remove from oven.
3. Arrange zucchini and tomato over dough; sprinkle with pepper and salt.
4. Bake at 450° for 10 to 12 minutes or until crust is lightly browned and vegetables are tender. **YIELD: 10 SERVINGS (SERVING SIZE: 1 SLICE).**

PER SERVING: Calories 137; Fat 2.7g (sat 0.2g, mono 1.1g, poly 1g); Protein 4.3g; Carb 25g; Fiber 1.1g; Chol 0mg; Iron 1.5mg; Sodium 329mg; Calc 4mg

WORKING WITH PIZZA DOUGH

Prebaking the pizza dough is an important step in preparing this appetizer. Fresh tomatoes and zucchini contain water that leaches out while they bake. Without prebaking the crust, you run the risk of that liquid creating a soggy pizza bottom. Piercing the dough with a fork prevents the crust from rising too much.

desserts

Ice Cream Truffle Cones, *page 41*

FRESH BLUEBERRY–LEMON FOOL

PointsPlus value per serving: 4

PREP: 9 minutes

The original English dessert is made from gooseberries, but any berry can be used. You can remove the remaining lemon rind with a vegetable peeler to use as a garnish, if you'd like.

> 2 cups blueberries
> 3 tablespoons powdered sugar
> 1 tablespoon water
> ½ teaspoon grated lemon rind
> 1 teaspoon fresh lemon juice
> 1 (8-ounce) container frozen reduced-calorie whipped topping, thawed and divided
> Lemon rind strips (optional)
> Mint sprigs (optional)

1. Place first 3 ingredients in a blender; process until smooth. Add rind and juice to blender; pulse.
2. Place blueberry puree in a large bowl; add ½ cup whipped topping, stirring with a whisk until combined. Fold remaining whipped topping into puree. Spoon blueberry mixture evenly into martini glasses. Garnish with reserved lemon rind strips and mint sprigs, if desired. YIELD: 6 SERVINGS (SERVING SIZE: ABOUT ⅔ CUP).

PER SERVING: Calories 127; Fat 4.4g (sat 4.2g, mono 0g, poly 0.1g); Protein 0.4g; Carb 23.7g; Fiber 1.2g; Chol 0mg; Iron 0.1mg; Sodium 1mg; Calc 3mg

CARAMEL-APPLE CRISP

PointsPlus value per serving: 6   *pictured on page 56*

PREP: 13 minutes ■ COOK: 45 minutes

Canned fried apples provide a jump-start to this homestyle dessert. Keep them stocked on your pantry shelf, and you'll always be ready for dessert.

> 3 (15-ounce) cans fried apples with cinnamon (such as Luck's), undrained
> Cooking spray
> 2 tablespoons fat-free caramel sundae syrup (such as Smucker's)
> 2.25 ounces all-purpose flour (about ½ cup)
> ½ cup packed brown sugar
> ¼ teaspoon salt
> ⅓ cup chilled butter, cut into small pieces
> ¾ cup old-fashioned rolled oats
> ¾ cup caramel light ice cream (such as Edy's)

1. Preheat oven to 350°.
2. Drain apples, reserving ¾ cup syrup. Place apples in an 11 x 7–inch glass or ceramic baking dish coated with cooking spray. Add 2 tablespoons caramel syrup to apple syrup, stirring well with a whisk. Pour syrup mixture over apples in dish.
3. Weigh or lightly spoon flour into a dry measuring cup; level with a knife. Combine flour, sugar, and salt in a bowl; cut in butter with a pastry blender or 2 knives until mixture is crumbly. Stir in oats. Sprinkle over apple mixture. Bake at 350° for 45 minutes or until topping is crisp. Top each serving with ice cream.
YIELD: 12 SERVINGS (SERVING SIZE: ½ CUP CRISP AND 1 TABLE-SPOON ICE CREAM).

PER SERVING: Calories 229; Fat 6.1g (sat 3.6g, mono 1.5g, poly 0.3g); Protein 1.7g; Carb 43.7g; Fiber 2.2g; Chol 16mg; Iron 0.5mg; Sodium 127mg; Calc 19mg

CHOCOLATE-ALMOND COBBLER

PointsPlus value per serving: 6   *pictured on page 57*

PREP: 15 minutes ■ COOK: 30 minutes

Remove this decadent dessert from the oven as soon as the cake is set to ensure an ooey, gooey, fudgy bottom layer.

> 2 tablespoons light butter
> Cooking spray
> 4.9 ounces self-rising flour (about 1 cup)
> 1 cup sugar, divided
> 5 tablespoons unsweetened cocoa, divided
> ⅔ cup 1% low-fat milk
> 1 teaspoon vanilla extract
> 3 tablespoons slivered almonds, toasted
> 2 tablespoons almond brickle chips (such as Heath)
> 1¼ cups boiling water
> ½ cup caramel light ice cream (such as Edy's)

1. Preheat oven to 350°.
2. Place butter in an 8-inch square glass or ceramic baking dish coated with cooking spray. Place in oven 5 to 6 minutes or until butter melts. Set aside.
3. Weigh or lightly spoon flour into a dry measuring cup; level with a knife. Combine flour, ½ cup sugar, and 2½ tablespoons cocoa in a medium bowl; stir well. Add milk and vanilla, stirring with a whisk until smooth. Pour batter over butter in dish.
4. Combine remaining ½ cup sugar, remaining 2½ tablespoons cocoa, almonds, and brickle chips in a small bowl; stir well. Sprinkle evenly over batter. Slowly pour 1¼ cups boiling water over sugar mixture

(do not stir). Bake at 350° for 25 to 28 minutes or until top springs back when lightly touched in center. Serve warm with ice cream. **YIELD: 8 SERVINGS (SERVING SIZE: ⅛ OF COBBLER AND 1 TABLESPOON ICE CREAM).**

PER SERVING: Calories 234; Fat 5.4g (sat 2.3g, mono 1g, poly 0.4g); Protein 3.8g; Carb 45.2g; Fiber 1.9g; Chol 9mg; Iron 1.3mg; Sodium 257mg; Calc 96mg

GRILLED FRUIT WITH BLUEBERRY BUTTER

PointsPlus value per serving: 6

PREP: 5 minutes ■ **COOK:** 6 minutes

The blueberry butter adds a nice rich flavor to grilled fruit. Make extra to spread on English muffins or whole-grain toast for breakfast. A ⅓-cup serving of vanilla fat-free ice cream has a *PointsPlus* value per serving of 3.

2 peaches, halved and pitted
2 plums, halved and pitted
4 (4.7-ounce) fresh pineapple slices
Cooking spray
⅓ cup blueberries
¼ cup light butter, softened
2 teaspoons brown sugar
½ teaspoon grated lemon rind
1⅓ cups vanilla fat-free ice cream (optional)

1. Preheat grill to medium-high heat.
2. Place peaches, plums, and pineapple on grill rack coated with cooking spray. Grill fruit 3 minutes on each side or until tender. Cut fruit into bite-sized pieces.
3. While fruit grills, place blueberries and next 3 ingredients in a food processor or blender; pulse until combined. Add blueberry butter to grilled fruit; toss until butter melts. Spoon fruit mixture over ice cream, if desired. Serve immediately. **YIELD: 4 SERVINGS (SERVING SIZE: 1 CUP).**

PER SERVING: Calories 191; Fat 6.6g (sat 3.5g, mono 1.7g, poly 0.3g); Protein 1.7g; Carb 37.3; Fiber 4g; Chol 15mg; Iron 0.8mg; Sodium 97mg; Calc 20mg

AMBROSIA-TOPPED ANGEL FOOD CAKE

PointsPlus value per serving: 4

PREP: 13 minutes ■ **COOK:** 8 minutes

This ambrosia topping can also be served over vanilla light ice cream or pancakes.

½ (15-ounce) angel food cake, cut into 8 slices
Cooking spray
2 large navel oranges
2 red grapefruit
¼ cup coarsely chopped maraschino cherries
½ cup flaked sweetened coconut, toasted

1. Preheat oven to 350°.
2. Place cake slices on a baking sheet coated with cooking spray. Bake at 350° for 8 to 10 minutes or until toasted.
3. Peel and section oranges and grapefruit over a bowl; squeeze membranes to extract juice. Add cherries to fruit in bowl, stirring well. Top each cake slice with about ⅓ cup fruit mixture; sprinkle with coconut. **YIELD: 8 SERVINGS (SERVING SIZE: 1 SLICE CAKE, ABOUT ⅓ CUP FRUIT, AND 1 TABLESPOON COCONUT).**

PER SERVING: Calories 148; Fat 1.9g (sat 1.5g, mono 0.1g, poly 0.1g); Protein 2.6g; Carb 32.2g; Fiber 2.8g; Chol 0mg; Iron 0.4mg; Sodium 215mg; Calc 67mg

✳ Maraschino Cherries
Typically made from the light, sweet Royal Ann, Rainier, or Gold cherry varieties, maraschino cherries are pitted and then macerated in a flavored sugar syrup. They're a staple garnish for cocktails, milkshakes, and desserts, as well as fruit salads and baked goods.

FIG PRESERVES CAKE

PointsPlus value per serving: 4

PREP: 8 minutes ▪ **COOK:** 40 minutes ▪ **OTHER:** 1 hour

Fig preserves give this cake a moist, tender texture and a subtle fig flavor.

1 (18.25-ounce) package spice cake mix
1 (1-ounce) package sugar-free vanilla instant pudding mix
1 (11.5-ounce) jar fig preserves
1 cup water
1 tablespoon vegetable oil
2 large eggs
2 large egg whites
Cooking spray
Powdered sugar (optional)

1. Preheat oven to 350°.
2. Combine cake mix and pudding mix in a large bowl; add fig preserves, 1 cup water, and oil. Beat with a mixer at medium speed until smooth. Add eggs and egg whites, 1 at a time, beating well after each addition.
3. Pour batter into a 13 x 9–inch metal baking pan coated with cooking spray. Bake at 350° for 40 minutes or until a wooden pick inserted in center comes out clean. Cool in pan on a wire rack. Sprinkle with powdered sugar before serving, if desired. **YIELD: 24 SERVINGS (SERVING SIZE: 1 SQUARE).**

PER SERVING: Calories 138; Fat 2.8g (sat 0.7g, mono 0.8g, poly 0.4g); Protein 1.8g; Carb 26.8g; Fiber 0g; Chol 18mg; Iron 0.4mg; Sodium 198mg; Calc 43mg

DOUBLE BROWNIE CHEESECAKE TORTE

PointsPlus value per serving: 8   *pictured on page 58*

PREP: 31 minutes ▪ **COOK:** 45 minutes
▪ **OTHER:** 10 hours

Cooking spray
1 (20.5-ounce) package low-fat brownie mix (such as Betty Crocker)
½ cup water
1 tablespoon vegetable oil
3 large eggs, divided
½ cup sugar
2 tablespoons all-purpose flour
2 teaspoons vanilla extract
1 (8-ounce) block ⅓-less-fat cream cheese, softened
1 (8-ounce) block fat-free cream cheese, softened
3 ounces bittersweet chocolate, melted
1 cup frozen fat-free whipped topping, thawed
4 teaspoons grated bittersweet chocolate

1. Preheat oven to 350°.
2. Coat a 9-inch springform pan with cooking spray. Coat a 9-inch round cake pan with cooking spray; line with wax paper. Coat wax paper with cooking spray. Set pans aside.
3. Prepare brownie mix according to package directions using ½ cup water, 1 tablespoon oil, and 1 egg. Divide batter evenly between prepared pans. Bake at 350° for 15 to 18 minutes (brownies will be set but not done).
4. Cool brownies in pans on wire rack 15 minutes; run a knife around outside edge to loosen. Invert brownie in cake pan onto a baking sheet or platter lined with wax paper, tapping bottom of pan lightly with a spoon to release. Carefully remove wax paper. Cool inverted brownie and brownie in springform pan while preparing cheesecake batter.
5. Reduce oven temperature to 325°.
6. Place sugar and next 4 ingredients in a large bowl; beat with a mixer at medium speed until smooth and fluffy. Add remaining 2 eggs, 1 at a time, beating just until combined. Pour half of batter into a separate bowl; stir melted chocolate into remaining batter.
7. Pour chocolate batter over brownie in springform pan, spreading gently. Place remaining brownie over chocolate batter; pour vanilla batter over brownie. Bake at 325° for 25 to 30 minutes or until edges are set and center barely moves when pan is touched. Remove cheesecake from oven; carefully run a knife around edge. Cool completely in pan on a wire rack. Cover and chill at least 8 hours.

8. Top each slice with whipped topping and grated chocolate. YIELD: 16 SERVINGS (SERVING SIZE: 1 SLICE CHEESECAKE, 1 TABLESPOON WHIPPED TOPPING, AND ¼ TEASPOON GRATED CHOCOLATE).

PER SERVING: Calories 291; Fat 10.3g (sat 4.6g, mono 3.5g, poly 1.9g); Protein 6.7g; Carb 45.6g; Fiber 1.7g; Chol 52mg; Iron 1.2mg; Sodium 320mg; Calc 65mg

HOW TO MAKE DOUBLE BROWNIE CHEESECAKE TORTE

1. Coat a 9-inch springform pan with cooking spray. Coat a 9-inch round cake pan with cooking spray; line with wax paper. Coat wax paper with cooking spray. Set pans aside.

2. Prepare brownie mix, and divide batter evenly between the prepared pans. Bake until brownies are set but not done.

3. Cool brownies in pans on wire rack 15 minutes; run a knife around outside edge to loosen.

4. Invert brownie in the cake pan onto a baking sheet or platter lined with wax paper, tapping bottom of pan lightly with a spoon to release. Carefully remove wax paper. Cool inverted brownie and brownie in springform pan while preparing cheesecake batter.

5. Prepare cheesecake batter. Pour half of batter into a separate bowl; stir melted chocolate into remaining batter.

6. Pour chocolate batter over brownie in springform pan, spreading gently.

7. Place remaining brownie over chocolate batter.

8. Pour vanilla batter over brownie. Bake until edges are set and center barely moves when pan is touched. Run a knife around edge. Cool completely in pan on a wire rack. Cover and chill at least 8 hours.

BAKED SWEET POTATO DUMPLINGS

PointsPlus value per serving: 6

PREP: 5 minutes ■ COOK: 40 minutes

These lightened dumplings were just as delicious as the full-fat original. They earned our Test Kitchens' highest rating. Fat-free vanilla ice cream would be a delicious topping.

½ cup refrigerated mashed sweet potatoes with brown sugar and cinnamon (such as Simply Potatoes)
2 teaspoons bottled cinnamon sugar, divided
1 (8-ounce) can refrigerated reduced-fat crescent dinner roll dough
Cooking spray
1 cup light brown sugar
1 tablespoon cornstarch
1 cup water
3 tablespoons light butter
2 teaspoons vanilla extract

1. Preheat oven to 350°.

2. Combine sweet potato and 1 teaspoon cinnamon sugar in a bowl. Unroll dough, separating into triangles with a knife. Spoon 2 tablespoons sweet potato mixture onto wide end of each triangle. Fold tips of wide ends over filling, and roll up triangles, beginning at wide end. Place rolls, point sides down, in an 11 x 7–inch glass or ceramic baking dish coated with cooking spray.

3. Combine brown sugar and cornstarch in a medium saucepan; stir in 1 cup water. Add butter; cook over medium–high heat just until sugar dissolves and butter melts, stirring constantly. Remove from heat, and stir in vanilla. Pour sugar mixture over rolls. Sprinkle with remaining 1 teaspoon cinnamon sugar.

4. Bake, uncovered, at 350° for 35 minutes or until rolls are lightly browned and sauce is bubbly. YIELD: 8 SERVINGS (SERVING SIZE: 1 DUMPLING).

PER SERVING: Calories 211; Fat 7.7g (sat 3.8g, mono 2.4g, poly 0.6g); Protein 2.5g; Carb 34.5g; Fiber 3.2g; Chol 6mg; Iron 1.5mg; Sodium 250mg; Calc 22mg

"FRIED" CHERRY PIES

PointsPlus value per serving: 4

PREP: 16 minutes ■ COOK: 30 minutes
■ OTHER: 20 minutes

If fresh cherries are out of season, substitute slightly thawed frozen cherries.

1 cup coarsely chopped pitted sweet cherries
¼ cup granulated sugar
2 teaspoons cornstarch
1½ tablespoons water
¼ teaspoon almond extract
½ (14.1-ounce) package refrigerated pie dough (such as
    Pillsbury)
Cooking spray
Powdered sugar (optional)
Frozen fat-free whipped topping, thawed (optional)

1. Combine cherries and granulated sugar in a small saucepan; bring to a boil. Reduce heat; simmer 10 minutes. Combine cornstarch and 1½ tablespoons water, stirring until smooth. Add to cherry mixture; bring to a boil. Cook 1 minute, stirring constantly. Remove from heat, and stir in extract. Cool completely.
2. Preheat oven to 400°.
3. Roll dough into a 12-inch circle on a lightly floured surface; cut with a 3½-inch biscuit cutter into 8 rounds. Top half of each dough round with about 1½ teaspoons cherry filling. Fold remaining half of dough over filling, pressing edges together to seal.
4. Place pies on a baking sheet coated with cooking spray. Coat tops of pies with cooking spray. Bake at 400° for 15 minutes or until golden brown. Dust with powdered sugar, and serve with whipped topping, if desired. YIELD: 8 SERVINGS (SERVING SIZE: 1 PIE).

PER SERVING: Calories 141; Fat 6.6g (sat 2.3g, mono 2.8g, poly 0.7g); Protein 1.1g; Carb 20.8g; Fiber 0.4g; Chol 0mg; Iron 0.1mg; Sodium 130mg; Calc 0mg

CARAMEL-BRICKLE PIE

PointsPlus value per serving: 6

PREP: 5 minutes ■ COOK: 8 hours ■ OTHER: 1 hour

Minimal prep work and hands-off cook time produce this too-good-to-be-true light dessert. Coffee might be the only accompaniment needed.

1 (14-ounce) can fat-free sweetened condensed milk
1 (6-ounce) reduced-fat graham cracker crust
2 cups frozen fat-free whipped topping, thawed
¼ cup almond brickle chips (such as Heath)

1. Pour milk into a 2-cup glass measuring cup; cover with foil. Place measuring cup in a 3½-quart electric slow cooker; add enough hot water to cooker to come to the level of milk in cup. Cover and cook on LOW 8 hours.
2. Pour caramelized milk into crust; cool 1 hour. Spread whipped topping over pie; sprinkle with brickle chips. Cover and chill until ready to serve. YIELD: 10 SERVINGS (SERVING SIZE: 1 SLICE).

PER SERVING: Calories 249; Fat 4.8g (sat 1.4g, mono 2.9g, poly 0.3g); Protein 3.9g; Carb 45g; Fiber 0g; Chol 7mg; Iron 0mg; Sodium 162mg; Calc 102mg

LIMONCELLO ICE BOX PIE

PointsPlus value per serving: 6   *pictured on page 55*

PREP: 15 minutes ■ COOK: 1 minute ■ OTHER: 1 hour

We tried a couple of different varieties of lemon yogurt, but found that lemon meringue was perfect for this tangy, summer-friendly pie. You can substitute lemonade for the limoncello, if you like.

2 teaspoons grated lemon rind
¼ cup fresh lemon juice
3 tablespoons limoncello
1 (14-ounce) can fat-free sweetened condensed milk
1 (6-ounce) carton lemon meringue fat-free yogurt (such as
    Yoplait)
1½ teaspoons unflavored gelatin
3 tablespoons water
1 (6-ounce) reduced-fat graham cracker crust
2 cups frozen fat-free whipped topping, thawed
10 very thin lemon slices (optional)

1. Combine first 5 ingredients in a bowl; stir well, and set aside. Sprinkle gelatin over 3 tablespoons water in a small bowl; let stand 1 minute. Microwave at HIGH

15 seconds, stirring until gelatin dissolves. Add gelatin mixture to lemon mixture, stirring with a whisk until well blended.

2. Spoon filling into crust. Cover and chill 1 hour or until set. Spread whipped topping over pie. Garnish with lemon slices, if desired. Store in refrigerator. **YIELD: 10 SERVINGS (SERVING SIZE: 1 SLICE).**

PER SERVING: Calories 232; Fat 2.8g (sat 0.4g, mono 2.1g, poly 0.2g); Protein 4.7g; Carb 43g; Fiber 0.1g; Chol 5mg; Iron 0.3mg; Sodium 127mg; Calc 123mg

✳ Limoncello
This Italian lemon liqueur, made by infusing the bracing citrusy flavor from lemon rind into vodka, is available in liquor stores. It's also delicious ice cold on its own, mixed with sparkling wine, added to a martini, or splashed over a bowl of fresh fruit.

GRASSHOPPER ICE CREAM SANDWICH DESSERT

PointsPlus value per serving: 8

PREP: 8 minutes ■ **OTHER:** 2 hours

You'll never believe this delicious dessert is light! For a double dose of chocolate, use chocolate ice cream sandwiches.

  1 (8-ounce) container frozen fat-free whipped topping, thawed
  2 cups chocolate-mint light ice cream (such as Edy's), softened
  1 cup chocolate wafer crumbs (about 15 cookies; such as Nabisco's Famous Chocolate Wafers), divided
  6 (4-ounce) reduced-fat ice cream sandwiches (such as Healthy Choice)
  ½ cup fat-free chocolate syrup

1. Spoon whipped topping into a large bowl; gently fold in softened ice cream and ½ cup cookie crumbs.
2. Arrange ice cream sandwiches in an 11 x 7–inch glass or ceramic baking dish. Spread whipped topping mixture evenly over ice cream sandwiches. Sprinkle with remaining ½ cup cookie crumbs. Cover and freeze at least 2 hours or until firm. Drizzle with chocolate syrup before serving. **YIELD: 10 SERVINGS (SERVING SIZE: ¹⁄₁₀ OF DESSERT).**

PER SERVING: Calories 317; Fat 6.4g (sat 2.8g, mono 1.6g, poly 1.3g); Protein 4.4g; Carb 58.7g; Fiber 0.7g; Chol 15mg; Iron 2mg; Sodium 277mg; Calc 46mg

ICE CREAM TRUFFLE CONES

PointsPlus value per serving: 7   *pictured on page 54*

PREP: 6 minutes ■ **COOK:** 5 minutes ■ **OTHER:** 1 hour

Act like a kid again by indulging in the ice cream treats that are rolled in a favorite childhood cereal and served in sugar cones.

  2 cups cookie dough light ice cream (such as Edy's)
  1 cup chocolate sweetened rice cereal (such as Cocoa Krispies)
  2 ounces white chocolate, finely chopped
  ¼ cup chopped pecans, toasted
  6 (0.42-ounce) sugar cones

1. Scoop ice cream into ⅓-cup balls. Combine cereal, chocolate, and pecans. Roll ice cream balls in cereal mixture. Place on a baking sheet lined with parchment paper. Freeze 1 hour or until firm.
2. Place 1 ice cream ball on each cone. Serve immediately. **YIELD: 6 SERVINGS (SERVING SIZE: 1 ICE CREAM CONE).**

PER SERVING: Calories 248; Fat 10.3g (sat 4.4g, mono 2.7g, poly 1.1g); Protein 4.4g; Carb 35.2g; Fiber 0.6g; Chol 15mg; Iron 2mg; Sodium 149mg; Calc 71mg

PRETZEL ICE CREAM SMASH

PointsPlus value per serving: 8

PREP: 4 minutes ■ **OTHER:** 30 minutes

Pretzels and chocolate chips give this ice cream treat a yummy sweet and salty contrast. This is "soft-serve" style, but if you'd prefer a firmer ice cream, feel free to return it to the freezer.

  1 cup vanilla light ice cream (such as Edy's), slightly softened
  1 tablespoon chocolate syrup
  ½ cup tiny pretzels, broken into pieces
  ¼ cup semisweet chocolate minichips

1. Place a large rimmed baking sheet in freezer for 30 minutes.
2. Spoon ice cream onto chilled baking sheet. Pour chocolate syrup over ice cream; sprinkle with pretzels and chocolate chips. Working quickly with 2 spoons, fold toppings into ice cream until blended. Serve immediately. **YIELD: 2 SERVINGS (SERVING SIZE: ABOUT ½ CUP).**

PER SERVING: Calories 296; Fat 10.5g (sat 6.1g, mono 3.1g, poly 0.4g); Protein 5.6g; Carb 48g; Fiber 1.9g; Chol 21mg; Iron 1.6mg; Sodium 285mg; Calc 129mg

KIWI SORBET

PointsPlus value per serving: 2   *pictured on page 56*

PREP: 14 minutes ■ COOK: 4 minutes
■ OTHER: 1 hour and 30 minutes

Try this refreshing sorbet on a hot summer day. Fresh strawberries add a nice punch of color to the light green sorbet.

1½ cups water
¼ cup sugar
3 cups coarsely chopped peeled kiwifruit (about
     10 kiwifruit)
2 tablespoons fresh lime juice
Sliced strawberries (optional)

1. Combine 1½ cups water and sugar in a medium saucepan. Bring mixture to a boil over medium–high heat; cook 1 minute or until sugar dissolves. Place pan in a large ice-filled bowl in refrigerator until syrup cools.
2. Place sugar syrup, kiwifruit, and lime juice in a blender; process until smooth. Pour mixture into the freezer can of an ice–cream freezer; freeze according to manufacturer's instructions. Spoon sorbet into a freezer–safe container; cover and freeze until firm. Garnish with strawberries, if desired. YIELD: 8 SERVINGS (SERVING SIZE: ½ CUP).

PER SERVING: Calories 66; Fat 0.4g (sat 0g, mono 0g, poly 0.2g); Protein 0.8g; Carb 16.4; Fiber 2g; Chol 0mg; Iron 0.2mg; Sodium 2mg; Calc 23mg

KIWIFRUIT

Kiwifruit's fuzzy brown exterior belies its emerald-green interior, which offers a refreshing flavor that's a cross between strawberry and pineapple. The smooth flesh is dotted with edible black seeds that provide a crunchy textural contrast. Kiwifruit is nutrient-rich, too. One delivers double the vitamin C of an orange and as much potassium as a banana. Kiwifruit is one of the few fruits that become sweeter after being picked. For the best ready-to-eat flavor, look for fruit that gives slightly when touched and is not wrinkled or bruised.

MOCHA-TOFU TIRAMISU

PointsPlus value per serving: 6

PREP: 10 minutes ■ COOK: 1 minute ■ OTHER: 2 hours

Don't let the tofu in this recipe dissuade you from preparing this delicious dessert. The tofu blends beautifully, creating a silky consistency. Be sure to use silken tofu for a creamy tiramisu. Regular soft tofu is too firm and doesn't blend as smoothly.

8 cakelike ladyfingers, split
3 tablespoons Kahlúa (coffee-flavored liqueur), divided
1 (12.3-ounce) package soft silken tofu
1 (6-ounce) carton cappuccino fat-free yogurt
1 (1-ounce) square semisweet chocolate, melted
½ cup frozen fat-free whipped topping, thawed
Shaved semisweet chocolate (optional)

1. Arrange 4 ladyfinger halves into each of 4 dessert dishes; brush ladyfingers evenly with 2 tablespoons Kahlúa; set aside.
2. Place tofu in a food processor; process until smooth. Add yogurt, melted chocolate, and remaining 1 table-spoon Kahlúa; process until smooth. Spoon tofu mixture evenly into center of each dessert dish. Chill 2 hours before serving. Top each serving with whipped topping and chocolate shavings, if desired. YIELD: 4 SERV-INGS (SERVING SIZE: 1 INDIVIDUAL TIRAMISU).

PER SERVING: Calories 177; Fat 4.4g (sat 1.5g, mono 1.4g, poly 1g); Protein 6.9g; Carb 26.1g; Fiber 0.8g; Chol 30mg; Iron 0.8mg; Sodium 135mg; Calc 82mg

WHITE CHOCOLATE PUDDING WITH AMARETTO CRANBERRIES

PointsPlus value per serving: 5

PREP: 7 minutes ■ COOK: 4 minutes
■ OTHER: 10 minutes

A double dose of almond flavor adds spark to a boxed pudding mix.

¼ cup amaretto (almond-flavored liqueur)
1 cup fresh cranberries
1 (1-ounce) package sugar-free white chocolate instant
     pudding mix
2 cups fat-free milk
1 cup frozen reduced-calorie whipped topping, thawed
¼ cup slivered almonds, toasted
White chocolate curls (optional)

1. Place amaretto in a medium saucepan; bring to a boil. Reduce heat; add cranberries, and cook 1 minute or until cranberries pop. Remove from heat; mash lightly. Let stand 10 minutes. Drain cranberries, reserving juice. Set mashed cranberries aside. Return cranberry juice to pan; bring to a boil. Boil 1 to 2 minutes or until syrupy.

2. While cranberries stand, prepare pudding according to package directions using 2 cups fat-free milk. When pudding is set, fold in cranberries and whipped topping. Spoon pudding mixture evenly into 4 dessert glasses; top with almonds, and drizzle with cranberry syrup. Garnish with chocolate curls, if desired. YIELD: 4 SERVINGS (SERVING SIZE: ¾ CUP PUDDING MIXTURE, 1 TABLESPOON ALMONDS, AND ABOUT ½ TEASPOON CRANBERRY SYRUP).

PER SERVING: Calories 182; Fat 5.5g (sat 2.3g, mono 2.1g, poly 0.8g); Protein 5.7g; Carb 26.2g; Fiber 2g; Chol 3mg; Iron 0.4mg; Sodium 336mg; Calc 173mg

BUTTERSCOTCH WALNUT BREAD PUDDING

PointsPlus value per serving: 8

PREP: 6 minutes ■ COOK: 30 minutes

For an even more decadent dessert, serve each bread pudding with 1 tablespoon store-bought butterscotch sauce and 1 tablespoon whipped topping. These toppings will bring the *PointsPlus* value per serving to 9.

    Cooking spray
    5 ounces French bread baguette, torn into 1-inch pieces
    2 large eggs
    1 cup evaporated low-fat milk
    ⅓ cup packed dark brown sugar
    ¼ cup coarsely chopped walnuts
    ¼ cup fat-free whipped topping (optional)

1. Preheat oven to 325°.
2. Coat 4 (6-ounce) ramekins or custard cups with cooking spray. Divide bread evenly among ramekins.
3. Place eggs in a medium bowl; stir with a whisk until foamy. Stir in milk and brown sugar. Pour custard evenly over bread. Press bread carefully with the back of a spoon to soak up custard. Sprinkle walnuts evenly over the top of each pudding.

4. Place ramekins in a 9-inch square metal baking pan; add hot water to pan to a depth of 1 inch. Bake at 325° for 30 minutes or until set. Garnish each serving with 1 tablespoon whipped topping, if desired. YIELD: 4 SERVINGS (SERVING SIZE: 1 PUDDING).

PER SERVING: Calories 307; Fat 9.1g (sat 2.4g, mono 1.7g, poly 4.1g); Protein 12.4g; Carb 45.1g; Fiber 1.3g; Chol 116mg; Iron 2.1mg; Sodium 341mg; Calc 211mg

RASPBERRY MOUSSE

PointsPlus value per serving: 3

PREP: 10 minutes ■ COOK: 2 minutes ■ OTHER: 2 hours

Frozen raspberries give this mousse its vibrant flavor and bright pink hue.

    2 (10-ounce) packages frozen raspberries in light syrup, thawed and undrained
    1½ teaspoons unflavored gelatin
    ¼ cup water
    1½ cups frozen fat-free whipped topping, thawed
    1 cup fresh raspberries

1. Drain raspberries, reserving ¼ cup syrup. Discard remaining syrup. Place ¼ cup syrup and thawed raspberries in a blender or food processor; process until blended. Strain raspberry mixture through a sieve into a bowl, pressing firmly on the solids. Discard solids.
2. Sprinkle gelatin over ¼ cup water in a small saucepan; let stand 1 minute. Cook over low heat until gelatin dissolves, stirring constantly. Add to raspberry mixture, stirring well.
3. Add ¼ cup whipped topping to raspberry mixture, stirring with a whisk. Gently fold in remaining 1¼ cups whipped topping. Spoon into dessert dishes. Cover and chill at least 2 hours. Top with fresh raspberries before serving. YIELD: 4 SERVINGS (SERVING SIZE: ABOUT ⅔ CUP MOUSSE AND ¼ CUP RASPBERRIES).

PER SERVING: Calories 150; Fat 0g (sat 0g, mono 0g, poly 0g); Protein 2g; Carb 35.3g; Fiber 7g; Chol 0mg; Iron 0.1mg; Sodium 22mg; Calc 6mg

FROZEN HONEY MOUSSE

PointsPlus value per serving: 3

PREP: 16 minutes ▪ **COOK:** 4 minutes ▪ **OTHER:** 4 hours

This mousse highlights the distinct flavor of honey in a refreshing way. Try a floral variety such as orange blossom or lavender.

Cooking spray
1 teaspoon unflavored gelatin
9 tablespoons water, divided
4 large pasteurized eggs, separated
7 tablespoons honey, divided
1½ cups frozen reduced-calorie whipped topping, thawed
¼ cup chopped pistachios, toasted

1. Line a 9 x 5–inch loaf pan with parchment paper, allowing the parchment paper to extend over outside edges. Coat paper with cooking spray.
2. Sprinkle gelatin over 5 tablespoons water in a small bowl; set aside.
3. While gelatin stands, combine egg yolks, 3 tablespoons water, and 2 tablespoons honey in the top of a double boiler. Cook over simmering water until a candy thermometer registers 160° (about 2 minutes), stirring constantly with a whisk. Remove from heat; add gelatin mixture, stirring until smooth.
4. Combine remaining 5 tablespoons honey and remaining 1 tablespoon water in a small saucepan. Cook until candy thermometer registers 220°. Place egg whites in a large bowl; beat with a mixer at high speed until foamy. Gradually pour hot honey mixture into egg white mixture, beating at medium speed and then at high speed until stiff peaks form.
5. Gently fold egg yolk mixture and whipped topping into egg white mixture. Spoon into prepared pan; cover and freeze at least 4 hours. To serve, place a platter upside down on top of loaf pan; invert pan onto platter, and remove parchment paper. Cut mousse crosswise into 12 slices. Sprinkle each serving with pistachios. **YIELD: 12 SERVINGS (SERVING SIZE: 1 SLICE MOUSSE AND 1 TEASPOON PISTACHIOS).**

PER SERVING: Calories 109; Fat 4.9g (sat 1.8g, mono 1.8g, poly 0.9g); Protein 3.3g; Carb 14.5g; Fiber 0.5g; Chol 71mg; Iron 0.6mg; Sodium 25mg; Calc 15mg

Honey Varieties

The color and flavor of a particular honey depend on its nectar source. Honey ranges from a light golden color that generally has a milder flavor, to a deep amber that has a more intense flavor. There are hundreds of varieties, and each area of the country offers its own options, so feel free to experiment with them. You can find locally produced artisanal honey in supermarkets, specialty stores, and at farmers' markets.

BANANA–MILK CHOCOLATE QUESADILLAS

PointsPlus value per serving: 5

PREP: 3 minutes ▪ **COOK:** 3 minutes

The chocolate-banana pairing proves ever popular in this crisp and yummy treat meant for dessert or an after-school snack. Flour tortillas have a soft texture and brown nicely without tearing.

1 large ripe banana, sliced
2 (8-inch) flour tortillas
⅓ cup milk chocolate chips
Butter-flavored cooking spray
2 teaspoons powdered sugar

1. Arrange banana slices over half of each tortilla; add chocolate chips, and fold each tortilla in half.
2. Heat a large nonstick skillet over medium–high heat. Coat pan with cooking spray. Place quesadillas in pan; coat tops with cooking spray. Cook 1 to 2 minutes on each side or until browned. Cut each quesadilla into 4 wedges. Sprinkle evenly with powdered sugar. **YIELD: 4 SERVINGS (SERVING SIZE: 2 WEDGES).**

PER SERVING: Calories 184; Fat 6.3g (sat 3.1g, mono 1.9g, poly 0.6g); Protein 3.4g; Carb 29.1g; Fiber 2.1g; Chol 3mg; Iron 1.2mg; Sodium 158mg; Calc 58mg

S'MORE POPPERS

PointsPlus value per serving: 1

PREP: 7 minutes ■ **COOK:** 1 minute

These two-bite desserts are like an inside-out s'more—gooey and satisfying!

- ½ cup milk chocolate chips
- 3 graham crackers, coarsely crumbled
- 18 wooden picks
- 18 regular size marshmallows

1. Place chocolate chips in a small glass bowl; microwave at HIGH 1 minute or until almost melted, stirring until smooth.
2. Place graham cracker pieces in a small shallow bowl.
3. Pierce 1 wooden pick into flat side of each marshmallow. Roll each marshmallow in chocolate, leaving ends uncoated. Immediately roll in graham crackers. Serve immediately, or store at room temperature in an airtight container. **YIELD: 18 SERVINGS (SERVING SIZE: 1 POPPER).**

PER SERVING: Calories 46; Fat 1.5g (sat 0.9g, mono 0.4g, poly 0.1g); Protein 0.6g; Carb 7.8g; Fiber 0.2g; Chol 1mg; Iron 0.1mg; Sodium 13mg; Calc 11mg

BITTERSWEET CHOCOLATE–HAZELNUT BROWNIES

PointsPlus value per serving: 4

PREP: 16 minutes ■ **COOK:** 23 minutes
■ **OTHER:** 45 minutes

Look for blanched hazelnuts, which have most of the skins removed, to save you from having to skin the hazelnuts.

- 5.6 ounces all-purpose flour (about 1¼ cups)
- ½ teaspoon baking powder
- ¼ teaspoon salt
- ½ cup butter
- 3 ounces bittersweet chocolate, coarsely chopped
- ½ cup hazelnut chocolate spread (such as Nutella)
- 1 cup sugar
- 2 teaspoons vanilla extract
- 2 large eggs
- Cooking spray
- 1 tablespoon finely chopped blanched hazelnuts

1. Preheat oven to 350°.
2. Weigh or lightly spoon flour into dry measuring cups; level with a knife. Combine flour, baking powder, and salt. Set aside.
3. Combine butter and chocolate in a medium saucepan; cook over low heat until chocolate and butter melt. Remove from heat; add hazelnut spread, stirring until blended. Stir in sugar and vanilla. Add eggs, 1 at a time, stirring well after each addition. Add flour mixture, stirring well.
4. Spread batter into a 13 x 9–inch metal baking pan coated with cooking spray. Sprinkle hazelnuts over batter. Bake at 350° for 22 to 23 minutes or until edges are set. Cool slightly before cutting. **YIELD: 28 BROWNIES (SERVING SIZE: 1 BROWNIE).**

PER SERVING: Calories 128; Fat 6.8g (sat 3.4g, mono 1.1g, poly 0.2g); Protein 1.8g; Carb 16.3g; Fiber 0.5g; Chol 24mg; Iron 0.5mg; Sodium 59mg; Calc 14mg

*Hazelnut Chocolate Spread

This creamy spread is made from ground hazelnuts, fat-free milk, oil, sugar, and a bit of cocoa. It's also delicious as a topping for toast or as a substitute in a PB & J Sandwich. One tablespoon has a *PointsPlus* value per serving of 3.

FUDGY BROWNIES WITH GOAT CHEESE

PointsPlus value per serving: 4

PREP: 12 minutes ■ COOK: 25 minutes
■ OTHER: 20 minutes

Tangy goat cheese lends an unexpected yum factor to these brownies.

  1 cup sugar, divided
  ⅓ cup light butter, softened
  1 large egg
  2 large egg whites, divided
  1 tablespoon vanilla extract
  2.25 ounces all-purpose flour (about ½ cup)
  ¼ cup unsweetened cocoa
  ⅛ teaspoon salt
  Cooking spray
  ½ cup (4 ounces) ⅓-less-fat cream cheese, softened
  ½ cup (4 ounces) goat cheese (such as Belle Chevre), softened

1. Preheat oven to 350°.
2. Place ¾ cup sugar and butter in a medium bowl; beat with a mixer at medium speed 2 minutes or until light and fluffy. Beat in egg, 1 egg white, and vanilla. Weigh or lightly spoon flour into a dry measuring cup; level with a knife. Add flour, cocoa, and salt to egg mixture, beating just until blended. Pour batter into an 8-inch square metal baking pan coated with cooking spray.
3. Place cheeses and remaining ¼ cup sugar in a medium bowl; beat with a mixer at medium-high speed just until smooth. Add remaining 1 egg white; beat until blended. Dollop cream cheese mixture over batter; swirl batters together using the tip of a knife.
4. Bake at 350° for 25 to 26 minutes. Cool in pan on a wire rack; cut into squares. **YIELD: 16 SERVINGS (SERVING SIZE: 1 SQUARE).**

PER SERVING: Calories 138; Fat 6.2g (sat 3.6g, mono 1.6g, poly 0.3g); Protein 3.6g; Carb 16.9g; Fiber 0.4g; Chol 27mg; Iron 0.6mg; Sodium 101mg; Calc 23mg

CHOCOLATE-CRANBERRY BLONDIES

PointsPlus value per serving: 6

PREP: 8 minutes ■ COOK: 24 minutes
■ OTHER: 20 minutes

Tart plump cranberries covered in milk chocolate update the flavor and wow factor in these melt-in-your-mouth bars.

  4.5 ounces all-purpose flour (about 1 cup)
  ¼ teaspoon baking powder
  ⅛ teaspoon baking soda
  ⅛ teaspoon salt
  6 tablespoons butter, melted
  ⅔ cup packed brown sugar
  1 large egg
  1 large egg yolk
  1 tablespoon light corn syrup
  1 teaspoon almond extract
  1 cup chocolate-covered dried cranberries (such as Craisins)
  Cooking spray

1. Preheat oven to 350°.
2. Weigh or lightly spoon flour into a dry measuring cup; level with a knife. Combine flour, baking powder, baking soda, and salt, stirring well. Place butter in a large microwave-safe bowl. Microwave at HIGH 30 seconds or until butter melts. Add sugar, stirring until combined. Add egg and next 3 ingredients, stirring with a whisk until smooth. Add flour mixture to butter mixture, stirring to combine. Fold in chocolate-covered cranberries.
3. Spoon batter into an 8-inch square metal baking pan coated with cooking spray, spreading evenly with a knife or rubber spatula. Bake at 350° for 23 minutes or until a wooden pick inserted in center comes out almost clean. Cool in pan on a wire rack; cut into bars. **YIELD: 12 SERVINGS (SERVING SIZE: 1 BAR).**

PER SERVING: Calories 213; Fat 9.4g (sat 5.3g, mono 1.8g, poly 0.4g); Protein 2.6g; Carb 30.8g; Fiber 1g; Chol 51mg; Iron 0.7mg; Sodium 107mg; Calc 23mg

CHEWY CHOCOLATE-ALMOND SANDWICH COOKIES

PointsPlus value per serving: 6   *pictured on page 53*

PREP: 9 minutes ■ **COOK:** 20 minutes
■ **OTHER:** 35 minutes

This recipe works best if the egg whites are at room temperature. To do this quickly, simply place whole, uncracked eggs in a bowl of warm water for about 5 minutes before proceeding with the recipe.

  1 cup sugar
  1 (7-ounce) tube almond paste
  ¼ teaspoon vanilla extract
  2 large egg whites
  4 ounces bittersweet chocolate, chopped

1. Preheat oven to 300°.
2. Place sugar and almond paste in a food processor; pulse 6 times or until paste is crumbly. Add vanilla and egg whites; pulse until smooth. Spoon batter by tablespoonfuls, 1 inch apart, onto baking sheets lined with parchment paper. Bake at 300° for 20 minutes or until puffed and lightly browned. Cool on pans on wire racks.
3. Place chocolate in a medium-sized glass bowl. Microwave at HIGH 30 seconds; stir. Microwave 15 seconds or until melted, stirring until smooth. Carefully remove cookies from paper. Spoon 1½ teaspoons chocolate onto half of cookies. Top with remaining cookies. Let stand 15 to 20 minutes or until chocolate is firm, or freeze 3 minutes. **YIELD: 12 SERVINGS (SERVING SIZE: 1 SANDWICH COOKIE).**

PER SERVING: Calories 191; Fat 8.7g (sat 2.5g, mono 3g, poly 1g); Protein 2.8g; Carb 29.5g; Fiber 1.5g; Chol 0mg; Iron 0.5mg; Sodium 11mg; Calc 29mg

PECAN-BLUEBERRY SHORTBREAD

PointsPlus value per serving: 3

PREP: 13 minutes ■ **COOK:** 30 minutes
■ **OTHER:** 25 minutes

These shortbread bars were a hit in our Test Kitchens. By using a combination of butter and canola oil, this shortbread retains its rich texture with fewer calories and less saturated fat. Swap out the dried blueberries or pecans with your favorite dried fruit and nuts, if you'd like.

  Cooking spray
  9 ounces all-purpose flour (about 2 cups)
  ¼ cup cornstarch
  ¼ teaspoon salt
  ½ cup butter, softened
  ½ cup canola oil
  ½ cup sugar
  ¾ cup dried blueberries
  ½ cup finely chopped pecans

1. Preheat oven to 350°.
2. Line bottom and sides of a 13 x 9–inch metal baking pan with foil; coat foil with cooking spray.
3. Weigh or lightly spoon flour into dry measuring cups; level with a knife. Combine flour, cornstarch, and salt in a large bowl; stir with a whisk.
4. Place butter in a medium bowl; beat with a mixer at medium speed 2 minutes until light and fluffy. Add oil; beat 3 minutes or until well blended. Gradually add sugar, beating well. Add flour mixture, beating at low speed just until blended. Stir in blueberries and pecans.
5. Spoon dough into prepared pan. Place a sheet of plastic wrap over dough; press to an even thickness. Discard wrap. Bake at 350° for 30 minutes or until edges are browned. Cool in pan 5 minutes on a wire rack. Carefully lift foil from pan; cut into 32 bars. Cool bars completely on wire rack. **YIELD: 32 SERVINGS (SERVING SIZE: 1 BAR).**

PER SERVING: Calories 126; Fat 7.8g (sat 2.2g, mono 3.7g, poly 1.5g); Protein 1.1g; Carb 12.6; Fiber 1g; Chol 8mg; Iron 0.4mg; Sodium 40mg; Calc 3mg

OATMEAL BARK

PointsPlus value per serving: 4

PREP: 5 minutes ■ COOK: 15 minutes
■ OTHER: 35 minutes

Use damp hands to press the dough onto the baking sheet to prevent the dough from sticking to your hands.

> 6 (1.58-ounce) packets instant high-fiber cinnamon swirl oatmeal
> 2 tablespoons all-purpose flour
> ½ teaspoon baking soda
> ¼ teaspoon baking powder
> ¼ cup butter, melted
> 2 large egg whites
> 2 ounces bittersweet chocolate, melted
> ⅓ cup dried cherries, chopped

1. Preheat oven to 350°.
2. Combine first 4 ingredients in a medium bowl. Combine butter and egg whites in a small bowl, stirring with a whisk. Add egg white mixture to oatmeal mixture, stirring until a soft dough forms. Press dough to ¼-inch thickness onto a rimmed baking sheet lined with parchment paper. Bake at 350° for 15 minutes or until lightly browned. Cool completely.
3. Drizzle chocolate over oatmeal mixture. Sprinkle evenly with cherries. Refrigerate 10 to 15 minutes or until chocolate is firm. Break bark into 12 pieces. YIELD: 12 SERVINGS (SERVING SIZE: 1 PIECE).

PER SERVING: Calories 160; Fat 6.9g (sat 3.7g, mono 1.5g, poly 0.4g); Protein 3.2g; Carb 23.8g; Fiber 5.8g; Chol 10mg; Iron 2.1mg; Sodium 202mg; Calc 61mg

LEMON CORNMEAL BISCOTTI

PointsPlus value per serving: 2

PREP: 10 minutes ■ COOK: 46 minutes
■ OTHER: 30 minutes

The rosemary flavor is very subtle in these crunchy, sweet treats. If you prefer a stronger rosemary flavor, increase to 1 tablespoon.

> 7.88 ounces all-purpose flour (about 1¾ cups)
> 1 cup yellow cornmeal
> 1 cup sugar
> 2 teaspoons baking powder
> 2 teaspoons chopped fresh rosemary
> ½ teaspoon salt
> 3 large eggs
> 2 tablespoons butter, melted
> 2 teaspoons grated lemon rind

1. Preheat oven to 350°.
2. Weigh or lightly spoon flour into dry measuring cups; level with a knife. Combine flour and next 5 ingredients in a large bowl; stir with a whisk. Combine eggs, butter, and rind in a small bowl; stir with a whisk. Add egg mixture to flour mixture, stirring until blended. Turn dough out onto a lightly floured surface; knead lightly 8 times. Divide dough into 2 equal portions. Shape each portion of dough into a 10-inch log. Place logs 4 inches apart on a baking sheet lined with parchment paper.
3. Bake at 350° for 25 minutes or until golden. Remove logs from pan; cool 15 minutes on a wire rack. Cut each log diagonally into 15 (½-inch-thick) slices. Place slices, cut sides down, on baking sheet.
4. Reduce oven temperature to 325°.
5. Bake at 325° for 10 minutes; turn biscotti over and bake an additional 10 minutes. Remove biscotti from pan; cool on wire racks. YIELD: 30 SERVINGS (SERVING SIZE: 1 BISCOTTO).

PER SERVING: Calories 86; Fat 1.4g (sat 0.7g, mono 0.4g, poly 0.2g); Protein 1.8g; Carb 16.6g; Fiber 0.4g; Chol 23mg; Iron 0.7mg; Sodium 78mg; Calc 21mg

Grilled Corn, Tomatillo, and Avocado
Salsa, *page 18*

Prosecco and Berries, *page 26*

Open-Faced Naan Quesadillas,
page 23

Cheese and Chives Drop
Biscuits, *page 30*

Apple Fritter
Pancakes, *page 28*

Gruyère Scones,
page 32

Chewy Chocolate-Almond Sandwich
Cookies, *page 47*

Ice Cream Truffle
Cones, *page 41*

54

Limoncello Ice Box Pie, *page 40*

Caramel-Apple Crisp,
page 36

Kiwi Sorbet,
page 42

Chocolate-Almond Cobbler,
page 36

Double Brownie Cheesecake
Torte, *page 38*

Grilled Scallops with Champagne
Vinaigrette and Peach Salsa, *page 73*

Shrimp and Linguine with Lemon-Basil
Cream Sauce, *page 76*

Lowcountry Boil Packets, *page 75*

Vietnamese-Style
Catfish, *page 66*

Curried Shepherd's Pie, *page 80*

Spicy Beer-Steamed Mussels,
page 72

63

Ziti with Cherry Tomatoes, Arugula, and Fresh Mozzarella, *page 85*

fish & shellfish

Watermelon-Glazed Salmon, *page 68*

VIETNAMESE-STYLE CATFISH

PointsPlus value per serving: 8   *pictured on page 62*

PREP: 7 minutes ■ COOK: 16 minutes

This highly seasoned dish is best paired with steamed jasmine rice and sautéed bok choy or cabbage. Double the chile paste for a spicier sauce.

    4 (6-ounce) catfish fillets
    Cooking spray
    1 tablespoon dark sesame oil
    1 tablespoon minced peeled fresh ginger
    2 garlic cloves, minced
    2 tablespoons brown sugar
    ½ teaspoon chile paste with garlic (such as sambal oelek)
    ¼ cup hot water
    4 teaspoons fish sauce
    1 cup fresh bean sprouts
    ¼ cup diagonally sliced green onions
    2 tablespoons chopped fresh cilantro
    4 lime wedges

1. Heat a large nonstick skillet over medium–high heat; coat fish with cooking spray. Add fish to pan; cook 3 to 4 minutes on each side. Remove from pan; set aside. Wipe pan with paper towels.
2. Heat oil in pan over medium–high heat. Add ginger and garlic; sauté 30 seconds. Add brown sugar and chile paste; cook 30 seconds. Stir in ¼ cup hot water and fish sauce. Return fish to pan, spooning sauce over fish to coat. Cover, reduce heat, and simmer 4 to 5 minutes or until desired degree of doneness.
3. Remove fish to a platter. Boil sauce in pan 30 seconds or until reduced slightly. Spoon about 1 tablespoon sauce over each fillet; top each serving with bean sprouts, green onions, and cilantro. Serve with lime wedges. **YIELD: 4 SERVINGS (SERVING SIZE: 1 FILLET, ABOUT 1 TABLESPOON SAUCE, ¼ CUP BEAN SPROUTS, 1 TABLESPOON GREEN ONIONS, AND 1½ TEASPOONS CILANTRO).**

PER SERVING: Calories 306; Fat 16.7g (sat 3.5g, mono 7.6g, poly 4.2g); Protein 27.8g; Carb 11.4g; Fiber 1.2g; Chol 80mg; Iron 1.3mg; Sodium 491mg; Calc 32mg

SESAME-ENCRUSTED GROUPER WITH GINGER SALAD

PointsPlus value per serving: 6

PREP: 7 minutes ■ COOK: 12 minutes

The lightly browned sesame coating elevates a simple fish fillet, making it a company-worthy dish.

    ½ cup plus 2 tablespoons light sesame-ginger dressing
        (such as Newman's Own), divided
    4 (6-ounce) grouper fillets
    ¼ teaspoon salt
    ¼ teaspoon freshly ground black pepper
    2 tablespoons sesame seeds
    Cooking spray
    4 cups torn Boston lettuce (about 2 small heads)
    4 radishes, thinly sliced

1. Preheat oven to 400°.
2. Brush 2 tablespoons dressing over fish; sprinkle with salt and pepper. Place sesame seeds in a shallow dish; press fish into sesame seeds to coat.
3. Place fish, skin sides down, on a baking sheet coated with cooking spray. Bake at 400° for 12 to 15 minutes or until desired degree of doneness and topping is crispy.
4. While fish bakes, combine lettuce and radishes. Toss with remaining ½ cup dressing. Divide salad among 4 plates; place fish over salad. Serve immediately. **YIELD: 4 SERVINGS (SERVING SIZE: 1 FILLET AND 1¼ CUPS SALAD).**

PER SERVING: Calories 238; Fat 6g (sat 0.7g, mono 1.6g, poly 2.8g); Protein 34.9g; Carb 9.4g; Fiber 1.5g; Chol 63mg; Iron 3.2mg; Sodium 732mg; Calc 120mg

✳ Sesame Seeds

Sesame seeds tend to go rancid quickly because of their high oil content, so be sure to store them in the refrigerator. They'll keep in the fridge for up to 6 months or in the freezer for up to a year.

HOMESTYLE FISH STICKS

PointsPlus value per serving: 6

PREP: 15 minutes ■ **COOK:** 14 minutes

Squeezing fresh lemon juice over the fish adds delicious tangy flavor.

3 (0.9-ounce) slices white-wheat bread
¼ cup chopped fresh cilantro
4 (6-ounce) skinless halibut fillets (about ¾ inch thick)
¼ cup tartar sauce
Cooking spray
1 lemon, cut into wedges

1. Preheat oven to 350°.
2. Place bread in a food processor; pulse 4 times or until fine crumbs measure 1¼ cups. Sprinkle crumbs on a baking sheet; bake at 350° for 5 minutes or until golden. Cool crumbs 5 minutes; stir in chopped cilantro. Place crumb mixture in a shallow dish. Increase oven temperature to 450°.
3. While crumbs cool, cut fish into 16 strips. Brush all sides of fish with tartar sauce. Dredge fish in breadcrumb mixture; place on a baking sheet coated with cooking spray. Coat fish with cooking spray.
4. Bake at 450° for 9 minutes or until lightly browned and fish is desired degree of doneness. Serve with lemon wedges. **YIELD: 4 SERVINGS (SERVING SIZE: 4 FISH STICKS).**

PER SERVING: Calories 268; Fat 7.5g (sat 1.1g, mono 2.2g, poly 3.3g); Protein 35.4g; Carb 11.7g; Fiber 2g; Chol 57mg; Iron 1.4mg; Sodium 292mg; Calc 85mg

---

✳ **White-Wheat Bread**

White-wheat bread is made from white-wheat flour, so it has all the nutrients and fiber of a whole grain but a milder flavor and softer texture than regular whole-wheat bread. It's a healthier alternative to bread made from refined white flour, which has been stripped of its fiber and most of its nutrients.

HALIBUT WITH HERBS AND GOAT CHEESE

PointsPlus value per serving: 7

PREP: 6 minutes ■ **COOK:** 13 minutes

Herbs and goat cheese add an elegant touch to halibut in this entrée.

4 (6-ounce) halibut fillets
¼ teaspoon salt
¼ teaspoon freshly ground black pepper
1 tablespoon olive oil
¼ cup dry white wine
2 tablespoons chopped green onions
1 tablespoon chopped fresh tarragon
1 tablespoon chopped fresh flat-leaf parsley
2 garlic cloves, minced
½ cup (2 ounces) crumbled goat cheese

1. Preheat oven to 450°.
2. Sprinkle fish evenly with salt and pepper. Heat oil in a large cast-iron or ovenproof skillet over medium-high heat; add fish to pan. Cook 2 minutes on each side or until browned.
3. Combine wine and next 4 ingredients; pour over fish in pan. Sprinkle fish evenly with goat cheese. Bake at 450° for 8 minutes or until desired degree of doneness. **YIELD: 4 SERVINGS (SERVING SIZE: 1 FILLET).**

PER SERVING: Calories 266; Fat 10.3g (sat 3.1g, mono 4.4g, poly 1.7g); Protein 38.2g; Carb 1.3g; Fiber 0.2g; Chol 61mg; Iron 1.9mg; Sodium 294mg; Calc 109mg

SALMON WITH CITRUS–WHITE WINE GLAZE

PointsPlus value per serving: 7

PREP: 4 minutes ■ **COOK:** 43 minutes

Roasting salmon at a low temperature ensures moist, even cooking. Serve with basmati rice and a mixed green salad.

1 cup dry white wine
½ cup orange juice
⅓ cup lower-sodium soy sauce
2 tablespoons grated peeled fresh ginger
2 tablespoons dark brown sugar
½ teaspoon coarsely ground black pepper
4 (6-ounce) skinless salmon fillets

1. Preheat oven to 275°.
2. Combine first 6 ingredients in a medium saucepan; bring to a boil. Cook until reduced to ½ cup (about 15 minutes).
3. Place fillets on a foil-lined baking sheet. Brush one-third of wine mixture over fillets. Bake at 275° for 15 minutes; brush with one-third of glaze. Bake an additional 10 minutes or until desired degree of doneness, basting with remaining glaze. **YIELD: 4 SERVINGS (SERVING SIZE: 1 FILLET).**

PER SERVING: Calories 260; Fat 6g (sat 1g, mono 1.6g, poly 2.3g); Protein 35.6g; Carb 12.6g; Fiber 0.2g; Chol 89mg; Iron 1.6mg; Sodium 637mg; Calc 36mg

HOW TO PEEL AND GRATE FRESH GINGER

Choose fresh, young-looking ginger. Old ginger is fibrous, tough, and flavorless. Store it tightly wrapped in plastic wrap in the vegetable crisper section of your refrigerator for up to 3 weeks.

1. Use a vegetable peeler to remove the tough skin and reveal the yellowish flesh.
2. For chopped or minced ginger, place a peeled piece on a cutting board. Cut with the grain into thin strips; stack the slices. Cut across the pile into small pieces.
3. For grated ginger, rub a peeled piece of ginger across a fine grater or the smallest holes of a box grater.

WATERMELON-GLAZED SALMON

PointsPlus value per serving: 7   *pictured on page 65*

PREP: 5 minutes ■ **COOK:** 22 minutes

Watermelon puree reduces to a sweet glaze that gets a kick from spicy red pepper jelly.

1½ cups cubed seeded watermelon
½ cup red pepper jelly
1 tablespoon fresh lime juice
1 teaspoon grated lime rind
4 (6-ounce) skinless salmon fillets
¼ teaspoon salt

1. Preheat broiler.
2. Place first 3 ingredients in a blender or food processor; process until smooth. Strain mixture through a colander into a medium saucepan; discard solids. Bring to a boil; cook 8 minutes or until mixture is syrupy and reduced to ½ cup. Stir in lime rind.
3. Sprinkle fish evenly with salt; place on a foil-lined broiler pan. Brush fish with half of watermelon mixture. Broil 12 minutes or until desired degree of doneness, basting with remaining glaze after 6 minutes. **YIELD: 4 SERVINGS (SERVING SIZE: 1 FILLET).**

PER SERVING: Calories 275; Fat 5.9g (sat 1g, mono 1.6g, poly 2.3g); Protein 34.1g; Carb 20.6g; Fiber 0.2g; Chol 89mg; Iron 1.5mg; Sodium 292mg; Calc 27mg

ROASTED RED SNAPPER AND TOMATOES

PointsPlus value per serving: 5

PREP: 6 minutes ■ COOK: 20 minutes

4 (6-ounce) red snapper or other firm white fish fillets
Cooking spray
1 tablespoon olive oil
1 tablespoon fresh lemon juice
½ teaspoon salt
¼ teaspoon freshly ground black pepper
2 garlic cloves, minced
1 pint grape tomatoes
2 tablespoons capers

1. Preheat oven to 425°.
2. Place fish, skin sides down, in a 13 x 9–inch glass or ceramic baking dish coated with cooking spray. Combine olive oil and next 4 ingredients in a medium bowl, stirring with a whisk. Drizzle 1½ tablespoons olive oil mixture over fish. Add tomatoes and capers to remaining olive oil mixture; toss well. Arrange tomato mixture around fish in baking dish.
3. Bake at 425° for 20 minutes or until desired degree of doneness. Spoon roasted tomato mixture over fish.
YIELD: 4 SERVINGS (SERVING SIZE: 1 FILLET AND ABOUT ⅓ CUP TOMATO MIXTURE).

PER SERVING: Calories 220; Fat 5.9g (sat 1g, mono 2.9g, poly 1.2g); Protein 35.6g; Carb 4.1g; Fiber 1.2g; Chol 63mg; Iron 0.4mg; Sodium 531mg; Calc 72mg

Capers
These tiny unopened flower buds of the Mediterranean caper shrub are cured in white vinegar for a sharp, salty-sour flavor that complements everything from this snapper dish to chicken piccata to tartar sauce.

POTATO CHIP–CRUSTED TILAPIA ON VEGGIE BEDS

PointsPlus value per serving: 8

PREP: 15 minutes ■ COOK: 15 minutes

A side of rice makes a nice accompaniment to this healthy dish. A ½-cup serving of cooked brown rice has a *PointsPlus* value per serving of 3.

1 (1-ounce) slice white bread, crumbled
1½ cups chopped tomato
1½ cups chopped leek
½ cup chopped green bell pepper
3 garlic cloves, finely chopped
½ cup coarsely crushed baked potato chips (such as Ruffles)
⅓ cup grated Parmesan cheese
¾ teaspoon dried Italian seasoning
4 (6-ounce) tilapia fillets
⅛ teaspoon salt
2 tablespoons butter, melted
1 tablespoon chopped fresh parsley
4 lemon wedges

1. Preheat oven to 425°.
2. Place bread in a food processor; pulse 10 times or until coarse crumbs measure ½ cup.
3. Combine tomato and next 3 ingredients in a bowl; toss gently. Spoon about 1 cup vegetables into 4 oval gratin dishes, or arrange vegetables into 4 mounds on a jelly-roll pan.
4. Combine breadcrumbs, potato chips, Parmesan cheese, and Italian seasoning in a small bowl; stir well. Place fillets on top of vegetables; sprinkle evenly with salt. Top each fillet with about ½ cup crumb mixture, and drizzle butter evenly over crumb mixture.
5. Bake at 425° for 15 minutes or until desired degree of doneness. Sprinkle with parsley, and serve with lemon wedges. YIELD: 4 SERVINGS (SERVING SIZE: 1 FILLET AND 1 CUP VEGETABLE MIXTURE).

PER SERVING: Calories 333; Fat 11.6g (sat 6.2g, mono 3.1g, poly 1.2g); Protein 39.4g; Carb 19.3g; Fiber 2.5g; Chol 106mg; Iron 2.3mg; Sodium 355mg; Calc 153mg

TEX-MEX FISH TACOS

PointsPlus value per serving: 7

PREP: 7 minutes ■ **COOK:** 14 minutes

Complete your Tex-Mex meal with black beans and rice.

    1 pound tilapia or other firm white fish fillets
    Cooking spray
    1½ tablespoons 40%-less-sodium taco seasoning
    3 limes, divided
    2 cups angel hair slaw
    ½ cup reduced-fat sour cream
    ⅓ cup chopped fresh cilantro
    ¼ cup chopped green onions
    ½ teaspoon 40%-less-sodium taco seasoning
    8 (6-inch) corn tortillas

1. Preheat oven to 425°.
2. Place fish on the rack of a broiler pan coated with cooking spray. Sprinkle 1½ tablespoons taco seasoning over fish. Cut 1 lime in half; squeeze over fish. Bake at 425° for 13 minutes or until desired degree of doneness.
3. While fish cooks, combine slaw and next 4 ingredients in a medium bowl.
4. Quickly flake fish into bite-sized pieces with 2 forks. Wrap tortillas in 2 layers of damp paper towels. Microwave at HIGH 30 to 40 seconds or until thoroughly heated. Divide fish evenly among tortillas; top each with about ¼ cup slaw. Cut remaining 2 limes into 8 wedges; serve with tacos. **YIELD: 4 SERVINGS (SERVING SIZE: 2 TACOS).**

PER SERVING: Calories 267; Fat 6.7g (sat 3g, mono 1.7g, poly 1.1g); Protein 26g; Carb 29.2g; Fiber 4.4g; Chol 68mg; Iron 1mg; Sodium 297mg; Calc 68mg

---

CORN VS. FLOUR TORTILLAS

A standard 6-inch corn tortilla contains about half the fat and calories and one-fourth the sodium of a similar-sized flour tortilla. In traditional Mexican tortillas, the fat comes from lard, but many brands now use vegetable shortening. Look for those made without trans fat.

GRILLED TUNA WITH TOMATO-OLIVE RELISH

PointsPlus value per serving: 8

PREP: 10 minutes ■ **COOK:** 8 minutes

Serve this versatile olive relish over crostini or with baked chips as an appetizer.

    4 (6-ounce) tuna steaks (1¼ inches thick)
    ¼ cup light red wine vinegar and olive oil vinaigrette, divided
    ½ teaspoon freshly ground black pepper
    Cooking spray
    1 small tomato, chopped
    ½ cup pitted kalamata olives, halved
    ¼ cup basil leaves, coarsely chopped

1. Preheat grill to medium-high heat.
2. Brush fish with 2 tablespoons vinaigrette; sprinkle with pepper. Place fish on grill rack coated with cooking spray; grill 4 to 6 minutes on each side or until desired degree of doneness. Transfer to a platter; keep warm.
3. Combine tomato, olives, remaining 2 tablespoons vinaigrette, and basil. Spoon tomato relish over grilled fish. **YIELD: 4 SERVINGS (SERVING SIZE: 1 TUNA STEAK AND ABOUT ⅓ CUP TOMATO RELISH).**

PER SERVING: Calories 327; Fat 15.5g (sat 3g, mono 6.3g, poly 3g); Protein 40.3g; Carb 3.8g; Fiber 0.5g; Chol 65mg; Iron 2mg; Sodium 551mg; Calc 28mg

CORIANDER AND FENNEL SEED TUNA SKEWERS

PointsPlus value per serving: 3

PREP: 6 minutes ■ COOK: 4 minutes

Using a quick rub of coriander and fennel seeds gives this tuna an exotic flavor. Don't skip the squeeze of fresh lime at the end.

1 tablespoon coriander seeds
1 tablespoon fennel seeds
¾ teaspoon freshly ground black pepper
¼ teaspoon salt
4 (4-ounce) tuna steaks, cut into 2-inch pieces
1 tablespoon light lime vinaigrette (such as Newman's Own)
4 (10-inch) metal skewers
1 lime, cut into wedges

1. Combine coriander and fennel seeds in a food processor or spice grinder; pulse 10 times. Transfer seeds to a shallow dish; stir in pepper and salt. Brush fish with vinaigrette. Dredge fish in spice mixture. Thread fish onto 4 (10-inch) metal skewers.
2. Heat a cast-iron skillet over high heat. Cook skewers 2 minutes on each side or until desired degree of doneness. Serve with lime wedges. **YIELD: 4 SERVINGS (SERVING SIZE: 1 SKEWER).**

PER SERVING: Calories 146; Fat 2.3g (sat 0.4g, mono 0.5g, poly 0.4g); Protein 27g; Carb 4g; Fiber 1.8g; Chol 51mg; Iron 1.4mg; Sodium 231mg; Calc 47mg

ABOUT CORIANDER AND CILANTRO

These two seasonings come from the same plant: The seeds are referred to as coriander, which when ground imparts a grassy, peppery flavor to foods. The leaves are known as cilantro, which is often used in salsas, as a garnish, or in stir-fries, soups, and stews.

THAI TUNA CAKES

PointsPlus value per serving: 3

PREP: 16 minutes ■ COOK: 10 minutes

Easy weeknight meals don't have to be ordinary. These flavor-packed cakes are superquick and tasty. Substitute canned salmon for tuna, if you prefer.

3 (5-ounce) cans very-low-sodium solid white albacore tuna in water, drained and flaked
2 large egg whites, lightly beaten
½ cup panko (Japanese breadcrumbs)
2 tablespoons chopped fresh cilantro
2 tablespoons light mayonnaise
1 tablespoon fresh lime juice
1½ teaspoons salt-free Thai seasoning
¼ teaspoon salt
Cooking spray
7 teaspoons sweet chili sauce (such as Maggi)

1. Combine first 8 ingredients in a bowl; mix well. Divide mixture into 7 equal portions, shaping each into a ½-inch-thick patty.
2. Heat a large nonstick skillet over medium-high heat. Coat pan with cooking spray. Add half of cakes; cook 2 minutes on each side or until golden brown and crisp. Remove from pan; keep warm. Repeat procedure with remaining cakes. Serve warm with chili sauce. **YIELD: 7 SERVINGS (SERVING SIZE: 1 CAKE AND 1 TEASPOON CHILI SAUCE).**

PER SERVING: Calories 122; Fat 2.8g (sat 0.3g, mono 0.9g, poly 1.5g); Protein 17.7g; Carb 5.5g; Fiber 0g; Chol 29mg; Iron 0.4mg; Sodium 174mg; Calc 1mg

SPICY BEER-STEAMED MUSSELS

PointsPlus value per serving: 9   *pictured on page 63*

PREP: 16 minutes ■ COOK: 12 minutes

Lager is an essential ingredient in this tasty sauce. Be sure to use a high-quality lager such as Samuel Adams or Stella Artois. Coat bread with cooking spray, and toast or grill it while the mussels steam.

1 tablespoon olive oil
Cooking spray
½ cup chopped onion
1 teaspoon crushed red pepper
4 garlic cloves, finely chopped
1 (11.2-ounce) bottle lager
56 mussels (about 2 pounds), scrubbed and debearded
2 tablespoons fresh lemon juice
⅛ teaspoon salt
4 (1-ounce) slices diagonally cut crusty peasant bread,
      toasted
1 tablespoon chopped fresh parsley (optional)

1. Heat oil in a large Dutch oven over medium heat. Coat pan with cooking spray. Add onion; sauté 2 minutes. Add red pepper and garlic; sauté 1 minute.
2. Add lager, and bring to a boil. Add mussels; cover and cook 5 minutes or until shells open. Remove from heat; discard any unopened shells. Sprinkle mussels with lemon juice and salt; stir well. Place mussels in wide, shallow bowls; ladle broth over mussels. Serve with toast. Sprinkle with parsley, if desired. YIELD: 4 SERVINGS (SERVING SIZE: ABOUT 14 MUSSELS, ABOUT ⅔ CUP BROTH, AND 1 SLICE TOAST).

PER SERVING: Calories 341; Fat 8.9g (sat 1.5g, mono 3.7g, poly 1.9g); Protein 30g; Carb 26.2g; Fiber 0.8g; Chol 64mg; Iron 9.8mg; Sodium 878mg; Calc 70mg

HOW TO SCRUB AND DEBEARD MUSSELS

It will take just a few seconds to scrub and debeard each mussel.

1. When ready to cook, scrub each mussel to remove any sand or dirt on the shell. Holding it under cool water, scrub each mussel's shell with a stiff-bristled brush, such as those used for cleaning vegetables.

2. Next, debeard to remove the byssal threads (or beard), which connect the mussel to rocks or pilings in the sea. Grab the fibers with your fingers, and pull them out, tugging toward the hinged point of the shell.

SCALLOPS WITH COCONUT, LIME, AND CHILE BROTH

PointsPlus value per serving: 6

PREP: 5 minutes ■ COOK: 8 minutes

This dish has a spicy punch with the addition of chile paste with garlic. Kick it up more with another teaspoon, if you really like it hot!

1 tablespoon canola oil
2 garlic cloves, minced
1 (13.5-ounce) can light coconut milk
1 tablespoon lemongrass paste
2 teaspoons chile paste with garlic (such as sambal oelek)
1 teaspoon fish sauce
1 teaspoon grated lime rind
1 tablespoon fresh lime juice
16 large sea scallops (about 1½ pounds)
Cilantro leaves (optional)

1. Heat oil in a large nonstick skillet over medium heat. Add garlic; sauté 1 minute or until tender. Add coconut milk and next 5 ingredients. Cook 3 minutes or until bubbly. Add scallops; cook 1½ minutes on each side or until scallops are done.
2. Divide scallops and broth evenly among 4 bowls. Top with cilantro, if desired. Serve immediately. YIELD: 4 SERVINGS (SERVING SIZE: 4 SCALLOPS AND ABOUT 1 CUP COCONUT BROTH).

PER SERVING: Calories 246; Fat 9.9g (sat 4.7g, mono 2.3g, poly 1.4g); Protein 29.9g; Carb 9.3g; Fiber 0.1g; Chol 56mg; Iron 0.9mg; Sodium 568mg; Calc 45mg

GRILLED SCALLOPS WITH CHAMPAGNE VINAIGRETTE AND PEACH SALSA

PointsPlus value per serving: 5   *pictured on page 59*

PREP: 7 minutes ■ COOK: 6 minutes

This restaurant-inspired dish is great served alongside steamed asparagus or salad greens to soak up the sweet salsa and vinaigrette.

12 large sea scallops (about 1½ pounds)
¼ teaspoon salt
¼ teaspoon freshly ground black pepper
Cooking spray
3 tablespoons Champagne vinegar
1 tablespoon extra-virgin olive oil
1 tablespoon minced shallots
2 teaspoons honey
1 teaspoon Dijon mustard
1 cup chopped peeled peach (about 1 large)
¼ cup minced red bell pepper
2 tablespoons minced red onion
1 tablespoon chopped fresh cilantro

1. Preheat grill to medium–high heat.
2. Sprinkle scallops evenly with salt and pepper. Place on grill rack coated with cooking spray. Grill 3 minutes on each side or until scallops are done.
3. While scallops grill, combine vinegar and next 4 ingredients, stirring well with a whisk. Set aside.
4. Combine peaches and next 3 ingredients. Divide scallops evenly among 4 plates; drizzle with vinaigrette, and top with salsa. YIELD: 4 SERVINGS (SERVING SIZE: 3 SCALLOPS, ABOUT ⅓ CUP SALSA, AND 1⅓ TABLESPOONS VINAIGRETTE).

PER SERVING: Calories 218; Fat 5.1g (sat 0.7g, mono 2.7g, poly 1g); Protein 29.1g; Carb 13g; Fiber 0.9g; Chol 56mg; Iron 0.7mg; Sodium 452mg; Calc 47mg

DRY- VS. WET-PACKED SCALLOPS

When buying scallops, opt for dry-packed scallops. "Wet-packed" scallops have been treated with a liquid solution containing sodium tripolyphosphate. The scallops absorb this mixture and plump up, resulting in a heavier weight and a higher market price. But when you cook them, the liquid portion will cook out, leaving you with smaller scallops and a higher sodium content. "Dry-packed" scallops are not chemically treated and are preferable over wet-packed for price and lower sodium content.

PAN-SEARED SCALLOPS WITH SUCCOTASH

PointsPlus value per serving: 8

PREP: 5 minutes ■ COOK: 27 minutes

Use fresh corn, lima beans, and tomatoes from the farmers' market during the summer. Substitute 2 seeded and chopped medium tomatoes for the canned tomatoes.

1½ cups frozen baby lima beans
12 large sea scallops (about 1½ pounds)
¼ teaspoon salt, divided
¼ teaspoon freshly ground black pepper, divided
Cooking spray
2 teaspoons olive oil
½ cup finely chopped onion
1½ cups frozen whole-kernel corn, thawed
1 (14.5-ounce) can diced tomatoes, drained
2 tablespoons sherry vinegar
2 teaspoons butter

1. Cook lima beans in boiling water 20 minutes or until tender; drain.
2. Meanwhile, pat scallops dry with paper towels. Sprinkle scallops evenly with ⅛ teaspoon salt and ⅛ teaspoon pepper. Heat a large skillet over medium-high heat. Coat pan with cooking spray. Add scallops to pan; cook 3 minutes on each side or until done. Remove scallops from pan; keep warm.
3. Heat olive oil in pan; add onion, and sauté 3 minutes or until tender. Add lima beans, corn, tomatoes, remaining ⅛ teaspoon salt, and remaining ⅛ teaspoon pepper. Cook 2 minutes or until thoroughly heated. Add vinegar; cook 2 minutes or until liquid almost evaporates. Remove from heat; add butter, stirring until butter melts. Serve scallops over succotash. YIELD: 4 SERVINGS (SERVING SIZE: 3 SCALLOPS AND ¾ CUP SUCCOTASH).

PER SERVING: Calories 354; Fat 6.7g (sat 1.8g, mono 2.4g, poly 1.1g); Protein 36g; Carb 36.1g; Fiber 6.5g; Chol 61mg; Iron 2.1mg; Sodium 560mg; Calc 68mg

GRILLED SHRIMP WITH WASABI DIP

PointsPlus value per serving: 6

PREP: 3 minutes ■ **COOK:** 7 minutes

Grilled shrimp gets a spicy kick from this low-calorie, yet full-flavored, wasabi dip. You can also serve this as an appetizer.

⅓ cup light mayonnaise
¼ cup plain fat-free Greek yogurt
1 tablespoon chopped green onions
2 teaspoons wasabi paste
1 teaspoon Worcestershire sauce
1 teaspoon fresh lemon juice
1½ pounds large shrimp, peeled and deveined
¼ teaspoon salt
¼ teaspoon freshly ground black pepper
Cooking spray

1. Preheat grill to medium–high heat.
2. Combine first 6 ingredients in a small bowl. Set aside.
3. Sprinkle shrimp evenly with salt and pepper; arrange in a grill basket coated with cooking spray. Grill 7 minutes or until shrimp are done, turning once. Serve shrimp with wasabi dip. **YIELD: 4 SERVINGS (SERVING SIZE: ABOUT 9 SHRIMP AND 3 TABLESPOONS WASABI DIP).**

PER SERVING: Calories 276; Fat 10.1g (sat 1.9g, mono 2g, poly 4.7g); Protein 35.8g; Carb 5.5g; Fiber 0.1g; Chol 265mg; Iron 4.2mg; Sodium 629mg; Calc 101mg

BBQ SHRIMP

PointsPlus value per serving: 6

PREP: 2 minutes ■ **COOK:** 11 minutes

Be sure to serve this traditional New Orleans dish with plenty of napkins—and French bread to sop up the flavorful sauce.

1 tablespoon olive oil
½ cup chopped onion
3 garlic cloves, minced
3 lemons, sliced
½ cup water
¼ cup lower-sodium Worcestershire sauce
¼ cup dry white wine
2 tablespoons chopped fresh parsley
1 tablespoon chopped fresh rosemary
¾ teaspoon Creole seasoning
2 pounds large shrimp, peeled and deveined

1. Heat oil in a large Dutch oven over medium–high heat. Add onion and garlic; sauté 3 minutes or until tender. Add lemon slices and next 6 ingredients; bring to a boil. Add shrimp. Cover, reduce heat, and simmer 3 minutes or until shrimp are done, stirring occasionally. Divide mixture evenly among 5 bowls. **YIELD: 5 SERVINGS (SERVING SIZE: ABOUT 1½ CUPS).**

PER SERVING: Calories 242; Fat 5.9g (sat 1g, mono 2.4g, poly 1.5g); Protein 37.3g; Carb 7.3g; Fiber 0.5g; Chol 276mg; Iron 4.7mg; Sodium 377mg; Calc 110mg

LOWCOUNTRY BOIL PACKETS

PointsPlus value per serving: 7   *pictured on page 61*

PREP: 12 minutes ■ COOK: 37 minutes

Bring this flavorful one-dish meal straight from the grill to the table.

    Cooking spray
    2 cups refrigerated potato wedges (such as Simply
        Potatoes)
    3 ears corn, each cut crosswise in half
    ½ cup water
    36 large shrimp (about 1½ pounds), peeled and deveined
    1 tablespoon Old Bay seasoning
    8 ounces reduced-fat smoked turkey sausage, cut into
        1-inch pieces
    1 large red onion, cut into 12 wedges
    3 large lemons, halved

1. Heat a large nonstick skillet over medium-high heat. Coat pan with cooking spray. Add potatoes; cover and cook 20 minutes or until potatoes are almost tender, stirring occasionally.

2. Preheat grill to medium heat.

3. Place corn and ½ cup water in a microwave-safe bowl. Cover with plastic wrap; vent. Microwave at HIGH 5 minutes or until tender.

4. Combine shrimp and Old Bay seasoning. Fold 6 (20 x 12–inch) sheets of heavy-duty foil in half lengthwise. Open foil; place 6 shrimp, ⅓ cup potatoes, 1 piece corn, 3 pieces sausage, 2 onion wedges, and 1 lemon half on 1 half of each foil sheet. Fold foil over shrimp and vegetables; tightly seal edges.

5. Place packets on grill rack. Grill 12 to 15 minutes or until shrimp are done and vegetables are tender. YIELD: 6 SERVINGS (SERVING SIZE: 1 FOIL PACKET).

PER SERVING: Calories 300; Fat 6.5g (sat 1.7g, mono 2g, poly 1.9g); Protein 33.1g; Carb 28.3g; Fiber 3.7g; Chol 194mg; Iron 3.5mg; Sodium 787mg; Calc 76mg

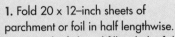

FOIL AND PARCHMENT PACKETS

This healthy cooking method is known in French as *en papillote*, which involves wrapping ingredients in a sealed foil or parchment package before cooking. Parchment paper works with all ingredients. Foil is a good substitute except in recipes containing lots of acidic foods—foil can react with those foods and create off flavors or colors. To prepare the packets, follow these tips:

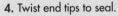

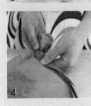

1. Fold 20 x 12–inch sheets of parchment or foil in half lengthwise.

2. Open the foil, and fill with the fish or shellfish and vegetables on 1 half of the sheet, making sure to leave a border around the edge. Sprinkle with any seasonings you like.

3. Fold paper over filling ingredients, and, starting at one end, fold paper, tightly sealing edges with narrow folds.

4. Twist end tips to seal.

Whether the packets are baked or grilled, this method steams the fish, meat, poultry, or vegetables inside, yielding flavorful, tender results.

SESAME-HONEY SHRIMP

PointsPlus value per serving: 8

PREP: 10 minutes ■ **COOK:** 10 minutes

Serve this as a much healthier alternative to take-out Chinese.

⅓ cup honey
¼ cup rice vinegar
1 tablespoon light brown sugar
2 tablespoons lower-sodium soy sauce
1 tablespoon cornstarch
2 tablespoons water
¼ teaspoon salt
36 large shrimp (about 1½ pounds), peeled and deveined
1 tablespoon toasted sesame seeds

1. Combine first 4 ingredients in a large nonstick skillet, stirring with a whisk. Bring to a boil, stirring frequently. Combine cornstarch and 2 tablespoons water; add to honey mixture. Cook 1 minute or until thickened. Stir in salt.
2. Add shrimp to pan; cook 3 to 5 minutes or until shrimp are done, stirring frequently. Sprinkle with sesame seeds before serving. **YIELD: 4 SERVINGS (SERVING SIZE: 9 SHRIMP).**

PER SERVING: Calories 299; Fat 4.1g (sat 0.7g, mono 0.9g, poly 1.6g); Protein 35.5g; Carb 29.9g; Fiber 0.4g; Chol 259mg; Iron 4.7mg; Sodium 667mg; Calc 115mg

✳ Cornstarch

Cornstarch, which is the starch that comes from the corn kernel, is used as a thickening agent in soups, sauces, gravies, and stir-fries.

SHRIMP AND LINGUINE WITH LEMON-BASIL CREAM SAUCE

PointsPlus value per serving: 8   *pictured on page 60*

PREP: 6 minutes ■ **COOK:** 11 minutes

Fresh shrimp and pasta paired with a citrusy basil cream sauce make this rich-tasting, yet healthy, dish a sure winner.

1 tablespoon olive oil
1¼ pounds peeled and deveined large shrimp
¼ teaspoon salt
¼ teaspoon freshly ground black pepper
2 garlic cloves, minced
1 (9-ounce) package refrigerated linguine
1 (10-ounce) container light Alfredo sauce (such as Buitoni)
¼ cup chopped fresh basil
1 teaspoon grated lemon rind
1 tablespoon fresh lemon juice

1. Heat oil in a large nonstick skillet over medium-high heat. Sprinkle shrimp with salt and pepper; add shrimp and garlic to hot oil. Cook 5 minutes or until shrimp are done, stirring occasionally. Remove shrimp from pan.
2. Cook pasta according to package directions, omitting salt and fat.
3. While pasta cooks, combine Alfredo sauce and next 3 ingredients in pan. Cook 1 minute or until thoroughly heated. Return shrimp to pan; cook 1 minute or until thoroughly heated. Toss shrimp mixture with pasta. Serve immediately. **YIELD: 6 SERVINGS (SERVING SIZE: 1 CUP).**

PER SERVING: Calories 304; Fat 9g (sat 3.4g, mono 3.4g, poly 1.1g); Protein 27.4g; Carb 28g; Fiber 1.1g; Chol 184mg; Iron 3.3mg; Sodium 499mg; Calc 141mg

meatless main dishes

Grilled Vegetable Tacos, *page 78*

GRILLED VEGETABLE TACOS

PointsPlus value per serving: 8   *pictured on page 77*

PREP: 10 minutes ■ COOK: 12 minutes

Crunchy taco shells and soft tortillas provide a pleasing texture contrast for a tasty grilled vegetable filling.

    1 red onion, quartered
    1 large zucchini, cut lengthwise into ¼-inch-thick slices
    1 yellow bell pepper, halved and seeded
    Cooking spray
    ½ teaspoon chili powder
    1½ teaspoons Worcestershire sauce
    ¼ teaspoon salt
    ¼ teaspoon freshly ground black pepper
    ½ cup refrigerated guacamole (such as Wholly)
    6 (6-inch) flour tortillas
    6 (0.3-ounce) hard taco shells
    ½ cup pico de gallo
    1 cup (4 ounces) shredded Monterey Jack cheese

1. Preheat grill to medium-high heat.
2. Place first 3 ingredients on grill rack coated with cooking spray; grill 10 minutes or until vegetables are tender, turning occasionally. Cut vegetables into bite-sized pieces. Combine vegetables, chili powder, and next 3 ingredients.
3. While vegetables grill, spread about 1 tablespoon guacamole in center of each tortilla, leaving a 1-inch border. Place a hard taco shell in center of each tortilla, and gently press flour tortillas around shells, allowing guacamole to adhere. Spoon vegetable mixture evenly into taco shells; top each with about 1 tablespoon pico de gallo and about 2½ tablespoons cheese. **YIELD: 6 SERVINGS (SERVING SIZE: 1 TACO).**

PER SERVING: Calories 291; Fat 12.3g (sat 4.7g, mono 3.6g, poly 0.6g); Protein 10.4g; Carb 37.2g; Fiber 4.5g; Chol 17mg; Iron 1mg; Sodium 649mg; Calc 177mg

GRILLING VEGETABLES

Grilling adds a whole new taste sensation to vegetables, especially when they take on a chargrilled flavor and appearance. Depending on the recipe, you can either grill the vegetables first and then slice them, or you can slice them first. The best vegetables to grill are sturdy ones such as eggplant, yellow squash, zucchini, tomatoes, bell peppers, potatoes, and onions.

BLACK BEAN AND RICE PATTIES

PointsPlus value per serving: 6

PREP: 6 minutes ■ COOK: 18 minutes

Black beans, brown rice, and a colorful confetti of bell pepper combine to make a healthy vegetarian meal with Southwestern flair.

    1 (3½-ounce) bag boil-in-bag brown rice
    1 (15-ounce) can no-salt-added black beans, rinsed and drained
    ½ cup refrigerated prechopped tri-color bell pepper
    3 tablespoons whole-wheat panko (Japanese breadcrumbs)
    1 tablespoon 40%-less-sodium taco seasoning
    ¼ teaspoon salt
    ¼ teaspoon black pepper
    2 garlic cloves, minced
    1 large egg, lightly beaten
    Cooking spray
    8 teaspoons light sour cream
    ½ cup (2 ounces) shredded part-skim mozzarella cheese
    ½ cup fresh salsa
    8 teaspoons chopped fresh cilantro
    4 lime wedges (optional)

1. Cook rice according to package directions, omitting salt and fat.
2. Place black beans in a medium bowl; mash. Add cooked rice, bell pepper, and next 6 ingredients, stirring until combined. Divide bean mixture into 8 equal portions, shaping each into a ½-inch-thick patty.
3. Heat a large nonstick skillet over medium-high heat. Coat pan with cooking spray. Add patties; cook 4 minutes. Carefully turn patties over; cook 4 minutes or until lightly browned and thoroughly heated. Serve patties with sour cream, cheese, and salsa; sprinkle with fresh cilantro. Serve with a lime wedge, if desired.
YIELD: 4 SERVINGS (SERVING SIZE: 2 PATTIES, 2 TEASPOONS SOUR CREAM, 2 TABLESPOONS CHEESE, 2 TABLESPOONS SALSA, AND 2 TEASPOONS CILANTRO).

PER SERVING: Calories 253; Fat 6.4g (sat 2.9g, mono 0.8g, poly 0.2g); Protein 12.5g; Carb 37.1g; Fiber 5.4g; Chol 64mg; Iron 1.6mg; Sodium 475mg; Calc 156mg

HOW TO MAKE VEGETABLE PATTIES

You can easily create vegetable burgers and patties at home using beans, grains, and fresh vegetables—nutrient-packed ingredients that are high in protein and fiber but low in saturated fat. Start with a protein source, such as beans or soy, and add a grain, such as rice or oatmeal. You can add in other layers of flavor by incorporating fresh or sautéed vegetables, herbs, and spices. A binding agent like breadcrumbs holds the mixture together and absorbs excess moisture so you can form patties and cook the patties on the grill or in a skillet with a small amount of oil.

BLACK BEAN AND AVOCADO QUESADILLAS

PointsPlus value per serving: 8

PREP: 3 minutes ■ COOK: 10 minutes

Spice up the quick guacamole with a little chopped jalapeño, if you like.

1 ripe peeled avocado
1 tablespoon fresh lime juice
¼ teaspoon salt
¼ teaspoon black pepper
4 (8-inch) flour tortillas
1 (15-ounce) can no-salt-added black beans, rinsed and drained
½ cup (2 ounces) preshredded reduced-fat 4-cheese Mexican blend cheese
Cooking spray
½ cup bottled salsa

1. Place first 4 ingredients in a small bowl; mash to desired consistency.
2. Spread avocado mixture evenly over 2 tortillas. Top each with half of beans, half of cheese, and 1 tortilla.
3. Place a large nonstick skillet over medium heat. Coat pan and 1 side of each quesadilla with cooking spray. Add 1 quesadilla to pan; cook 2 to 3 minutes on each side or until lightly browned and cheese melts. Remove quesadilla from pan, and keep warm. Repeat with remaining quesadilla. Cut each quesadilla into 6 wedges; serve with salsa. YIELD: 4 SERVINGS (SERVING SIZE: 3 WEDGES AND 2 TABLESPOONS SALSA).

PER SERVING: Calories 315; Fat 11.8g (sat 3.8g, mono 3.3g, poly 1.6g); Protein 11.7g; Carb 41.5g; Fiber 9.3g; Chol 13mg; Iron 3mg; Sodium 660mg; Calc 247mg

CRISPY POLENTA ROUNDS WITH BLACK-EYED PEA SALAD

PointsPlus value per serving: 6

PREP: 7 minutes ■ COOK: 7 minutes

Cotija is a hard, white Mexican cheese that is typically crumbled or grated. You can easily substitute Parmesan, feta, or goat cheese.

1 (18-ounce) tube of polenta, cut into 12 slices
Cooking spray
1 (15-ounce) can black-eyed peas, rinsed and drained
1½ cups chopped tomato
¼ cup chopped fresh cilantro
3 tablespoons finely chopped red onion
2 tablespoons red wine vinegar
2 teaspoons garlic-flavored olive oil
¼ teaspoon freshly ground black pepper
⅛ teaspoon salt
⅔ cup crumbled cotija cheese

1. Heat a large nonstick skillet over medium–high heat. Coat both sides of polenta slices with cooking spray; cook 3 minutes on each side or until lightly browned.
2. While polenta cooks, combine peas and next 7 ingredients in a medium bowl, tossing to coat. Serve black-eyed pea salad over polenta rounds; sprinkle evenly with cheese. YIELD: 4 SERVINGS (SERVING SIZE: 3 POLENTA ROUNDS, ¾ CUP BLACK-EYED PEA SALAD, AND ABOUT 2½ TABLESPOONS CHEESE).

PER SERVING: Calories 270; Fat 8g (sat 3.7g, mono 3.2g, poly 0.6g); Protein 10.9g; Carb 36g; Fiber 6.2g; Chol 20mg; Iron 2.2mg; Sodium 727mg; Calc 149mg

LENTILS AND RICE WITH CARAMELIZED ONIONS

PointsPlus value per serving: 6

PREP: 5 minutes ■ **COOK:** 45 minutes

Farmer cheese is a form of cottage cheese from which most of the liquid has been pressed out. It has a mild, slightly tangy flavor and is usually sliced or crumbled. Goat cheese and feta cheese are good substitutes.

1 tablespoon olive oil
2 medium-sized white onions (about 1½ pounds), cut into
        ¼-inch-thick slices
1 tablespoon balsamic vinegar
1 (32-ounce) container organic vegetable broth
1¼ cups dried lentils
¼ teaspoon salt
¼ teaspoon freshly ground black pepper
¾ cup instant brown rice
3 tablespoons crumbled soft skim-milk farmer cheese

1. Heat oil in a large nonstick skillet over medium heat. Add sliced onion; cook 25 to 30 minutes or until deep golden brown, stirring frequently. Remove from heat; stir in balsamic vinegar.
2. While onions cook, bring broth to a boil in a large saucepan. Add lentils, salt, and pepper; boil 2 minutes. Cover, reduce heat, and simmer 25 minutes. Add rice; cover and simmer 7 minutes or until lentils and rice are tender and liquid is almost absorbed.
3. Remove from heat; let stand 10 minutes. Stir in half of onion. Spoon into bowls; top with remaining half of onion, and sprinkle with cheese. YIELD: 6 SERVINGS (SERVING SIZE: 1 CUP LENTIL MIXTURE, ABOUT 2½ TABLESPOONS ONIONS, AND 1½ TEASPOONS CHEESE).

PER SERVING: Calories 244; Fat 3.5g (sat 0.8g, mono 1.9g, poly 0.4g); Protein 14.1g; Carb 41.5g; Fiber 6.5g; Chol 3mg; Iron 3.8mg; Sodium 493mg; Calc 32mg

CURRIED SHEPHERD'S PIE

PointsPlus value per serving: 7   *pictured on page 62*

PREP: 6 minutes ■ **COOK:** 21 minutes

Curry powders can range in flavor from mild and sweet to hot and spicy. Choose the curry powder that reflects your preference for this meatless comfort dish.

2 cups steam-and-mash frozen garlic-seasoned potatoes
        (such as Ore-Ida Steam n' Mash Garlic Seasoned
        Potatoes)
1 cup light coconut milk, divided
1 tablespoon curry powder, divided
Cooking spray
1 (12-ounce) package frozen meatless crumbles (such as
        Morningstar Farms), thawed
½ cup chopped onion
1 cup frozen petite peas, thawed
1 (14.5-ounce) can diced tomatoes with onion and garlic,
        undrained

1. Preheat oven to 400°.
2. Place potatoes in a medium microwave-safe bowl. Cover with plastic wrap; vent. Microwave at HIGH 5 minutes or until tender. Uncover; add ½ cup coconut milk and 1½ teaspoons curry powder. Mash until smooth.
3. While potatoes cook, heat a large nonstick skillet over medium-high heat. Coat pan with cooking spray. Add meatless crumbles and onion; cook 5 minutes or until onion is tender, stirring frequently. Add peas and remaining 1½ teaspoons curry powder; cook 1 minute. Stir in tomatoes and remaining ½ cup coconut milk; cook 1 minute.
4. Spoon mixture into an 8-inch square glass or ceramic baking dish coated with cooking spray. Spread mashed potatoes over meatless mixture, smoothing with the back of a spoon. Bake at 400° for 15 minutes or until thoroughly heated. YIELD: 4 SERVINGS (SERVING SIZE: 1½ CUPS).

PER SERVING: Calories 295; Fat 10.1g (sat 4.6g, mono 2.1g, poly 3.5g); Protein 20.5g; Carb 33.4g; Fiber 7.6g; Chol 7mg; Iron 4.8mg; Sodium 818mg; Calc 35mg

GREEK TEMPEH ROLL-UPS

PointsPlus value per serving: 7

PREP: 4 minutes ■ COOK: 4 minutes

Tempeh is made from cooked soybeans and has an earthy, mild flavor. It has a firm texture, making it perfect to cut into strips for stir-fries or cubes for soups.

> 1 (6-ounce) carton plain 2% reduced-fat Greek yogurt
> ½ cup chopped seeded peeled cucumber
> 1 teaspoon salt-free garlic and herb seasoning blend (such as Mrs. Dash)
> 1 (8-ounce) package garden veggie tempeh (such as Lightlife), cut into 8 strips
> 1 cup shredded iceberg lettuce
> ½ cup chopped seeded tomato
> 4 tablespoons (1 ounce) crumbled reduced-fat feta cheese
> 4 (8-inch) flour tortillas

1. Preheat panini grill.
2. Combine first 3 ingredients in a small bowl. Cover and chill until ready to serve.
3. Cut each tempeh strip into 3 pieces. Arrange 6 pieces tempeh, ¼ cup lettuce, 2 tablespoons tomato, 1 tablespoon yogurt sauce, and 1 tablespoon feta in center of each tortilla; roll up tightly.
4. Place tortillas, seam sides down, on panini grill; cook 4 minutes or until lightly browned. Serve with remaining yogurt sauce. **YIELD: 4 SERVINGS (SERVING SIZE: 1 ROLL-UP AND 2 TABLESPOONS YOGURT SAUCE).**

PER SERVING: Calories 269; Fat 7.6g (sat 2.7g, mono 1.8g, poly 0.8g); Protein 18.6g; Carb 31.8g; Fiber 5.6g; Chol 5mg; Iron 3mg; Sodium 490mg; Calc 190mg

Tempeh

Tempeh's nutty, subtle, tangy flavor comes from the fermentation process used to make this pebbled soybean cake. When the temperature changes, the bacteria present in tempeh may cause small patches of gray or black spores to bloom on the surface of the cake. These spores are harmless and only add to tempeh's unique yeasty flavor.

BLACKENED TOFU WITH EDAMAME MAQUE CHOUX

PointsPlus value per serving: 8

PREP: 13 minutes ■ COOK: 12 minutes

Leave the seeds in the jalapeño pepper if you like extra-spicy foods. Blackening creates a lot of smoke, so be sure to cook in a well-ventilated area.

> 2 (8-ounce) packages smoked tofu (such as SoyBoy)
> Butter-flavored cooking spray
> 2½ cups frozen whole-kernel corn
> ½ cup chopped onion
> ½ cup chopped green bell pepper
> 1½ tablespoons finely chopped seeded jalapeño pepper
> 2 garlic cloves, minced
> 1 cup chopped tomato
> 1½ teaspoons salt-free blackened Creole seasoning, divided (such as Frontier)
> ½ teaspoon salt, divided
> 1 cup frozen shelled edamame (green soybeans), thawed

1. Cut each tofu block into 5 slices.
2. Place a large nonstick skillet over medium–high heat. Coat pan with cooking spray. Add corn and next 4 ingredients; sauté 5 minutes or until corn begins to brown. Add tomato, ½ teaspoon blackened seasoning, and ¼ teaspoon salt; cook 2 minutes or until vegetables are tender, stirring occasionally. Stir in edamame; cook 1 minute. Spoon into a bowl; keep warm. Wipe pan with paper towels.
3. Combine remaining 1 teaspoon blackened seasoning and remaining ¼ teaspoon salt. Rub evenly over both sides of tofu; coat both sides of tofu slices with cooking spray. Heat pan over medium–high heat. Add tofu slices; cook 2 minutes on each side or until lightly browned. Serve with maque choux. **YIELD: 5 SERVINGS (SERVING SIZE: 4 SLICES TOFU AND ABOUT ¾ CUP MAQUE CHOUX).**

PER SERVING: Calories 300; Fat 10.3g (sat 1.7g, mono 2.2g, poly 5.7g); Protein 23.4g; Carb 32.4g; Fiber 4.9g; Chol 0mg; Iron 1.9mg; Sodium 629mg; Calc 31mg

GREEN PIZZA

PointsPlus value per serving: 8

PREP: 5 minutes ■ **COOK:** 11 minutes

A trio of green replaces traditional, less-healthy toppings in this tasty meatless pizza.

Olive oil–flavored cooking spray
2½ cups broccoli florets, coarsely chopped
2 cups bagged baby spinach leaves
2 garlic cloves, crushed
½ teaspoon crushed red pepper
½ cup reduced-fat commercial pesto (such as Buitoni)
1 (10-ounce) Italian cheese-flavored thin pizza crust (such as Boboli)
1 cup (4 ounces) shredded part-skim mozzarella cheese

1. Preheat oven to 450°.
2. Heat a large nonstick skillet over medium–high heat. Heavily coat pan with cooking spray. Add broccoli; sauté 2 minutes. Add spinach, garlic, and red pepper; sauté 30 seconds. Remove pan from heat.
3. Spread pesto over pizza crust; top with broccoli mixture, and sprinkle with cheese. Bake at 450° for 8 minutes or until crust is golden brown. Cut into 6 slices. **YIELD: 6 SERVINGS (SERVING SIZE: 1 SLICE).**

PER SERVING: Calories 292; Fat 13.2g (sat 5g, mono 2.3g, poly 5g); Protein 13.4g; Carb 29.8g; Fiber 2.8g; Chol 15mg; Iron 2.2mg; Sodium 574mg; Calc 293mg

MAKING PESTO

Store-bought pesto is definitely convenient, but making your own from scratch is another option. There are endless variations, and we offer you a broccoli-walnut pesto option on page 84—one-fourth of the pesto has a *PointsPlus* value per serving of 4.

Smoked Tofu

Smoked tofu is firm, water-packed tofu that has been baked, seasoned, and smoked, which lends it a rich, savory taste perfect for quick recipes or as a stand-in for smoked cheese.

SMOKED BBQ TOFU PIZZA

PointsPlus value per serving: 7   *pictured on page 129*

PREP: 8 minutes ■ **COOK:** 13 minutes

The smoky flavor comes from the tofu, which is then doused with your favorite BBQ sauce. To add a unique twist and a more peppery flavor, use white BBQ sauce in place of the red. The *PointsPlus* value per serving will remain the same.

1 (10-ounce) Italian whole-wheat thin pizza crust (such as Boboli)
Cooking spray
¾ cup barbecue sauce, divided
1 (8-ounce) package smoked tofu, cubed
½ cup chopped green onions
1½ cups (6 ounces) shredded part-skim mozzarella cheese
¼ cup torn fresh cilantro leaves

1. Preheat oven to 450°.
2. Place pizza crust on a baking sheet; coat crust with cooking spray. Spread ¼ cup barbecue sauce over pizza crust, leaving a ½-inch border. Combine tofu and remaining ½ cup barbecue sauce in a small bowl. Arrange tofu mixture and onions over crust; sprinkle with cheese.
3. Bake at 450° for 13 minutes or until cheese melts and pizza is warmed through. Remove pizza from oven; sprinkle with cilantro. Cut into 8 wedges. **YIELD: 8 SERVINGS (SERVING SIZE: 1 WEDGE).**

PER SERVING: Calories 250; Fat 8.8g (sat 3.5g, mono 1.8g, poly 1.6g); Protein 14.9g; Carb 29.6g; Fiber 2.9g; Chol 11mg; Iron 1.1mg; Sodium 715mg; Calc 213mg

FETTUCCINE ALFREDO WITH ASPARAGUS

PointsPlus value per serving: 7

PREP: 10 minutes ■ COOK: 6 minutes

Asparagus brightens up a favorite comfort food.

1 pound asparagus spears
1 (9-ounce) package refrigerated fresh fettuccine
1 (8-ounce) carton 2% low-fat cottage cheese
¼ cup (1 ounce) shredded Asiago cheese
3 tablespoons fat-free milk
¼ teaspoon salt
¼ teaspoon freshly ground black pepper
Dash of grated whole nutmeg

1. Snap off tough ends of asparagus, and cut spears into 2-inch pieces.
2. Cook pasta and asparagus according to pasta package directions, omitting salt and fat. Drain; keep warm.
3. While pasta and asparagus cook, combine cottage cheese and next 5 ingredients in a blender or food processor; process until smooth. Place cottage cheese mixture in a medium saucepan; cook 3 minutes or until mixture is thoroughly heated. Pour sauce over pasta mixture; toss well to coat. YIELD: 4 SERVINGS (SERVING SIZE: ¾ CUP).

PER SERVING: Calories 286; Fat 5.2g (sat 1.9g, mono 0.5g, poly 0.7g); Protein 18.4g; Carb 40.2g; Fiber 4.3g; Chol 12mg; Iron 2.5mg; Sodium 538mg; Calc 144mg

CREAMY BLUE CHEESE FETTUCCINE

PointsPlus value per serving: 8

PREP: 2 minutes ■ COOK: 15 minutes

When tossed with hot pasta, the blue cheese partially melts to create a creamy, flavorful sauce. Pine nuts add the perfect crunch.

6 ounces tomato, carrot, and spinach blend fettuccine
    (such as Ronzoni Garden Delight)
1 tablespoon olive oil, divided
2 garlic cloves, minced
¾ cup (3 ounces) blue cheese, crumbled
1 teaspoon grated lemon rind
1 tablespoon fresh lemon juice
¼ teaspoon salt
¼ teaspoon freshly ground black pepper
2 tablespoons pine nuts, toasted

1. Cook pasta according to package directions, omitting salt and fat. Drain pasta in a colander over a bowl, reserving ¼ cup cooking liquid.
2. Meanwhile, heat 1 teaspoon oil in a large nonstick skillet over medium-high heat. Add garlic; sauté 30 seconds. Remove from heat; add pasta, blue cheese, reserved cooking liquid, lemon rind, lemon juice, remaining 2 teaspoons olive oil, salt, and pepper. Toss well. Sprinkle with pine nuts. YIELD: 4 SERVINGS (SERVING SIZE: ¾ CUP).

PER SERVING: Calories 281; Fat 13.1g (sat 4.6g, mono 5g, poly 2.3g); Protein 10.6g; Carb 32.4g; Fiber 3.3g; Chol 16mg; Iron 1.1mg; Sodium 456mg; Calc 132mg

BROCCOLI-WALNUT PESTO PASTA

PointsPlus value per serving: 8

PREP: 3 minutes ■ **COOK:** 11 minutes

Traditional pesto is made with basil and pine nuts, but here we replace those ingredients with broccoli and walnuts, and add a twist with a hit of lemon.

    2 cups uncooked penne (tube-shaped pasta)
    1 (12-ounce) package fresh broccoli florets
    1 cup organic vegetable broth
    ⅓ cup chopped walnuts, toasted
    ¼ cup (1 ounce) shredded fresh Parmigiano-Reggiano
        cheese
    1 tablespoon extra-virgin olive oil
    1 teaspoon grated lemon rind
    1 tablespoon lemon juice
    ¼ teaspoon salt
    ¼ teaspoon freshly ground black pepper
    2 garlic cloves, halved
    ¼ teaspoon crushed red pepper (optional)

1. Cook pasta according to package directions, omitting salt and fat. Drain pasta in a colander over a bowl, reserving 1 cup cooking liquid.
2. While pasta cooks, microwave broccoli according to package directions. Remove broccoli from microwave. Place broccoli and next 9 ingredients in a food processor; process until well blended. Add 1 cup reserved cooking liquid to processor; process until smooth.
3. Combine broccoli mixture and pasta, tossing to coat. Divide pasta evenly among 4 plates; top with crushed red pepper, if desired. **YIELD: 4 SERVINGS (SERVING SIZE: ABOUT 1 CUP).**

PER SERVING: Calories 302; Fat 11.9g (sat 2.3g, mono 3.9g, poly 4.6g); Protein 11.8g; Carb 38.2g; Fiber 4g; Chol 5mg; Iron 1.6mg; Sodium 434mg; Calc 142mg

PENNE RIGATE WITH ROASTED BELL PEPPER "CREAM"

PointsPlus value per serving: 8

PREP: 8 minutes ■ **COOK:** 13 minutes

Pureed tofu creates the creamy base for this healthy pasta sauce. Be sure to use "silken" tofu for optimum creaminess.

    1 (14.5-ounce) package uncooked penne rigate pasta
        (such as Ronzoni Smart Taste)
    1 cup silken soft tofu, drained
    1 cup drained bottled roasted red bell peppers
    2 tablespoons balsamic vinegar
    ½ teaspoon salt
    ¼ teaspoon freshly ground black pepper
    2 garlic cloves, halved
    ½ cup chopped fresh basil
    6 tablespoons grated fresh Parmesan cheese

1. Cook pasta according to package directions, omitting salt and fat.
2. While pasta cooks, place tofu and next 5 ingredients in a blender or food processor; process until smooth.
3. Drain pasta; immediately toss hot pasta with sauce and basil. Sprinkle with Parmesan cheese. Serve warm.
YIELD: 6 SERVINGS (SERVING SIZE: 1½ CUPS PASTA MIXTURE AND 1 TABLESPOON CHEESE).

PER SERVING: Calories 316; Fat 4.3g (sat 1.3g, mono 1g, poly 1.2g); Protein 14.6g; Carb 54.7g; Fiber 2.3g; Chol 5mg; Iron 2.8mg; Sodium 434mg; Calc 134mg

---

BUYING TOFU

Tofu is low in calories and loaded with vitamins and minerals, including folic acid and iron. It comes in a variety of textures—from silken to extra-firm. Nutritionally, there's not a huge difference among the various textures, but when buying it, make sure you purchase a brand that's fortified with calcium sulfate. A 3-ounce serving of fortified tofu can contain 30% or more of the daily recommendation for calcium; unfortified has a small fraction of that.

ZITI WITH CHERRY TOMATOES, ARUGULA, AND FRESH MOZZARELLA

PointsPlus value per serving: 9   *pictured on page 64*

PREP: 2 minutes ■ COOK: 19 minutes

Look for red, juicy, ripe summer tomatoes for this simple fresh pasta dish.

    2 cups uncooked ziti (short tube-shaped pasta)
    1 tablespoon olive oil
    2 pints cherry tomatoes
    3 large garlic cloves, minced
    ¼ cup organic vegetable broth
    ¼ teaspoon salt
    ¼ teaspoon freshly ground black pepper
    ¼ teaspoon crushed red pepper
    3 cups loosely packed arugula
    1 (8-ounce) container ciliegine mozzarella cheese

1. Cook pasta according to package directions, omitting salt and fat. Drain, reserving ¾ cup pasta water.
2. While pasta cooks, heat oil in a large nonstick skillet over medium-high heat. Add tomatoes and garlic; sauté 2 minutes or until tomatoes begin to burst and garlic is tender. Add broth and next 3 ingredients. Cook 2 minutes or until sauce reduces slightly. Add pasta, pasta water, arugula, and mozzarella; toss gently to coat. Serve immediately. **YIELD: 4 SERVINGS (SERVING SIZE: 1½ CUPS).**

PER SERVING: Calories 345; Fat 13.7g (sat 5.7, mono 5.3g, poly 1.1g); Protein 19.3g; Carb 38.2g; Fiber 2.9g; Chol 0mg; Iron 1.3mg; Sodium 270mg; Calc 292mg

INDIVIDUAL BROCCOLI-CHEDDAR QUICHES

PointsPlus value per serving: 6

PREP: 12 minutes ■ COOK: 50 minutes

Baking these in a water bath ensures even, slow cooking of the egg mixture.

    1 (10-ounce) package frozen chopped broccoli
    4 large eggs
    1½ cups fat-free milk
    2 teaspoons Dijon mustard
    ¼ teaspoon salt
    ¼ teaspoon freshly ground black pepper
    Cooking spray
    1 cup (4 ounces) reduced-fat shredded extrasharp
        cheddar cheese

1. Preheat oven to 325°.
2. Place broccoli in a medium glass bowl; microwave at HIGH 3 minutes or until thawed. Drain and pat dry with paper towels.
3. While broccoli thaws, place eggs in a medium bowl, stirring well with a whisk. Add milk and next 3 ingredients, stirring until blended. Stir in broccoli.
4. Divide broccoli mixture among 4 (10-ounce) custard cups coated with cooking spray; sprinkle cheese over broccoli mixture. Place cups in a 13 x 9–inch metal baking pan; add hot water to pan to a depth of 1 inch. Bake at 325° for 50 minutes or until set. **YIELD: 4 SERVINGS (SERVING SIZE: 1 QUICHE).**

PER SERVING: Calories 217; Fat 11.5g (sat 5.7g, mono 3.9g, poly 1g); Protein 18.5g; Carb 9.9g; Fiber 2.2g; Chol 234mg; Iron 1.5mg; Sodium 576mg; Calc 384mg

OVEN-BAKED OMELET WITH ARUGULA, GOAT CHEESE, AND MUSHROOMS

PointsPlus value per serving: 4

PREP: 10 minutes ■ COOK: 22 minutes

Goat cheese adds creaminess to this fluffy baked omelet. Try using an herbed goat cheese for extra flavor.

Cooking spray
2 cups fat-free milk
1½ cups egg substitute
½ teaspoon salt
¼ teaspoon freshly ground black pepper
2 (4-ounce) packages presliced exotic mushroom blend
1 (4-ounce) package goat cheese, crumbled
1½ cups loosely packed arugula

1. Preheat oven to 325°.
2. Coat a jelly-roll pan with cooking spray; line with parchment paper, allowing parchment to extend over edge of pan. Coat parchment with cooking spray.
3. Combine milk and next 3 ingredients, stirring well with a whisk. Pour into prepared pan. Bake at 325° for 22 minutes or until set.
4. While omelet bakes, place a large nonstick skillet over medium-high heat. Coat pan with cooking spray. Add mushrooms; cook 6 minutes or until tender, stirring occasionally.
5. Remove baked omelet from oven; sprinkle with goat cheese. Lightly spread goat cheese, leaving a ½-inch border. Top with arugula and mushrooms. Starting at long edge of pan, roll up omelet jelly-roll fashion. Place omelet, seam side down, on a platter. Cut into 6 slices. YIELD: 6 SERVINGS (SERVING SIZE: 1 SLICE).

PER SERVING: Calories 143; Fat 6.5g (sat 3.2g, mono 1.5g, poly 1.2g); Protein 15.2g; Carb 6.1g; Fiber 0.5g; Chol 11mg; Iron 2mg; Sodium 414mg; Calc 172mg

GREEK EGGS

PointsPlus value per serving: 8

PREP: 2 minutes ■ COOK: 13 minutes

These eggs are like Huevos Rancheros but with a Greek spin. If you like soft-set eggs, cook them only 7 minutes.

1 (8.5-ounce) package precooked whole-grain vegetable harvest–flavored rice (such as Uncle Ben's)
1 (14.5-ounce) can no-salt-added diced tomatoes with basil, garlic, and oregano, undrained
8 large eggs
¼ teaspoon freshly ground black pepper
¼ cup (1 ounce) crumbled reduced-fat feta cheese with basil and sun-dried tomatoes
¼ cup chopped pitted kalamata olives

1. Prepare rice according to package directions.
2. Pour tomatoes into a large skillet; cook over medium heat 5 minutes or just until simmering. Stir in rice.
3. Make 8 wells in rice mixture using the back of a spoon. Break 1 egg into a small custard cup; carefully pour egg into 1 well in rice. Repeat with remaining eggs. Sprinkle eggs with pepper. Cover and cook 8 minutes or until eggs are done.
4. Spoon about ½ cup rice, 2 eggs, 1 tablespoon feta, and 1 tablespoon olives onto each of 4 plates. YIELD: 4 SERVINGS.

PER SERVING: Calories 311; Fat 16.2g (sat 4.2g, mono 7g, poly 1.8g); Protein 17.7g; Carb 23.7g; Fiber 3.1g; Chol 426mg; Iron 3.1mg; Sodium 758mg; Calc 107mg

✳ Canned Vegetables

While it's often thought that fresh vegetables are better than canned, canned options in fact stack up well nutritionally against fresh. They retain many of the vitamins and minerals that are found in fresh vegetables. The primary nutritional concern in canned vegetables is the sodium content. The best bet is to opt for no-salt-added or lower-sodium varieties. Organic options are often lower in sodium, too.

meats

Pan-Seared Steaks with Warm Tomatoes
and Feta, *page 90*

BEEF SOUVLAKI KEBABS

PointsPlus value per serving: 5

PREP: 12 minutes ■ **COOK:** 5 minutes
■ **OTHER:** 30 minutes

Serve these with basmati or jasmine rice, or stuff the meat and veggies in a pita for a hearty sandwich.

¼ cup fresh lemon juice
1 tablespoon olive oil
1 tablespoon chopped fresh oregano
3 garlic cloves, minced
1 pound top sirloin steak, cut into 1-inch pieces
¼ teaspoon salt
¼ teaspoon freshly ground black pepper
2 cups cherry tomatoes
1 medium-sized red onion, cut into 16 wedges
Cooking spray
½ cup fat-free, lower-sodium beef broth

1. Preheat grill to medium-high heat.
2. Combine first 4 ingredients in a large zip-top plastic bag. Add steak; seal and marinate in refrigerator at least 30 minutes.
3. Remove steak from bag, reserving marinade. Sprinkle steak evenly with salt and pepper. Thread steak alternately with tomatoes and onion onto each of 8 (12-inch) metal skewers. Place skewers on grill rack coated with cooking spray; grill 2 minutes on each side or until desired degree of doneness.
4. While steak grills, place marinade in a small saucepan; add broth to marinade. Bring to a boil; cook until reduced to about ⅓ cup. Pour sauce over grilled kebabs.
YIELD: 4 SERVINGS (SERVING SIZE: 2 KEBABS AND 1½ TABLESPOONS SAUCE).

PER SERVING: Calories 213; Fat 8.2g (sat 2.2g, mono 4.4g, poly 0.6g); Protein 26.5g; Carb 7.8g; Fiber 1.5g; Chol 48mg; Iron 2.2mg; Sodium 272mg; Calc 52mg

METAL AND WOOD SKEWERS

Skewering small chunks of meat and vegetables on long, thin, pointed metal rods or wooden sticks is a grilling tradition. If you grill often, invest in a set of metal skewers, which can be reused. If you use wooden skewers, soak them in water for at least 30 minutes before using them or they'll burn, and discard them after use.

BEEF STIR-FRY RICE BOWL

PointsPlus value per serving: 9

PREP: 8 minutes ■ **COOK:** 12 minutes
■ **OTHER:** 10 minutes

Round out this meal with a steaming cup of green tea and fortune cookies.

1 (1½-pound) flank steak, trimmed
1 cup salt-free spicy teriyaki marinade (such as Mrs. Dash)
1 (7-ounce) package frozen pearled barley, sugar snap peas, and julienne carrots in herb sauce (such as Green Giant)
1 (8.5-ounce) package precooked jasmine rice (such as Uncle Ben's Ready Rice)
¼ teaspoon salt
Cooking spray

1. Cut steak diagonally across grain into thin slices; place steak and marinade in a large heavy-duty zip-top plastic bag. Seal bag; marinate 10 minutes, turning once.
2. While steak marinates, cook vegetables according to package directions; place in a large bowl. Prepare rice according to package directions; add to vegetables in bowl. Add salt; toss well.
3. Remove steak from bag, discarding marinade. Heat a large nonstick skillet over medium-high heat. Coat pan with cooking spray. Add steak; sauté 5 minutes. Add vegetable mixture; cook 1 to 2 minutes or until thoroughly heated. YIELD: 5 SERVINGS (SERVING SIZE: ABOUT 1 CUP).

PER SERVING: Calories 342; Fat 9.5g (sat 2.9g, mono 3.5g, poly 0.7g); Protein 32g; Carb 29.9g; Fiber 1.2g; Chol 45mg; Iron 3mg; Sodium 283mg; Calc 50mg

FLANK STEAK WITH SALSA VERDE

PointsPlus value per serving: 6

PREP: 5 minutes ■ **COOK:** 12 minutes
■ **OTHER:** 5 minutes

The Italian version of this "green sauce" is a bold, flavorful condiment for most grilled meats.

1½ cups fresh flat-leaf parsley leaves
½ cup basil leaves
3 tablespoons extra-virgin olive oil
1 tablespoon fresh lemon juice
1 tablespoon drained capers
1 garlic clove, crushed
½ teaspoon salt, divided
1 (1½-pound) flank steak, trimmed
¼ teaspoon freshly ground black pepper
Cooking spray

1. Preheat grill to medium–high heat.
2. Place first 6 ingredients and ¼ teaspoon salt in a blender or food processor; pulse until finely chopped, scraping down sides of bowl occasionally. Set salsa verde aside.
3. Sprinkle steak with remaining ¼ teaspoon salt and pepper. Place on grill rack coated with cooking spray; grill 6 to 8 minutes per side or until desired degree of doneness. Let steak stand 5 minutes. Cut steak diagonally across grain into thin slices. Serve with salsa verde. **YIELD: 6 SERVINGS (SERVING SIZE: 3 OUNCES STEAK AND 1⅓ TABLESPOONS SALSA VERDE).**

PER SERVING: Calories 225; Fat 13.3g (sat 3.4g, mono 7.2g, poly 1.3g); Protein 24.9g; Carb 1.1g; Fiber 0.4g; Chol 37mg; Iron 2.4mg; Sodium 306mg; Calc 45mg

✳ Flank Steak

Flank steak has a distinct, visible grain, and it should be cut across this grain into ⅛- to ¼-inch-thick slices for maximum tenderness. Allow 5 minutes of stand time before slicing so the flavorful juices will reabsorb and redistribute, and they won't run out as freely when you carve. Tilt your knife diagonally, and slice away from you to ensure the largest surface area possible for each piece.

FAJITA SKEWERS

PointsPlus value per serving: 6

PREP: 19 minutes ■ **COOK:** 10 minutes
■ **OTHER:** 2 minutes

Remove the meat and veggies from the skewers, and serve over rice or wrapped in warmed flour tortillas with shredded lettuce and reduced-fat cheddar cheese.

1 (1-pound) flank steak, trimmed
1 large green bell pepper, cut into 18 (1-inch) pieces
1 large red bell pepper, cut into 18 (1-inch) pieces
1 small red onion, cut into 18 wedges
½ cup light balsamic vinaigrette
½ teaspoon freshly ground black pepper
4 garlic cloves, crushed
Cooking spray
1 lime, cut into 4 wedges

1. Preheat grill to medium–high heat.
2. Cut steak across grain into thin slices. Thread steak slices onto 4 (12-inch) metal skewers. Thread bell peppers and onion onto 6 (12-inch) metal skewers. Place skewers on a jelly-roll pan.
3. Combine vinaigrette, black pepper, and garlic in a small bowl; brush half of vinaigrette mixture evenly over skewers. Let stand 2 minutes.
4. Place skewers on grill rack coated with cooking spray. Grill meat skewers 8 minutes or until desired degree of doneness, turning once and basting with vinaigrette mixture. Grill vegetable skewers 10 minutes or until tender, turning once and basting with remaining vinaigrette mixture. Squeeze lime over skewers before serving. **YIELD: 4 SERVINGS (SERVING SIZE: 3 OUNCES STEAK AND ¼ OF VEGETABLES).**

PER SERVING: Calories 239; Fat 10.6g (sat 2.9g, mono 2.8g, poly 1g); Protein 25.5g; Carb 9.2g; Fiber 1.7g; Chol 37mg; Iron 2.2mg; Sodium 536mg; Calc 45mg

SANTA FE STEAKS

PointsPlus value per serving: 7

PREP: 3 minutes ■ COOK: 6 minutes

Perk up a prepared salsa with a few stir-ins for a Southwestern spin on fillets.

4 (4-ounce) beef tenderloin steaks, trimmed (about ½ inch thick)
2 teaspoons chili powder
¼ teaspoon salt
Cooking spray
1 cup frozen whole-kernel corn, thawed
½ cup fresh salsa
1 small chopped peeled avocado
Lime wedges (optional)

1. Heat a large nonstick skillet over medium-high heat. Sprinkle steaks with chili powder and salt; coat steaks with cooking spray. Add steaks to pan; cook 3 minutes on each side or until desired degree of doneness. Transfer steaks to a serving platter; keep warm.
2. While steaks cook, combine corn, salsa, and avocado in a medium bowl. Serve steaks topped with salsa. Garnish with lime wedges, if desired. YIELD: 4 SERVINGS (SERVING SIZE: 1 STEAK AND ½ CUP SALSA).

PER SERVING: Calories 282; Fat 13.7g (sat 3.5g, mono 6.8g, poly 1.2g); Protein 27g; Carb 11.9g; Fiber 2.2g; Chol 82mg; Iron 2.4mg; Sodium 300mg; Calc 35mg

PAN-SEARED STEAKS WITH WARM TOMATOES AND FETA

PointsPlus value per serving: 8   *pictured on page 90*

PREP: 10 minutes ■ COOK: 10 minutes

Multicolored cherry tomatoes make for a beautiful presentation over fillets, but feel free to use all red cherry tomatoes or grape tomatoes.

4 (4-ounce) beef tenderloin steaks (about 1 inch thick), trimmed
Cooking spray
½ teaspoon salt, divided
½ teaspoon freshly ground black pepper, divided
1 tablespoon olive oil, divided
6 garlic cloves, thinly sliced
4 cups multicolored cherry, grape, or heirloom tomatoes
2 teaspoons chopped fresh oregano
½ cup (2 ounces) crumbled feta cheese

1. Coat steaks with cooking spray; sprinkle evenly with ¼ teaspoon salt and ¼ teaspoon pepper. Heat 2 teaspoons oil in a large nonstick skillet over medium-high heat. Add steaks; cook 3 to 4 minutes on each side or until desired degree of doneness. Transfer steaks to 4 plates; keep warm.
2. Heat remaining 1 teaspoon oil in pan over medium-high heat. Add garlic; cook 1 minute or until golden brown. Remove garlic from pan.
3. Add tomatoes, remaining ¼ teaspoon salt, and remaining ¼ teaspoon pepper to pan; sauté 2 minutes or until tomatoes begin to burst. Stir in oregano and garlic. Spoon tomato mixture over steaks; sprinkle with feta. YIELD: 4 SERVINGS (SERVING SIZE: 1 STEAK, ABOUT ⅔ CUP TOMATO MIXTURE, AND 2 TABLESPOONS FETA).

PER SERVING: Calories 323; Fat 15.9g (sat 6.1g, mono 6.9g, poly 0.9g); Protein 36g; Carb 8.2g; Fiber 2g; Chol 102mg; Iron 2.7mg; Sodium 529mg; Calc 118mg

"BLACK AND BLUE" STEAK PIZZAS

PointsPlus value per serving: 6

PREP: 6 minutes ■ COOK: 16 minutes

2 (4-ounce) beef tenderloin steaks
½ teaspoon freshly ground black pepper
¼ teaspoon salt
Cooking spray
½ cup creamy yogurt blue cheese dressing (such as Bolthouse Farms)
3 (3-ounce) whole-wheat naan
1 medium-sized red bell pepper, sliced
2 cups loosely packed arugula

1. Preheat oven to 400°.
2. Heat a small skillet over medium-high heat. Sprinkle steaks with black pepper and salt. Coat pan with cooking spray. Add steaks to pan; cook 3 minutes on each side or until desired degree of doneness. Remove steaks from pan; keep warm.
3. While steaks cook, spread about 2½ tablespoons dressing over each naan. Place one-third of bell pepper on each naan. Bake at 400° for 10 minutes or until bell pepper is tender.
4. Cut steaks into thin slices. Arrange steak slices over pizzas, and top with arugula. YIELD: 6 SERVINGS (SERVING SIZE: ½ PIZZA).

PER SERVING: Calories 251; Fat 9.1g (sat 2.8g, mono 3g, poly 2.8g); Protein 17.6g; Carb 25.2g; Fiber 4.7g; Chol 40mg; Iron 2.3mg; Sodium 379mg; Calc 80mg

BEEF POT PIE

PointsPlus value per serving: 7

PREP: 15 minutes ■ **COOK:** 37 minutes

Cooking spray
¾ pound ground sirloin
2 cups frozen mixed vegetables
2 cups frozen hash brown potatoes with onions and
        peppers (such as Ore-Ida Potatoes O'Brien)
1 (14.5-ounce) can fat-free, lower-sodium beef broth
2 tablespoons all-purpose flour
1 tablespoon tomato paste
½ teaspoon salt
¼ teaspoon freshly ground black pepper
⅓ cup light sour cream
½ (14.1-ounce) package refrigerated pie dough

1. Preheat oven to 425°.
2. Heat a large nonstick skillet over medium-high heat. Coat pan with cooking spray. Add beef; cook 6 minutes or until browned, stirring to crumble. Drain, if necessary, and return beef to pan. Add mixed vegetables and potatoes; cook 3 minutes or until thoroughly heated.
3. Combine broth and next 4 ingredients, stirring with a whisk. Add broth mixture to pan. Cook 3 minutes or until mixture begins to thicken. Stir in sour cream. Spoon into an 8-inch square glass or ceramic baking dish coated with cooking spray.
4. Cut pie dough into 6 (8½ x 1–inch) strips. Reserve remaining dough for another use. Arrange strips in a lattice pattern over filling; coat dough with cooking spray. Bake at 425° for 25 minutes or until filling is bubbly and crust is browned. **YIELD: 6 SERVINGS (SERVING SIZE: ABOUT ¾ CUP).**

PER SERVING: Calories 251; Fat 11g (sat 4.8g, mono 4.1g, poly 0.7g); Protein 14.8g; Carb 23.1g; Fiber 1.7g; Chol 43mg; Iron 1.8mg; Sodium 475mg; Calc 35mg

CORNED BEEF HASH AND EGGS

PointsPlus value per serving: 5

PREP: 4 minutes ■ **COOK:** 22 minutes

We used pasteurized eggs to ensure they're safe when served "over easy." When the yolk runs over the hearty hash, it's a food match made in heaven. Be sure to look for lean corned beef with only 1 gram of fat per ounce.

2 teaspoons canola oil
4 cups frozen hash brown potatoes with onions and
        peppers (such as Ore-Ida Potatoes O'Brien)
2 garlic cloves, minced
1 cup diced deli corned beef (about ¼ pound)
½ cup fat-free, lower-sodium chicken broth
½ teaspoon freshly ground black pepper
¼ teaspoon salt
Cooking spray
4 large pasteurized eggs
4 teaspoons chopped parsley (optional)

1. Heat oil in a large cast-iron or nonstick skillet over medium-high heat. Add potatoes and garlic; cook 10 minutes or until potatoes brown, stirring occasionally. Add corned beef and next 3 ingredients. Cook 5 minutes, stirring frequently. Remove mixture from pan; keep warm.
2. Heat pan over medium heat. Coat pan with cooking spray. Gently break 2 eggs into pan. Cook 2 minutes. Carefully turn eggs; cook 1 minute or until desired degree of doneness. Remove eggs from pan. Repeat procedure with remaining 2 eggs. Serve eggs over hash; sprinkle with parsley, if desired. **YIELD: 4 SERVINGS (SERVING SIZE: ¾ CUP HASH AND 1 EGG).**

PER SERVING: Calories 197; Fat 8.3g (sat 2.3g, mono 3.4g, poly 1.3g); Protein 13.3g; Carb 17.2g; Fiber 1.4g; Chol 227mg; Iron 2.2mg; Sodium 449mg; Calc 30mg

❋ Pasteurized Eggs
Pasteurized eggs are rapidly heated and held at a minimum required temperature for a specified time. This process destroys salmonella without cooking the eggs or affecting their color, flavor, or nutritional value, so cooking eggs and leaving the yolks runny won't compromise food safety.

GRILLED ROSEMARY LAMB CHOPS WITH RUBY PORT–FIG CHUTNEY

PointsPlus value per serving: 8   *pictured on page 130*

PREP: 8 minutes ■ **COOK:** 15 minutes ■ **OTHER:** 5 minutes

Serve with sautéed Brussels sprouts for a quick side. The chutney also pairs well with grilled steak or pork tenderloin.

1⅓ cups ruby port
1 cup finely chopped dried Black Mission figs
⅓ cup water
2 teaspoons brown sugar
1½ teaspoons grated lemon rind
⅛ teaspoon salt
8 (4-ounce) lamb loin chops, trimmed
2 teaspoons olive oil
2 tablespoons finely chopped fresh rosemary
½ teaspoon freshly ground black pepper
¼ teaspoon salt
Cooking spray

1. Preheat grill to high heat.
2. Combine first 6 ingredients in a medium saucepan; bring to a boil. Cook 12 minutes or until most of liquid evaporates, stirring occasionally.
3. While chutney cooks, rub lamb chops with olive oil; sprinkle with rosemary, pepper, and salt. Place chops on grill rack coated with cooking spray; cover and grill 6 minutes on each side or until desired degree of doneness. Let stand 5 minutes. Serve with chutney. **YIELD: 4 SERVINGS (SERVING SIZE: 2 LAMB CHOPS AND ¼ CUP CHUTNEY).**

PER SERVING: Calories 377; Fat 12g (sat 3.7g, mono 5.8g, poly 1.1g); Protein 29.9g; Carb 26.8g; Fiber 3.9g; Chol 91mg; Iron 2.8mg; Sodium 306mg; Calc 85mg

LAMB-TABBOULEH MEAT LOAF

PointsPlus value per serving: 7

PREP: 10 minutes ■ **COOK:** 1 hour ■ **OTHER:** 15 minutes

You'll love having leftovers from this meal. Smear a little hummus inside a pita, and stuff it with a slice of meat loaf, lettuce, and tomato. Serve both warm slices and sandwiches with a dollop of low-fat or fat-free Greek yogurt.

½ cup (2 ounces) crumbled feta cheese
¼ cup pine nuts, toasted
2 tablespoons pepperoncini pepper liquid
3 garlic cloves, minced
2 large egg whites
1 (5.25-ounce) package tabbouleh wheat salad mix (such as Near East)
2 pounds lean ground lamb
Cooking spray
½ cup chopped tomato
¼ cup drained sliced pepperoncini peppers

1. Preheat oven to 350°.
2. Combine first 6 ingredients in a large bowl; stir well. Crumble lamb over mixture, and stir just until ingredients are blended.
3. Shape mixture into a 9 x 3–inch loaf on a broiler pan coated with cooking spray. Bake at 350° for 1 hour or until a thermometer registers 160°. Let stand 15 minutes before slicing.
4. Combine tomato and peppers; toss gently. Serve with meat loaf slices. **YIELD: 10 SERVINGS (SERVING SIZE: 1 SLICE MEAT LOAF AND ABOUT 1 TABLESPOON TOMATO-PEPPER MIXTURE).**

PER SERVING: Calories 281; Fat 19.2g (sat 7.6g, mono 7.4g, poly 2.3g); Protein 21.9g; Carb 4.8g; Fiber 1g; Chol 82mg; Iron 1.8mg; Sodium 235mg; Calc 58mg

GRILLED KEFTA WITH MINT YOGURT

PointsPlus value per serving: 8

PREP: 16 minutes ■ **COOK:** 8 minutes

Popular in Morocco, Greece, and the Middle East, these spiced meatballs are superb when skewered and grilled. A minted yogurt sauce is the perfect accompaniment to the seasoned meat.

3 tablespoons minced fresh mint
2 tablespoons minced fresh parsley
2 tablespoons minced fresh cilantro
¾ teaspoon ground cumin
¾ teaspoon pumpkin pie spice
½ teaspoon ground coriander
½ teaspoon freshly ground black pepper
¾ teaspoon salt, divided
4 garlic cloves, minced and divided
1 pound lean ground lamb or ground round
Cooking spray
1 (6-ounce) carton plain fat-free Greek yogurt
2 tablespoons minced fresh mint
1 teaspoon fresh lemon juice
Mint sprigs (optional)

1. Preheat grill to high heat.
2. Combine first 7 ingredients, ½ teaspoon salt, and 3 garlic cloves in a large bowl; stir well. Add lamb, mixing until blended.
3. Divide lamb mixture into 16 equal portions, shaping each into a 2 x 1–inch oval meatball. Thread 4 meatballs onto each of 4 (10-inch) metal skewers. Place skewers on grill rack coated with cooking spray; grill 8 to 10 minutes or until lamb is done, turning frequently.
4. Combine remaining ¼ teaspoon salt, remaining garlic clove, yogurt, 2 tablespoons mint, and lemon juice; stir well. Serve with kefta. Garnish with mint sprigs, if desired. **YIELD: 4 SERVINGS (SERVING SIZE: 4 KEFTA AND ABOUT 2 TABLESPOONS YOGURT SAUCE).**

Note: If using wooden skewers, soak them in water 30 minutes before grilling. See page 88 for more information.

PER SERVING: Calories 311; Fat 19.4g (sat 7.9g, mono 8g, poly 1.4g); Protein 28.2g; Carb 4.2g; Fiber 1g; Chol 94mg; Iron 2.9mg; Sodium 541mg; Calc 79mg

PORK MEDALLIONS WITH SAUTÉED APPLES

PointsPlus value per serving: 6

PREP: 9 minutes ■ **COOK:** 20 minutes

Pork and apples are a timeless combination; this version is accented with fresh thyme.

1 tablespoon chopped fresh thyme
¼ teaspoon salt
¼ teaspoon freshly ground black pepper
1 (1-pound) pork tenderloin, cut into ½-inch-thick slices
Cooking spray
¾ cup thinly sliced onion
2 cups sliced peeled Fuji apple (about ¾ pound)
1 cup apple cider
1 tablespoon butter

1. Combine first 3 ingredients in a small bowl; sprinkle evenly over pork slices.
2. Heat a large nonstick skillet over medium-high heat. Coat pan with cooking spray. Add pork; cook 3 minutes on each side or until browned. Remove pork from pan; keep warm.
3. Recoat pan with cooking spray. Add onion; sauté 2 minutes. Add apple; cook 4 minutes or until tender and deep golden brown, stirring occasionally. Return pork to pan; add cider, and bring to a boil. Cook until cider is reduced by half (about 6 minutes). Remove from heat. Add butter, stirring until butter melts. Cut pork into 8 slices, and serve apple mixture over pork. **YIELD: 4 SERVINGS (SERVING SIZE: 2 PORK MEDALLIONS AND ½ CUP APPLE MIXTURE).**

PER SERVING: Calories 222; Fat 5.7g (sat 2.7g, mono 1.8g, poly 0.6g); Protein 24.5g; Carb 18g; Fiber 1.2g; Chol 81mg; Iron 1.3mg; Sodium 229mg; Calc 17mg

MU SHU PORK TENDERLOIN WITH STIR-FRIED SLAW

PointsPlus value per serving: 8

PREP: 3 minutes ■ COOK: 18 minutes
■ OTHER: 10 minutes

Five-spice powder is a blend of ground cinnamon, cloves, fennel seed, star anise, and Szechuan peppercorns. Look for this fragrant spice blend in large supermarkets or Asian markets.

1 (1-pound) pork tenderloin
Cooking spray
2 teaspoons roasted peanut oil or vegetable oil
2 tablespoons bottled ground fresh ginger (such as Spice World)
¼ teaspoon five-spice powder
¼ teaspoon crushed red pepper
½ cup red plum jam
¼ cup rice vinegar, divided
1 tablespoon lower-sodium soy sauce
¼ teaspoon dark sesame oil
1 (10-ounce) package angel hair slaw
¼ teaspoon salt
1 tablespoon sesame seeds, toasted
2 green onions, sliced (optional)

1. Preheat grill to medium–high heat.
2. Place pork on grill rack coated with cooking spray; cover and grill 15 to 18 minutes or until a thermometer registers 145°, turning occasionally. Remove pork from grill; cover and let stand 10 minutes.
3. While pork grills, heat oil in a small nonstick skillet over medium heat. Add ginger, five-spice powder, and red pepper; sauté 1 minute. Add jam, 2 tablespoons vinegar, and soy sauce; cook 3 to 5 minutes or until sauce thickens. Remove from heat; stir in sesame oil.
4. Heat a large nonstick skillet over medium–high heat. Coat pan and slaw with cooking spray. Add slaw; sauté 3 minutes or until slaw wilts and is lightly browned. Stir in remaining 2 tablespoons vinegar and salt. Remove from heat.
5. Cut tenderloin into ½-inch-thick slices; combine pork and ½ cup plum sauce, tossing well. Arrange pork slices on a bed of slaw; drizzle with remaining ¼ cup sauce. Sprinkle with sesame seeds, and top with green onions, if desired. YIELD: 4 SERVINGS (SERVING SIZE: 3 OUNCES PORK, ABOUT ⅔ CUP SLAW, 1 TABLESPOON PLUM SAUCE, AND ABOUT 1 TEASPOON SESAME SEEDS).

PER SERVING: Calories 309; Fat 7.8g (sat 1.8g, mono 2.7g, poly 1.5g); Protein 25g; Carb 31.9g; Fiber 1.8g; Chol 74mg; Iron 4.5mg; Sodium 421mg; Calc 10mg

PORK STROGANOFF

PointsPlus value per serving: 8

PREP: 4 minutes ■ COOK: 16 minutes

A traditional beef dish is reworked with lean, flavorful pork tenderloin.

6 ounces uncooked egg noodles
Cooking spray
1 (1-pound) pork tenderloin, trimmed and cut into 1-inch pieces
½ teaspoon salt, divided
¼ teaspoon freshly ground black pepper, divided
1 (8-ounce) package presliced mushrooms
1 tablespoon butter
2 tablespoons all-purpose flour
¼ teaspoon ground allspice
1½ cups fat-free, lower-sodium chicken broth
½ cup light sour cream
Chopped fresh parsley (optional)
Freshly ground black pepper (optional)

1. Cook egg noodles according to package directions, omitting salt and fat. Drain and keep warm.
2. While noodles cook, heat a large nonstick skillet over medium–high heat. Coat pan with cooking spray. Sprinkle pork evenly with ¼ teaspoon salt and ⅛ teaspoon pepper. Add pork to pan; cook 4 minutes or until pork pieces are browned on all sides, stirring frequently. Remove pork from pan; keep warm.
3. Recoat pan with cooking spray. Add mushrooms; sauté 4 minutes or until browned. Remove mushrooms from pan.
4. Melt butter in pan over medium heat. Add flour, allspice, remaining ¼ teaspoon salt, and remaining ⅛ teaspoon pepper; cook 1 minute, stirring constantly. Add broth, stirring with a whisk. Bring to a boil, reduce heat, and simmer 2 minutes or until sauce thickens. Remove from heat; stir in sour cream, pork, and mushrooms. Add egg noodles, and toss well. Sprinkle with parsley and black pepper, if desired. YIELD: 5 SERVINGS (SERVING SIZE: 1 CUP).

PER SERVING: Calories 313; Fat 8.5g (sat 3.9g, mono 2.5g, poly 1.3g); Protein 28.1g; Carb 30.2g; Fiber 1.8g; Chol 113mg; Iron 2.4mg; Sodium 499mg; Calc 68mg

PORK AND PINEAPPLE TACOS

PointsPlus value per serving: 7

PREP: 4 minutes ■ **COOK:** 11 minutes

Stir in the slaw and radishes at the end to preserve the fresh, crispy texture. Fresh pineapple is key here, too. You can start with a whole, fresh pineapple (see tips for cutting it below) or take advantage of the precored whole pineapples or prechopped pineapple available in most grocery stores.

> **1 (1-pound) pork tenderloin, cut into thin strips**
> **1 teaspoon chili powder**
> **¼ teaspoon salt**
> **¼ teaspoon freshly ground black pepper**
> **2 teaspoons canola oil**
> **½ cup chopped onion**
> **1½ cups chopped fresh pineapple**
> **1½ cups angel hair slaw**
> **¼ cup shredded radishes**
> **Chopped fresh cilantro (optional)**
> **8 (6-inch) corn tortillas, warmed**
> **Salsa verde (optional)**

1. Combine first 4 ingredients, tossing well. Heat oil in a large nonstick skillet over medium–high heat. Add onion; sauté 3 minutes or until tender. Add pork; sauté 6 minutes or until pork is done. Add pineapple; cook 2 minutes or until thoroughly heated.
2. Remove pan from heat. Combine slaw, radishes, and cilantro, if desired. Divide pork mixture evenly among tortillas. Top with slaw mixture and salsa, if desired.
YIELD: 4 SERVINGS (SERVING SIZE: 2 TACOS).

PER SERVING: Calories 273; Fat 6g (sat 1g, mono 2.4g, poly 1.7g); Protein 26.7g; Carb 29.9g; Fiber 4.1g; Chol 74mg; Iron 1.5mg; Sodium 233mg; Calc 42mg

HOW TO CHOP FRESH PINEAPPLE

1. Lay the pineapple horizontally on a cutting board, and cut off the leafy top (the plume) and the base.
2. Stand the pineapple upright, and cut down the sides to remove the rind. Try to remove as little of the flesh as possible.
3. While the pineapple is upright, cut it into thirds by carefully slicing downward as shown to remove the fibrous core. You can then slice it into cubes.

DRIED CHERRY AND ROSEMARY–STUFFED PORK CHOPS

PointsPlus value per serving: 8

PREP: 15 minutes ■ **COOK:** 24 minutes

This is a good use for a small chunk of leftover cornbread, or purchase prepared cornbread from the deli section of your grocer.

> **½ cup orange juice**
> **¼ cup dried cherries**
> **2 tablespoons minced shallots**
> **1 cup crumbled prepared cornbread**
> **1 tablespoon chopped fresh rosemary**
> **½ teaspoon salt, divided**
> **½ teaspoon black pepper, divided**
> **4 (6-ounce) bone-in center-cut pork chops**
> **1 tablespoon olive oil**

1. Combine first 3 ingredients in a small saucepan; bring to a boil. Reduce heat; simmer until reduced by half (about 8 minutes). Remove from heat; drain cherries and shallots, reserving cherry mixture and orange juice.
2. Combine cornbread, rosemary, ¼ teaspoon salt, ¼ teaspoon pepper, and reserved cherry mixture in a medium bowl. Add 1 tablespoon reserved orange juice, gently stirring until cornbread is moist.
3. Cut a horizontal slit through thickest portion of each pork chop to form a pocket. Stuff ¼ cup cornbread mixture into each pocket; close opening with a wooden pick. Sprinkle pork chops with remaining ¼ teaspoon salt and remaining ¼ teaspoon pepper.
4. Heat oil in a large nonstick skillet over medium-high heat. Add pork; cook 7 minutes on each side or until pork is done. Spoon remaining reserved orange juice over pork. **YIELD: 4 SERVINGS (SERVING SIZE: 1 PORK CHOP AND ABOUT 1 TABLESPOON ORANGE JUICE).**

PER SERVING: Calories 313; Fat 12.6g (sat 2.7g, mono 5.9g, poly 1.4g); Protein 24.5g; Carb 22.8g; Fiber 1.2g; Chol 81mg; Iron 1.4mg; Sodium 456mg; Calc 46mg

BAKED SPAGHETTI

PointsPlus value per serving: 7   *pictured on page 131*

PREP: 20 minutes ■ **COOK:** 41 minutes

Lean ground pork offers a variation from the traditional ground beef or ground poultry options. When buying, look for packages labeled "lean." Pound for pound, ground pork contains less saturated fat and fewer calories than ground sirloin, which has 10% fat.

    8 ounces uncooked spaghetti
    1 pound lean ground pork
    1 tablespoon dried Italian seasoning
    1 (24-ounce) jar fire-roasted tomato and garlic pasta
        sauce
    Cooking spray
    2 tablespoons all-purpose flour
    1 (12-ounce) can evaporated fat-free milk
    ½ teaspoon salt
    ½ teaspoon freshly ground black pepper
    1 (8-ounce) package shredded reduced-fat Italian
        blend cheese

1. Preheat oven to 375°.
2. Cook pasta according to package directions, omitting salt and fat. Drain; keep warm.
3. Heat a large nonstick skillet over medium-high heat. Add pork and Italian seasoning to pan; cook 6 minutes or until browned, stirring to crumble. Drain. Combine pasta, pork, and pasta sauce. Spoon pasta mixture into a 13 x 9–inch glass or ceramic baking dish coated with cooking spray.
4. Place flour in a small saucepan. Gradually add milk, stirring constantly with a whisk until blended. Stir in salt and pepper. Place over medium heat; cook until thick (about 5 minutes), stirring constantly. Spoon sauce evenly over pasta mixture in dish; sprinkle with cheese. Bake at 375° for 20 minutes or until filling is bubbly and cheese melts. **YIELD: 10 SERVINGS (SERVING SIZE:** ¹⁄₁₀ **OF CASSEROLE).**

PER SERVING: Calories 283; Fat 8.5g (sat 4.2g, mono 1.3g, poly 0.4g); Protein 22.2g; Carb 28.5g; Fiber 2g; Chol 48mg; Iron 1.7mg; Sodium 535mg; Calc 293mg

SMOKED SAUSAGE–POTATO BAKE

PointsPlus value per serving: 8

PREP: 9 minutes ■ **COOK:** 33 minutes

Potatoes, cheese, and sausage combine for a quick weeknight comfort food dish. Using instant potato flakes gets this in the oven in less than 10 minutes.

    1¾ cups water
    1¼ cups fat-free milk
    1 tablespoon light butter
    2⅔ cups instant potato flakes
    1 (8-ounce) carton fat-free sour cream
    1 cup (4 ounces) reduced-fat shredded sharp cheddar
        cheese, divided
    Butter-flavored cooking spray
    1 (14-ounce) package light smoked sausage with
        turkey, pork, and beef (such as Hillshire Farm),
        chopped

1. Preheat oven to 350°.
2. Bring first 3 ingredients to a boil in a large saucepan. Remove from heat; stir in potato flakes. Stir with a fork until potatoes are fluffy. Stir in sour cream and ⅔ cup cheese.
3. Spoon half of potato mixture into an 8-inch square glass or ceramic baking dish coated with cooking spray. Sprinkle sausage over potatoes and top with remaining potatoes. Sprinkle with remaining ⅓ cup cheese. Bake at 350° for 30 minutes or until thoroughly heated. **YIELD: 6 SERVINGS (SERVING SIZE: ABOUT 1 CUP).**

PER SERVING: Calories 301; Fat 15.2g (sat 7.4g, mono 5.5g, poly 1.9g); Protein 20g; Carb 21.3g; Fiber 0g; Chol 56mg; Iron 0.6mg; Sodium 812mg; Calc 387mg

Chicken Broccoli Stir-Fry, *page 103*

CHICKEN CURRY

PointsPlus value per serving: 7   *pictured on page 133*

PREP: 4 minutes ■ **COOK:** 15 minutes

This Eastern-inspired dish bursts with the fresh tastes of curry powder and coconut milk. Squeeze a lime wedge over each serving for a bright hit of flavor.

1 (8.8-ounce) package microwavable precooked
      basmati rice (such as Uncle Ben's Ready Rice)
Cooking spray
1½ cups vertically sliced onion
1 pound skinless, boneless chicken breast, cut into
      1-inch cubes
1 tablespoon curry powder
1 (14.5-ounce) can diced tomatoes, drained
1 (13.5-ounce) can light coconut milk
½ teaspoon salt
3 cups bagged baby spinach leaves

1. Prepare rice in microwave according to package directions. Keep warm.
2. Heat a large nonstick skillet over medium-high heat. Coat pan with cooking spray. Add onion and chicken; sauté 7 minutes or until chicken is browned. Reduce heat to medium.
3. Add curry powder; cook 1 minute. Add tomatoes, coconut milk, and salt; stir well. Cover and simmer 5 minutes or until slightly thick, stirring occasionally. Remove from heat; add spinach, stirring until spinach wilts. Serve chicken mixture over rice. **YIELD: 4 SERVINGS (SERVING SIZE: ABOUT 1¼ CUPS CHICKEN MIXTURE AND ½ CUP RICE).**

PER SERVING: Calories 284; Fat 5.6g (sat 1.8g, mono 1.2g, poly 1.4g); Protein 27.5g; Carb 30.9g; Fiber 3.1g; Chol 63mg; Iron 3.1mg; Sodium 530mg; Calc 62mg

LAPSANG SOUCHONG–POACHED CHICKEN WITH GINGER SAUCE

PointsPlus value per serving: 5

PREP: 15 minutes ■ **COOK:** 23 minutes

Lapsang Souchong is a black tea with a smoky flavor that easily infuses into foods.

4 (6-ounce) skinless, boneless chicken breast
      halves
2 cups fat-free, lower-sodium chicken broth,
      divided
1 cup cold water
2 tablespoons grated peeled fresh ginger, divided
2 tablespoons Lapsang Souchong tea leaves
2 tablespoons lower-sodium soy sauce, divided
1 tablespoon thawed orange juice concentrate
2 teaspoons cornstarch
2 garlic cloves, minced
2 tablespoons sliced green onions (optional)

1. Combine chicken, 1 cup broth, 1 cup water, 1 tablespoon ginger, tea, and 1 tablespoon soy sauce in a large deep skillet. Bring to a boil; cover and simmer 20 minutes or until chicken is done.
2. While chicken cooks, combine remaining 1 cup broth, remaining 1 tablespoon ginger, remaining 1 tablespoon soy sauce, orange juice concentrate, cornstarch, and garlic in a small saucepan. Bring to a boil; reduce heat, and simmer, uncovered, 6 minutes or until thick. Place 1 chicken breast half on each of 4 plates. Spoon sauce evenly over chicken. Sprinkle evenly with green onions, if desired. **YIELD: 4 SERVINGS (SERVING SIZE: 1 CHICKEN BREAST HALF AND ¼ CUP SAUCE).**

PER SERVING: Calories 217; Fat 2.2g (sat 0.6g, mono 0.5g, poly 0.5g); Protein 40.9g; Carb 5.5g; Fiber 0.3g; Chol 99mg; Iron 1.6mg; Sodium 533mg; Calc 32mg

CHICKEN CORDON BLEU SPIRALS

PointsPlus value per serving: 8

PREP: 15 minutes ■ **COOK:** 17 minutes

This elegant and palate-pleasing dish is accompanied by a simple pan sauce. It works well for a weeknight dinner or entertaining friends.

- 4 (6-ounce) skinless, boneless chicken breast halves
- ¼ teaspoon salt
- ¼ teaspoon freshly ground black pepper
- 4 (1-ounce) slices smoked ham
- 4 (0.8-ounce) slices reduced-fat Swiss cheese
- Cooking spray
- ¼ cup minced shallots (1 large)
- ½ cup dry white wine
- ⅓ cup half-and-half
- 1 tablespoon whole-grain Dijon mustard
- 1 tablespoon chopped fresh tarragon

1. Preheat oven to 450°.
2. Place chicken breast halves between 2 sheets of heavy-duty plastic wrap; pound to ¼-inch thickness using a meat mallet or small heavy skillet. Sprinkle chicken evenly with salt and pepper. Layer 1 ham slice and 1 cheese slice in center of each chicken breast. Roll up jelly-roll fashion and secure with wooden picks.
3. Heat a large nonstick skillet over medium-high heat. Coat pan with cooking spray. Add chicken to pan; cook 2 minutes on each side or until browned. Remove from heat. Transfer chicken to an 11 x 7–inch glass or ceramic baking dish coated with cooking spray.
4. Bake, uncovered, at 450° for 13 minutes or until a thermometer inserted in center registers 165°. Cut each chicken breast crosswise into spirals.
5. While chicken cooks, return pan to medium heat. Recoat pan with cooking spray. Add shallots to pan; sauté 1 minute. Add wine; cook, stirring constantly, 1 minute or until wine is reduced by half. Add half-and-half and mustard. Cook, stirring constantly, 1 minute or until sauce thickens. Stir in tarragon. Spoon sauce evenly over chicken. **YIELD: 4 SERVINGS (SERVING SIZE: 1 STUFFED CHICKEN BREAST HALF AND 2 TABLESPOONS SAUCE).**

PER SERVING: Calories 333; Fat 10.6g (sat 4.7g, mono 2.3g, poly 0.9g); Protein 52.4g; Carb 4.5g; Fiber 0g; Chol 130mg; Iron 1.4mg; Sodium 700mg; Calc 263mg

CHICKEN WITH DIJON-TARRAGON PAN SAUCE

PointsPlus value per serving: 5

PREP: 8 minutes ■ **COOK:** 13 minutes

- 4 (6-ounce) skinless, boneless chicken breast halves
- ¼ teaspoon salt
- ¼ teaspoon freshly ground black pepper
- ¼ cup dry white wine
- ¼ cup fat-free half-and-half
- 2 tablespoons country-style Dijon mustard
- 1 tablespoon olive oil
- 2 garlic cloves, minced
- 2 teaspoons chopped fresh tarragon

1. Sprinkle chicken evenly with salt and pepper. Combine wine, half-and-half, and mustard in a small bowl. Heat oil in a large nonstick skillet over medium-high heat. Add chicken to pan. Cook 6 minutes on each side or until done. Remove from pan; keep warm.
2. Add garlic to pan; cook 30 seconds or until tender. Stir in wine mixture. Cook 1 minute or until sauce thickens. Stir in tarragon. Place 1 chicken breast half on each of 4 plates. Spoon sauce evenly over chicken.
YIELD: 4 SERVINGS (SERVING SIZE: 1 CHICKEN BREAST HALF AND 2 TABLESPOONS SAUCE).

PER SERVING: Calories 249; Fat 6.1g (sat 1g, mono 3g, poly 0.8g); Protein 39.9g; Carb 3.6g; Fiber 0.4g; Chol 99mg; Iron 1.5mg; Sodium 425mg; Calc 40mg

GREEK CHICKEN POCKETS

PointsPlus value per serving: 6

PREP: 7 minutes ■ COOK: 25 minutes

Serve this chicken with orzo tossed with fresh oregano and lemon juice.

½ cup part-skim ricotta cheese
½ cup julienne-cut sun-dried tomatoes, packed without oil
1 tablespoon chopped fresh oregano
2 teaspoons Greek seasoning, divided
½ teaspoon freshly ground black pepper, divided
4 (6-ounce) skinless, boneless chicken breast halves
Cooking spray

1. Preheat oven to 400°.
2. Combine first 3 ingredients, 1 teaspoon Greek seasoning, and ¼ teaspoon pepper in a small bowl.
3. Cut a horizontal slit through thickest portion of each chicken breast half to form a pocket. Stuff ¼ cup ricotta mixture into each pocket; close openings with wooden picks. Sprinkle chicken evenly with remaining 1 teaspoon Greek seasoning and remaining ¼ teaspoon pepper.
4. Heat a large nonstick skillet over medium–high heat. Coat pan with cooking spray. Add chicken to pan. Cook 2 minutes on each side or until chicken is browned.
5. Place chicken in an 11 x 7–inch glass or ceramic baking dish coated with cooking spray. Bake, uncovered, at 400° for 20 minutes or until done. Remove and discard wooden picks. Serve immediately. YIELD: 4 SERVINGS (SERVING SIZE: 1 POCKET).

PER SERVING: Calories 275; Fat 4.6g (sat 2.1g, mono 1.2g, poly 0.6g); Protein 44g; Carb 10.6g; Fiber 2.2g; Chol 108mg; Iron 1.8mg; Sodium 222mg; Calc 109mg

CHEESE-STUFFED CHICKEN BREASTS WITH JALAPEÑO-RASPBERRY GLAZE

PointsPlus value per serving: 8

PREP: 9 minutes ■ COOK: 22 minutes

Spicy jalapeño jelly paired with raspberry jam creates a spicy-sweet glaze for the juicy chicken and creamy Monterey Jack cheese.

6 (6-ounce) skinless, boneless chicken breast halves
6 (0.8-ounce) slices Monterey Jack cheese with jalapeño peppers
¼ teaspoon salt
¼ teaspoon black pepper
Cooking spray
1 cup red bell pepper slices (about 1 medium)
⅓ cup seedless raspberry jam
¼ cup hot jalapeño jelly

1. Preheat oven to 350°.
2. Cut a horizontal slit through thickest portion of each chicken breast half to form a pocket. Stuff 1 cheese slice into each pocket; close openings with wooden picks. Sprinkle chicken evenly with salt and black pepper.
3. Heat a large nonstick skillet over medium–high heat. Coat pan with cooking spray. Add chicken to pan; cook 2 minutes on each side or until browned.
4. Place bell pepper slices in a 13 x 9–inch glass or ceramic baking dish coated with cooking spray. Place browned chicken on top of peppers. Combine jam and jelly in a small bowl. Microwave jam mixture at HIGH 30 seconds; stir until jelly melts. Spoon jam mixture over chicken.
5. Bake, uncovered, at 350° for 18 minutes or until chicken is done. Remove and discard wooden picks. Serve immediately. YIELD: 6 SERVINGS (SERVING SIZE: 1 CHICKEN BREAST HALF, ⅙ OF PEPPERS, AND 3 TABLESPOONS SAUCE).

PER SERVING: Calories 347; Fat 8.5g (sat 4.2g, mono 2.5g, poly 0.7g); Protein 44.6g; Carb 19.2g; Fiber 0.3g; Chol 119mg; Iron 1.3mg; Sodium 354mg; Calc 175mg

If a marinade is used as a basting liquid or sauce, it's important to bring the mixture to a boil after removing the raw meat. This ensures that any potentially harmful bacteria are killed and that the marinade is safe to eat.

LIMEADE-GLAZED CHICKEN KEBABS

PointsPlus value per serving: 7

PREP: 10 minutes ■ COOK: 14 minutes
■ OTHER: 1 hour

Limeade concentrate adds citrus flavor to the marinade for these tangy kebabs.

- ¼ cup thawed limeade concentrate, undiluted
- 1 tablespoon chopped fresh mint
- 2 teaspoons olive oil
- ¼ teaspoon freshly ground black pepper
- 1½ pounds skinless, boneless chicken breast, cut into 1½-inch pieces
- 8 (1½-inch) pieces green bell pepper
- 8 cherry tomatoes
- 1 small red onion, cut into 8 wedges
- Cooking spray
- ⅛ teaspoon salt

1. Combine first 4 ingredients in a large bowl, stirring with a whisk. Add chicken, bell pepper, and tomatoes to marinade, tossing to coat. Cover and chill 1 hour.
2. Preheat grill to medium-high heat.
3. Remove chicken and vegetables from marinade, reserving marinade. Transfer marinade to a small saucepan. Bring to a boil; cook 1 minute. Cut onion wedges in half crosswise. Thread onion pieces, marinated vegetables, and chicken alternately onto 4 (12-inch) metal skewers.
4. Place skewers on grill rack coated with cooking spray; grill 12 minutes or until chicken is done and vegetables are crisp-tender, turning occasionally and basting with reserved marinade. Remove kebabs from grill, and sprinkle evenly with salt. YIELD: 4 SERVINGS (SERVING SIZE: 1 KEBAB).

PER SERVING: Calories 283; Fat 4.8g (sat 0.9g, mono 2.2g, poly 0.8g); Protein 40.3g; Carb 17.9g; Fiber 1.7g; Chol 99mg; Iron 1.6mg; Sodium 189mg; Calc 36mg

CHICKEN MARSALA

PointsPlus value per serving: 8

PREP: 3 minutes ■ COOK: 15 minutes

- 1½ pounds chicken cutlets (4 cutlets)
- ¼ teaspoon freshly ground black pepper
- ⅛ teaspoon salt
- 3 tablespoons all-purpose flour
- 1 tablespoon olive oil
- 2 ounces prosciutto, chopped
- 3 tablespoons minced shallots (about 1 large)
- 1 (8-ounce) package presliced mushrooms
- ½ cup fat-free, lower-sodium chicken broth
- ½ cup Marsala wine
- 2 teaspoons chopped fresh parsley (optional)

1. Sprinkle chicken evenly with pepper and salt. Place flour in a shallow bowl. Dredge chicken in flour, shaking off excess.
2. Heat oil in a large nonstick skillet over medium-high heat. Add chicken to pan. Cook 3 minutes on each side or until done. Remove from pan; keep warm. Add prosciutto, shallots, and mushrooms to drippings in pan. Cook 6 minutes or until tender. Stir in chicken broth and wine. Return chicken to pan. Cook 3 minutes or until sauce begins to thicken. Sprinkle evenly with parsley, if desired. YIELD: 4 SERVINGS (SERVING SIZE: 1 CHICKEN CUTLET AND ¼ CUP SAUCE).

PER SERVING: Calories 316; Fat 7.3g (sat 1.6g, mono 3g, poly 0.9g); Protein 46; Carb 10.5g; Fiber 0.8g; Chol 110mg; Iron 2.1mg; Sodium 625mg; Calc 26mg

ABOUT MARSALA

Originating in the Sicilian city that shares its name, Marsala wine is one of the best wines a cook can have on hand. It has a light caramel-like fruitiness and, because it's fortified with a little more alcohol than table wine, a long shelf life.

CHICKEN CUTLETS WITH WARM LEMON-ARTICHOKE RELISH

PointsPlus value per serving: 4   *pictured on page 132*

PREP: 2 minutes ■ COOK: 10 minutes

Artichokes and lemon are a natural flavor combination that brightens up boneless chicken. Using thinner cutlets shortens cook time. Serve with steamed green beans.

4 (4-ounce) chicken cutlets
¼ teaspoon freshly ground black pepper
⅛ teaspoon salt
Cooking spray
1 teaspoon bottled minced garlic
1 (14-ounce) can artichoke hearts, drained and chopped
2 tablespoons water
1½ teaspoons grated lemon rind
2 teaspoons fresh lemon juice
1 tablespoon chopped fresh parsley
¼ cup (1 ounce) shredded Parmesan cheese (optional)

1. Sprinkle chicken with pepper and salt. Heat a large nonstick skillet over medium-high heat. Coat pan with cooking spray. Add chicken; cook 3 minutes on each side or until done. Remove chicken from pan; keep warm.
2. Recoat pan with cooking spray; add garlic. Cook 1 minute. Add artichokes and next 3 ingredients; cook 2 minutes or until thoroughly heated. Stir in parsley. Spoon artichoke relish over chicken, and sprinkle with Parmesan cheese, if desired. YIELD: 4 SERVINGS (SERVING SIZE: 1 CHICKEN CUTLET AND ¼ CUP RELISH).

PER SERVING: Calories 164; Fat 1.8g (sat 0.4g, mono 0.5g, poly 0.4g); Protein 28.4g; Carb 7.2g; Fiber 2.3g; Chol 66mg; Iron 0.9mg; Sodium 514mg; Calc 16mg

MUSHROOM CHICKEN FRICASSEE

PointsPlus value per serving: 6

PREP: 3 minutes ■ COOK: 22 minutes

"Fricassee" refers to a dish typically made with poultry stewed in rich gravy.

1½ pounds chicken breast tenders
½ teaspoon salt, divided
½ teaspoon freshly ground black pepper, divided
Cooking spray
¼ cup finely chopped shallots
1 (8-ounce) package presliced mushrooms
1 cup fat-free, lower-sodium chicken broth
½ cup light sour cream
1 tablespoon chopped fresh tarragon

1. Sprinkle chicken evenly with ¼ teaspoon salt and ¼ teaspoon pepper.
2. Heat a large nonstick skillet over medium heat. Coat pan with cooking spray. Add chicken to pan, and cook 4 to 5 minutes on each side or until golden brown. Remove chicken from pan. Cover and keep warm.
3. Recoat pan with cooking spray. Add shallots to pan; sauté 1 minute. Add mushrooms; cook 4 minutes or until lightly browned, stirring occasionally. Stir in chicken broth, scraping pan to loosen browned bits. Bring to a boil; reduce heat and simmer, uncovered, 5 minutes or until broth is reduced by half.
4. Stir in remaining ¼ teaspoon salt, remaining ¼ teaspoon pepper, sour cream, and tarragon. Return chicken to pan, turning to coat. Bring to a simmer; cook 2 minutes or just until thoroughly heated. YIELD: 4 SERVINGS (SERVING SIZE: ABOUT 4 OUNCES CHICKEN AND ½ CUP SAUCE).

PER SERVING: Calories 257; Fat 5.9g (sat 2.7g, mono 1.5g, poly 0.7g); Protein 43.1g; Carb 6.3g; Fiber 0.9g; Chol 110mg; Iron 1.8mg; Sodium 529mg; Calc 75mg

BAKED HONEY MUSTARD CHICKEN TENDERS

PointsPlus value per serving: 6

PREP: 8 minutes ■ **COOK:** 30 minutes

The familiar flavor of these chicken tenders will please both adults and children.

Cooking spray
6 tablespoons honey
¼ cup Dijon mustard
½ teaspoon paprika
1 tablespoon water
¼ cup all-purpose flour
1 cup panko (Japanese breadcrumbs)
¼ teaspoon salt
¼ teaspoon freshly ground black pepper
1½ pounds chicken breast tenders

1. Preheat oven to 425°.
2. Place a wire rack coated with cooking spray in a large jelly-roll pan.
3. Combine honey, mustard, and paprika in a shallow bowl, stirring with a whisk. Reserve half of honey mixture in a small bowl to use as a dipping sauce. Stir 1 tablespoon water into remaining honey mixture to thin. Lightly spoon flour into a dry measuring cup; level with a knife. Place flour in a bowl; place panko in another bowl.
4. Sprinkle salt and pepper evenly over chicken. Dredge chicken in flour, shaking off excess; dip into thinned honey mixture. Dredge in panko. Lightly coat chicken tenders with cooking spray, and place on prepared rack.
5. Bake at 425° for 20 minutes. Turn chicken over; cook 10 minutes or until done. **YIELD: 6 SERVINGS (SERVING SIZE: ABOUT 3 OUNCES CHICKEN TENDERS AND ABOUT 1 TABLESPOON DIPPING SAUCE).**

PER SERVING: Calories 256; Fat 2g (sat 0.5g, mono 0.5g, poly 0.5g); Protein 28.2g; Carb 30.1g; Fiber 0.6g; Chol 66mg; Iron 1.2mg; Sodium 440mg; Calc 15mg

Panko

These Japanese breadcrumbs are both larger and lighter than American dried breadcrumbs. The irregular-shaped crumbs stay remarkably crisp when cooked and provide a satisfying crunch.

CHICKEN BROCCOLI STIR-FRY

PointsPlus value per serving: 7   *pictured on page 131*

PREP: 5 minutes ■ **COOK:** 10 minutes

This Asian-inspired dish combines chicken and broccoli with meaty shiitake mushrooms for a flavorful weeknight meal.

Cooking spray
¾ pound chicken breast tenders, cubed
4½ cups large broccoli florets
2 (3.5-ounce) packages shiitake mushrooms, sliced
1½ cups fat-free, lower-sodium beef broth
2 tablespoons cornstarch
2 tablespoons oyster sauce
2 teaspoons lower-sodium soy sauce
1 teaspoon sugar
⅛ teaspoon salt
2 cups cooked brown rice

1. Heat a large nonstick skillet over medium-high heat. Coat pan with cooking spray. Add chicken; cook 4 minutes, stirring frequently. Add broccoli and mushrooms; cook 3 minutes, stirring frequently.
2. Combine broth and next 5 ingredients in a small bowl; add to chicken mixture. Cook 3 minutes or until sauce thickens, stirring constantly. Serve immediately over rice. **YIELD: 4 SERVINGS (SERVING SIZE: ABOUT 1⅔ CUPS CHICKEN MIXTURE AND ½ CUP RICE).**

PER SERVING: Calories 266; Fat 2.5g (sat 0.5g, mono 0.6g, poly 0.7g); Protein 26.4g; Carb 34.2g; Fiber 4.3g; Chol 49mg; Iron 2mg; Sodium 659mg; Calc 63mg

MOROCCAN CHICKEN THIGHS

PointsPlus value per serving: 9

PREP: 5 minutes ■ **COOK:** 31 minutes

Olive oil–flavored cooking spray
8 (5-ounce) bone-in chicken thighs, skinned
¼ teaspoon salt
¼ teaspoon freshly ground black pepper
2 lemons, halved crosswise
1 large onion, halved vertically and thinly sliced crosswise
1 tablespoon minced peeled fresh ginger
1 tablespoon paprika
2 teaspoons ground cumin
½ teaspoon ground cinnamon
1 (14.5-ounce) can fat-free, lower-sodium chicken broth

1. Heat a large nonstick skillet over medium-high heat. Coat pan with cooking spray. Sprinkle chicken evenly with salt and pepper. Add chicken to pan. Cook 3 minutes on each side or until browned. Remove chicken from pan, and keep warm.
2. Add lemon halves, cut sides down, to pan. Cook 1 minute or until browned. Remove from pan and add to chicken.
3. Add onion and ginger to pan. Cook over medium-high heat 5 minutes or until onion is tender, stirring occasionally. Stir in paprika, cumin, and cinnamon. Cook 30 seconds. Return chicken and lemon halves to pan. Add chicken broth to chicken mixture. Cover and cook 14 minutes or until chicken is done, stirring after 7 minutes.
4. Transfer chicken to a serving platter. Remove and discard lemon halves. Bring onion mixture to a boil; cook, uncovered, 3 minutes or until reduced to 2 cups. Pour onion mixture over chicken. **YIELD: 4 SERVINGS (SERVING SIZE: 2 CHICKEN THIGHS AND ½ CUP ONION MIXTURE).**

PER SERVING: Calories 365; Fat 16.9g (sat 4.6g, mono 6.3g, poly 3.9g); Protein 41g; Carb 10.4g; Fiber 2.7g; Chol 143mg; Iron 3mg; Sodium 512mg; Calc 54mg

SMOKED CHICKEN CHIPOTLE QUESADILLAS

PointsPlus value per serving: 6

PREP: 9 minutes ■ **COOK:** 8 minutes

Instead of the traditional shredded cheese base, cream cheese mixed with chipotle chiles becomes the binder in this fiery quesadilla. If you want to decrease the heat, use less of the chipotle chiles.

½ cup (4 ounces) ⅓-less-fat cream cheese, softened
2 tablespoons chopped chipotle chiles in adobo sauce
4 (6-inch) whole-wheat tortillas
2 cups shredded smoked cooked chicken
¼ cup chopped green onions
Cooking spray
¼ cup chipotle salsa (optional)
¼ cup light sour cream (optional)

1. Combine cream cheese and chiles in a small bowl. Spread cream cheese mixture evenly over tortillas. Sprinkle chicken and green onions evenly over half of each tortilla. Fold tortillas in half.
2. Heat a large nonstick skillet over medium heat; coat pan with cooking spray. Place 2 tortillas, folded sides together, in pan. Cook 2 to 3 minutes or until lightly browned; turn quesadillas over, keeping folded sides in center of pan. Cook 2 to 3 minutes or until lightly browned. Remove from pan and keep warm. Repeat procedure with remaining quesadillas. Cut each quesadilla into 4 wedges. Serve with salsa and sour cream, if desired. **YIELD: 4 SERVINGS (SERVING SIZE: 4 WEDGES).**

PER SERVING: Calories 274; Fat 10.9g (sat 5.8g, mono 2.3g, poly 0.7g); Protein 26.9g; Carb 15.3g; Fiber 8.8g; Chol 80mg; Iron 1.3mg; Sodium 466mg; Calc 95mg

FLUFFY CHICKEN PIE

PointsPlus value per serving: 6

PREP: 10 minutes ■ COOK: 46 minutes

Use rotisserie chicken in this kid-friendly, one-dish meal.

3 cups shredded skinless, boneless rotisserie chicken breast
1½ cups fat-free, lower-sodium chicken broth
2 teaspoons fresh thyme leaves
½ teaspoon freshly ground black pepper
1 (10¾-ounce) can condensed fat-free cream of chicken
    soup, undiluted
2 cups frozen peas and carrots
4.5 ounces self-rising flour (about 1 cup)
½ cup chilled light butter, cut into small pieces
¾ cup fat-free half-and-half
Cooking spray

1. Preheat oven to 400°.
2. Combine first 5 ingredients in a saucepan. Bring to a boil; stir in peas and carrots. Cover; return to a boil, reduce heat, and cook 2 minutes.
3. While chicken mixture cooks, weigh or lightly spoon flour into a dry measuring cup; level with a knife. Place flour in a bowl. Cut in butter with a pastry blender or 2 knives until mixture resembles coarse meal. Add half-and-half, stirring with a fork just until moist.
4. Pour chicken mixture into an 11 x 7–inch glass or ceramic baking dish coated with cooking spray. Dollop topping in 8 portions over chicken mixture.
5. Bake at 400° for 35 minutes or until browned.
YIELD: 8 SERVINGS (SERVING SIZE: ⅛ OF PIE).

PER SERVING: Calories 249; Fat 9.1g (sat 4.4g, mono 2.6g, poly 1.1g); Protein 19.9g; Carb 22g; Fiber 2g; Chol 63mg; Iron 1.7mg; Sodium 648mg; Calc 86mg

SELF-RISING FLOUR

Self-rising flour is all-purpose flour with baking powder and salt added. To make your own to use in place of 1 cup self-rising flour, combine 1 cup all-purpose flour with 1 teaspoon baking powder and ½ teaspoon salt. But pay attention to the shelf life of store-bought and homemade self-rising flour: Baking powder loses its potency over time, which means eventually your baked goods won't rise as they should.

LOADED CHICKEN NACHOS

PointsPlus value per serving: 8

PREP: 4 minutes ■ COOK: 5 minutes

Using rotisserie chicken allows this dish to come together in a snap.

4 cups baked tortilla chips
2 cups shredded skinless, boneless rotisserie chicken breast
3 tablespoons fresh lime juice
2 tablespoons chopped fresh cilantro
1½ cups (6 ounces) reduced-fat shredded white cheddar
    cheese with jalapeño peppers
1 cup shredded lettuce
1 cup fresh salsa
½ cup fat-free sour cream
½ cup diced avocado (optional)
Chopped fresh cilantro (optional)

1. Preheat oven to 425°.
2. Spread tortilla chips in a single layer on a large foil-lined jelly-roll pan. Combine chicken, lime juice, and cilantro. Spread chicken mixture evenly over chips; top with cheese.
3. Bake, uncovered, at 425° for 5 minutes or until cheese melts. Top with lettuce, salsa, and sour cream. Garnish with avocado and cilantro, if desired. Serve immediately. YIELD: 5 SERVINGS (SERVING SIZE: ⅕ OF NACHOS).

PER SERVING: Calories 326; Fat 11.2g (sat 5g, mono 3.1g, poly 1.7g); Protein 30.3g; Carb 24.5g; Fiber 1.5g; Chol 69mg; Iron 1mg; Sodium 613mg; Calc 324mg

BBQ CHICKEN TWICE-BAKED POTATOES

PointsPlus value per serving: 7

PREP: 7 minutes ■ COOK: 1 hour and 5 minutes

These twice-baked potatoes are not only full-flavored and satisfying, but they also require very little hands-on time.

2 baking potatoes (about 1½ pounds)
1⅓ cups shredded skinless, boneless rotisserie chicken breast
½ cup (2 ounces) reduced-fat shredded extrasharp cheddar cheese
⅓ cup sliced green onions
¼ teaspoon salt
¼ teaspoon freshly ground black pepper
¼ cup barbecue sauce

1. Preheat oven to 450°.
2. Bake potatoes at 450° for 50 minutes or until tender and done; cool slightly. Reduce oven temperature to 400°.
3. Cut each potato in half lengthwise; scoop out pulp, leaving a ¼-inch-thick shell. Place potato pulp in a large bowl; mash with a potato masher. Add chicken and next 4 ingredients to potato pulp, stirring to blend. Spoon potato mixture into shells. Place potatoes in a single layer on a baking sheet.
4. Bake at 400° for 15 minutes or until thoroughly heated. Drizzle each potato with 1 tablespoon barbecue sauce. **YIELD: 4 SERVINGS (SERVING SIZE: 1 STUFFED POTATO HALF).**

PER SERVING: Calories 287; Fat 4.9g (sat 2.5g, mono 1.5g, poly 0.5g); Protein 21.7g; Carb 38.3g; Fiber 2.7g; Chol 50mg; Iron 2.1mg; Sodium 511mg; Calc 140mg

HOW TO MAKE STUFFED POTATOES

1. Pierce each potato with a fork. Bake the potatoes at 450° for 50 minutes or until tender and done. Cut them in half lengthwise.

2. Scoop out the flesh from each potato, leaving about a ¼-inch-thick shell. Combine the potato flesh and the filling ingredients, and mash with a potato masher to reach the desired consistency. Divide the mixture evenly among the potato shells. Place the filled potatoes in a single layer on a baking sheet, and bake until thoroughly heated.

JAPANESE TERIYAKI CHICKEN CAKES

PointsPlus value per serving: 6   *pictured on page 132*

PREP: 18 minutes ■ COOK: 10 minutes

These small cakes, called *tsukune* in Japan, are glazed with teriyaki sauce and topped with green onions.

1 green onion
1 pound ground chicken
¼ cup finely chopped onion
2 tablespoons egg substitute
1½ teaspoons sugar
1½ teaspoons lower-sodium soy sauce
2 teaspoons minced peeled fresh ginger
4 teaspoons cornstarch, divided
Cooking spray
1 teaspoon dark sesame oil, divided
½ teaspoon canola oil, divided
2 tablespoons sugar
2 tablespoons mirin (sweet rice wine)
2 tablespoons lower-sodium soy sauce
4 lime wedges (optional)

1. Remove green top of onion; reserve for another use. Cut white part of onion into very thin sticks; place in ice water.
2. Combine chicken and next 5 ingredients in a medium bowl; mix well. On a large piece of wax paper, divide chicken mixture into 12 equal portions, shaping each into a 2½-inch patty; dust tops of patties with 2 teaspoons cornstarch.
3. Heat a large nonstick skillet over medium-high heat. Coat pan with cooking spray. Add ½ teaspoon sesame oil and ¼ teaspoon canola oil to pan. Using a rubber spatula, gently add half of chicken patties, cornstarch sides down, to pan; reshape patties, if necessary. Dust tops of patties with 1 teaspoon cornstarch. Cook 2 minutes on each side. Remove patties from pan. Repeat procedure with remaining oils, patties, and cornstarch. Return all patties to pan; reduce heat to medium.
4. Combine 2 tablespoons sugar, mirin, and 2 tablespoons soy sauce; stir well, and pour over chicken patties. Cook 1 minute or until chicken is done and patties are glazed, turning occasionally and stirring sauce to prevent burning. Top patties evenly with green onions. Serve with lime wedges, if desired. **YIELD: 4 SERVINGS (SERVING SIZE: 3 CHICKEN CAKES AND ABOUT 1 TEASPOON GLAZE).**

PER SERVING: Calories 243; Fat 11.3g (sat 2.8g, mono 4.8g, poly 2.4g); Protein 19.8g; Carb 14.6g; Fiber 0.3g; Chol 75mg; Iron 0.3mg; Sodium 324mg; Calc 12mg

CHICKEN PICADILLO

PointsPlus value per serving: 5

PREP: 12 minutes ■ **COOK:** 17 minutes

Many of these ingredients are kitchen staples, and the prep is simple. Serve with black beans and flour tortillas or baked tortilla chips.

Cooking spray
1 pound ground chicken breast
¾ cup chopped onion
½ cup chopped green bell pepper
3 garlic cloves, minced
1 cup bottled hot salsa
⅓ cup golden raisins
¼ cup sliced pimiento-stuffed olives
1½ teaspoons ground cumin
¼ teaspoon ground cinnamon
2 tablespoons slivered almonds, toasted
2 tablespoons chopped fresh cilantro

1. Heat a large nonstick skillet over medium–high heat. Coat pan with cooking spray. Add chicken, onion, bell pepper, and garlic; cook 5 minutes or until chicken is done, stirring to crumble chicken.

2. Stir in salsa and next 4 ingredients. Cover, reduce heat, and simmer 10 minutes, stirring occasionally. Remove from heat; sprinkle with almonds and cilantro. **YIELD: 5 SERVINGS (SERVING SIZE: 1 CUP).**

PER SERVING: Calories 182; Fat 3.2g (sat 0.1g, mono 1.4g, poly 0.9g); Protein 22.6g; Carb 17.5g; Fiber 3.3g; Chol 53mg; Iron 0.6mg; Sodium 602mg; Calc 29mg

HERBED TURKEY TENDERLOINS

PointsPlus value per serving: 6

PREP: 4 minutes ■ **COOK:** 20 minutes
■ **OTHER:** 10 minutes

You can replace these herbs with others you have on hand, such as oregano or rosemary.

1½ teaspoons dried thyme
1½ teaspoons dried marjoram
¾ teaspoon rubbed sage
½ teaspoon salt
½ teaspoon freshly ground black pepper
2 (¾-pound) turkey tenderloins
2 teaspoons olive oil
Cooking spray

1. Preheat grill to medium–high heat.

2. Combine first 5 ingredients. Brush turkey with olive oil, and rub evenly with herb mixture. Place turkey on grill rack coated with cooking spray. Grill 10 to 12 minutes on each side or until a thermometer registers 165°. Let turkey stand 10 minutes. Cut each tenderloin into 6 slices. **YIELD: 4 SERVINGS (SERVING SIZE: 3 SLICES).**

PER SERVING: Calories 237; Fat 5.7g (sat 2g, mono 1.9g, poly 0.7g); Protein 43g; Carb 5.7g; Fiber 2.4g; Chol 68mg; Iron 3mg; Sodium 402mg; Calc 91mg

✳ Turkey Tenderloins

There are two types of meat in poultry: light meat and dark meat. Light meat includes the breast and tenderloin, which is a thin, tender strip of meat under the breast. Dark meat includes the thigh, wing, and leg. Light meat contains about 50% less saturated fat than dark.

MOROCCAN-STYLE TURKEY CUTLETS

PointsPlus value per serving: 6

PREP: 10 minutes ■ COOK: 8 minutes

A bed of hot, cooked couscous is all you need to complete this quick and flavorful meal.

    1½ pounds turkey cutlets (about 10 cutlets)
    ¼ teaspoon freshly ground black pepper
    ⅛ teaspoon salt
    Cooking spray
    2 teaspoons olive oil, divided
    1 cup chopped onion
    2 teaspoons paprika
    1 teaspoon minced peeled fresh ginger
    ½ teaspoon ground cumin
    ¼ teaspoon ground cinnamon
    2 garlic cloves, minced
    ½ cup sliced Sicilian-style pitted green olives
    ¼ cup fat-free, lower-sodium chicken broth
    2 tablespoons fresh lemon juice

1. Sprinkle turkey cutlets evenly with pepper and salt.
2. Heat a large nonstick skillet over medium-high heat. Coat pan with cooking spray. Add 1 teaspoon oil to pan. Add half of turkey; cook 1 minute on each side or until browned. Remove from pan; keep warm. Repeat procedure with remaining oil and turkey. Reduce heat to medium-low. Recoat pan with cooking spray.
3. Add onion and next 5 ingredients to pan; sauté 1 minute. Stir in olives, chicken broth, and lemon juice. Nestle cutlets into onion mixture; cover and cook 2 minutes. YIELD: 4 SERVINGS (SERVING SIZE: 5 OUNCES TURKEY AND ¼ CUP ONION MIXTURE).

PER SERVING: Calories 263; Fat 6.8g (sat 0.4g, mono 4.1g, poly 1.2g); Protein 43g; Carb 7.7g; Fiber 1.4g; Chol 68mg; Iron 2.5mg; Sodium 612mg; Calc 20mg

TURKEY AND DRESSING ROULADE

PointsPlus value per serving: 6

PREP: 6 minutes ■ COOK: 46 minutes
■ OTHER: 5 minutes

Traditional Thanksgiving favorites are transformed into a stuffed turkey roll that's quick enough to serve on busy weeknights.

    2 (¾-pound) turkey tenderloins
    ¼ teaspoon salt
    ¼ teaspoon freshly ground black pepper
    1 tablespoon butter
    Cooking spray
    1 cup refrigerated prechopped celery, onion, and bell pepper mix
    1 cup herb-seasoned stuffing mix (such as Pepperidge Farm)
    ¾ cup fat-free, lower-sodium chicken broth
    1 cup whole-berry cranberry sauce
    1 teaspoon prepared horseradish
    Chopped fresh parsley (optional)

1. Preheat oven to 425°.
2. Place turkey tenderloins between 2 sheets of heavy-duty plastic wrap. Pound to ½-inch thickness using a meat mallet or small heavy skillet. Sprinkle tenderloins evenly with salt and pepper.
3. Melt butter over medium heat in a large nonstick skillet coated with cooking spray. Add celery mixture. Sauté 9 minutes or until tender. Remove from heat; stir in stuffing mix and chicken broth.
4. Spread stuffing mixture down center of tenderloins to within ½ inch of sides. Roll up tenderloins, jelly-roll fashion, starting with short side. Secure at 2-inch intervals with twine.
5. Return pan to medium-high heat; recoat pan with cooking spray. Add turkey to pan; cook 1 to 2 minutes on each side or until browned. Place turkey on a broiler pan coated with cooking spray. Bake at 425° for 30 minutes or until a thermometer registers 165°. Let stand, covered, 5 minutes before slicing each tenderloin into 6 slices.
6. Combine cranberry sauce and horseradish. Serve cranberry mixture with turkey. Garnish with parsley, if desired. YIELD: 6 SERVINGS (SERVING SIZE: 2 SLICES).

PER SERVING: Calories 250; Fat 3.9g (sat 1.2g, mono 0.5g, poly 0.1g); Protein 29.5g; Carb 26.2g; Fiber 1.8g; Chol 50mg; Iron 1.9mg; Sodium 383mg; Calc 15mg

ASIAN TURKEY CUTLETS

PointsPlus value per serving: 5

PREP: 6 minutes ▪ **COOK:** 8 minutes

Steamed snow peas and rice are the ideal sides for these quick-and-easy cutlets.

> Cooking spray
> 1 tablespoon dark sesame oil
> ¼ teaspoon crushed red pepper
> 1 pound turkey cutlets (about 6 cutlets)
> 3 tablespoons hoisin sauce
> 2 tablespoons water
> 1 tablespoon lower-sodium soy sauce
> 1 tablespoon rice vinegar
> 1 teaspoon grated peeled fresh ginger
> 3 garlic cloves, minced
> 1 tablespoon chopped fresh cilantro

1. Heat a large nonstick skillet over medium–high heat. Coat pan with cooking spray. Add oil. Add crushed red pepper, and sauté in hot oil 1 minute. Add cutlets; cook 2 minutes on each side or until browned.
2. While cutlets cook, combine hoisin sauce and next 5 ingredients. Pour over cutlets, turning to coat. Cook 1 minute; remove from heat. Sprinkle with cilantro.
YIELD: 4 SERVINGS (SERVING SIZE: 3 OUNCES TURKEY, 2 TABLESPOONS SAUCE, AND ¾ TEASPOON CILANTRO).

PER SERVING: Calories 186; Fat 4.7g (sat 0.6g, mono 1.6g, poly 1.7g); Protein 28.8g; Carb 6.6g; Fiber 0.4g; Chol 45mg; Iron 1.7mg; Sodium 392mg; Calc 9mg

✳ Ground Poultry

Poultry can be an excellent alternative to beef, but you'll need to closely watch what you're buying. Packages labeled "ground turkey" contain a mix of white meat, dark meat, and skin, which means it could contain anywhere from 10 to 15% fat. While it's still leaner than ground round, which has 15% fat, it's not the leanest choice available. Look for packages labeled ground turkey *breast*. It's the leanest ground poultry option out there.

EASY TURKEY CHILI MAC

PointsPlus value per serving: 6

PREP: 1 minute ▪ **COOK:** 7 minutes

This kid-friendly chili mac is an ideal weeknight option. If you want to add some heat, stir ⅛ teaspoon ground red pepper into the turkey mixture.

> ½ cup uncooked multigrain elbow macaroni
> Cooking spray
> ¾ pound ground turkey breast
> ¼ cup refrigerated prechopped onion
> 1 (15-ounce) can vegetarian chili with beans
> ¼ teaspoon salt
> ¼ teaspoon freshly ground black pepper
> ½ cup (2 ounces) shredded reduced-fat sharp
>   cheddar cheese

1. Cook pasta according to package directions, omitting salt and fat. Drain and keep warm.
2. Heat a large nonstick skillet over medium–high heat. Coat pan with cooking spray. Add turkey and onion; cook 4 minutes or until onion is tender, stirring to crumble turkey.
3. Add chili, salt, and pepper to turkey mixture. Bring to a simmer. Cook 2 minutes or until turkey is done. Stir in pasta. Spoon turkey mixture evenly onto 4 plates; top evenly with cheese, and serve immediately.
YIELD: 4 SERVINGS (SERVING SIZE: ABOUT 1 CUP CHILI MAC AND 2 TABLESPOONS CHEESE).

PER SERVING: Calories 266; Fat 5g (sat 2.5g, mono 1.3g, poly 0.3g); Protein 30.2g; Carb 24.2g; Fiber 5.1g; Chol 44mg; Iron 2.1mg; Sodium 669mg; Calc 149mg

SAUSAGE-STUFFED PORTOBELLOS

PointsPlus value per serving: 6

PREP: 4 minutes ■ COOK: 25 minutes

Portobello caps make the perfect edible baking vessels for this delicious sausage stuffing.

12 ounces turkey breakfast sausage
Cooking spray
1 (8-ounce) package refrigerated prechopped tricolor bell pepper
½ cup (4 ounces) tub-style light chive and onion cream cheese
2 teaspoons chopped fresh oregano, divided
4 (4-inch) portobello caps

1. Preheat oven to 400°.
2. Brown sausage in a large skillet coated with cooking spray over medium heat; stir to crumble. Add bell pepper, and sauté 3 minutes. Add cream cheese and 1 teaspoon oregano, stirring until cheese melts. Remove from heat.
3. Remove brown gills from the undersides of mushrooms using a spoon; discard gills. Place mushrooms on a broiler pan coated with cooking spray. Spoon sausage mixture evenly onto mushrooms.
4. Bake, uncovered, at 400° for 15 minutes or until tops are brown. Sprinkle remaining 1 teaspoon oregano evenly over mushrooms. YIELD: 4 SERVINGS (SERVING SIZE: 1 STUFFED MUSHROOM).

PER SERVING: Calories 237; Fat 11.9g (sat 4.7g, mono 2.2g, poly 2.1g); Protein 21.6g; Carb 10.1g; Fiber 2.2g; Chol 79mg; Iron 1.7mg; Sodium 682mg; Calc 71mg

TURKEY KIELBASA AND PINEAPPLE KEBABS

PointsPlus value per serving: 6

PREP: 9 minutes ■ COOK: 12 minutes

These easy-to-serve kebabs are reminiscent of kielbasa dinners. You can find the wooden skewers that come packaged with a salt-free spice packet in larger grocery stores and kitchenware stores.

1 (14-ounce) package turkey kielbasa, cut diagonally into ¾-inch-thick slices
1 cup (1½-inch) pieces red bell pepper (about 1 pepper)
1 cup (1½-inch) pieces green bell pepper (about 1 pepper)
1 cup (1½-inch) pieces onion (1 large)
2 cups (1½-inch) chunks fresh pineapple
4 single-use wooden skewers with no-salt-added mustard-and-herb spice pack (such as Fire & Flavor)
Cooking spray

1. Preheat grill to medium-high heat.
2. Thread kielbasa slices and pieces of pepper, onion, and pineapple alternately onto skewers. Sprinkle contents of mustard-and-herb spice pack evenly over kebabs.
3. Place kebabs on grill rack coated with cooking spray; grill 6 minutes on each side or until vegetables are crisp-tender and kielbasa is browned. YIELD: 4 SERVINGS (SERVING SIZE: 1 KEBAB).

PER SERVING: Calories 207; Fat 6.3g (sat 2.8g, mono 1.8g, poly 1.7g); Protein 16.7g; Carb 25.5g; Fiber 4.4g; Chol 25mg; Iron 2.4mg; Sodium 503mg; Calc 205mg

salads

Fruit and Nut Tossed Salad, *page 114*

AVOCADO, ORANGE, AND JICAMA CHOPPED SALAD

PointsPlus value per serving: 3

PREP: 15 minutes

Try this refreshing citrus salad alongside a piece of grilled fish or chicken.

    1 large navel orange
    2 tablespoons olive oil
    2 teaspoons fresh lemon juice
    ¼ teaspoon salt
    ¼ teaspoon ground cumin
    ¼ teaspoon crushed red pepper
    3 cups chopped romaine lettuce
    1 cup diced peeled jicama
    1 cup chopped English cucumber
    1 diced peeled avocado

1. Peel and section orange over a large bowl; squeeze membranes to extract juice, reserving 1 tablespoon juice. Set sections aside. Add olive oil and next 4 ingredients to reserved orange juice in bowl, stirring with a whisk.

2. Add lettuce, jicama, and cucumber; toss well. Add reserved orange sections and avocado; toss gently. YIELD: 6 SERVINGS (SERVING SIZE: 1 CUP).

PER SERVING: Calories 120; Fat 9.6g (sat 1.4g, mono 6.6g, poly 1.1g); Protein 1.5g; Carb 9g; Fiber 4.5g; Chol 0mg; Iron 0.7mg; Sodium 104mg; Calc 28mg

HOW TO PEEL AND DICE AVOCADO

To easily dice, start with an 8- to 10-inch chef's knife. Insert it into the top where the stem was (it will be a darker area), and gently press down until you reach the pit. Then follow these tips.

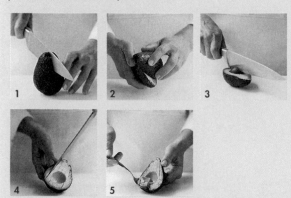

1. Holding the knife steady, rotate the fruit so the knife moves around the pit, cutting the entire avocado.
2. Remove the knife; then slowly and gently twist the two sides away from each other to separate.
3. Strike the pit, and pierce it with the blade. Then twist and remove the knife; the pit will come with it.
4. Use the knife's tip to cut the flesh in horizontal and vertical rows. Be careful not to cut through the skin.
5. Remove the flesh gently with a spoon. To prevent browning, squeeze lemon juice on the flesh.

BERRY GINGER SALAD

PointsPlus value per serving: 1

PREP: 6 minutes ■ OTHER: 30 minutes

Serve this salad with whole-wheat toast at breakfast or paired with a sandwich for lunch.

    1 tablespoon honey
    2 teaspoons fresh lime juice
    ½ teaspoon grated peeled fresh ginger
    2 cups mixed berries (such as blackberries, blueberries, and strawberries)
    1 tablespoon chopped fresh mint

1. Combine first 3 ingredients in a medium bowl. Add berries and mint; toss gently. Chill at least 30 minutes. YIELD: 4 SERVINGS (SERVING SIZE: ½ CUP).

PER SERVING: Calories 50; Fat 0.3g (sat 0g, mono 0g, poly 0.2g); Protein 0.8g; Carb 12.5g; Fiber 2.4g; Chol 0mg; Iron 0.5mg; Sodium 2mg; Calc 16mg

WATERMELON-TOMATO SALAD

PointsPlus value per serving: 3   *pictured on page 135*

PREP: 12 minutes

Watermelon cutouts offer a creative presentation. You can also chop the melon and stir everything together.

4 (1-inch-thick) seedless watermelon slices
1 cup finely chopped tomato
⅓ cup vertically sliced red onion
⅓ cup fresh lime juice
¼ cup torn fresh mint leaves
1 tablespoon sugar
1 tablespoon canola oil
½ teaspoon freshly ground black pepper
¼ teaspoon salt

1. Cut watermelon with a 3-inch biscuit cutter into 4 rounds; place rounds on a serving platter. Sprinkle with tomato and onion. Reserve remaining watermelon for another use.
2. Combine lime juice and next 5 ingredients, stirring well. Drizzle over watermelon rounds. Cover and chill until ready to serve. YIELD: 4 SERVINGS (SERVING SIZE: 1 WATERMELON ROUND).

PER SERVING: Calories 111; Fat 3.6g (sat 0.3g, mono 2.2g, poly 1g); Protein 1.3g; Carb 20.7g; Fiber 1.6g; Chol 0mg; Iron 0.7mg; Sodium 151mg; Calc 27mg

BLUEBERRY SPINACH SALAD WITH POPPY SEED DRESSING

PointsPlus value per serving: 4

PREP: 10 minutes ■ COOK: 2 minutes

Make the dressing ahead to prepare this salad in a snap. Dressing can keep stored in the refrigerator for up to 1 week.

1½ tablespoons minced shallots (about 1 small)
2 tablespoons olive oil
1 tablespoon white wine vinegar
1 tablespoon honey
2 teaspoons poppy seeds
¼ teaspoon salt
8 cups fresh baby spinach
1½ cups blueberries
½ cup (2 ounces) crumbled goat cheese
¼ cup sliced almonds, toasted

1. Combine first 6 ingredients in a large bowl, stirring with a whisk. Add spinach and remaining ingredients; toss gently. YIELD: 6 SERVINGS (SERVING SIZE: 1 CUP).

PER SERVING: Calories 141; Fat 9g (sat 2.2g, mono 5g, poly 1.4g); Protein 3.9g; Carb 13.6g; Fiber 3g; Chol 4mg; Iron 1.7mg; Sodium 186mg; Calc 65mg

PEAR-WALNUT SALAD WITH GORGONZOLA BUTTERMILK DRESSING

PointsPlus value per serving: 4   *pictured on page 136*

PREP: 8 minutes ■ COOK: 2 minutes

Gorgonzola cheese adds full flavor to this homemade, ranch-style dressing that complements sweet pears and crunchy walnuts. Tossing the sliced pears with lemon juice helps prevent browning.

¼ cup nonfat buttermilk
¼ cup plain fat-free Greek yogurt
1½ tablespoons white wine vinegar
¼ teaspoon salt
¼ teaspoon freshly ground pepper
¼ cup (1 ounce) crumbled Gorgonzola cheese
1 (5-ounce) package spring mix salad greens
2 Bartlett or Anjou pears, cored and cut lengthwise into ½-inch-thick slices
1 tablespoon fresh lemon juice
¼ cup chopped walnuts, toasted

1. Combine first 5 ingredients in a medium bowl, stirring with a whisk. Stir in Gorgonzola cheese.
2. Arrange 2 cups salad greens on each of 4 plates. Toss pears with lemon juice. Top salad greens evenly with pears and walnuts. Drizzle with dressing. YIELD: 4 SERVINGS (SERVING SIZE: 2 CUPS SALAD GREENS, ⅓ CUP PEAR SLICES, 1 TABLESPOON WALNUTS, AND 3 TABLESPOONS DRESSING).

PER SERVING: Calories 164; Fat 6.9g (sat 2g, mono 1.2g, poly 3.6g); Protein 5.4g; Carb 23.4g; Fiber 5.4g; Chol 7mg; Iron 0.7mg; Sodium 278mg; Calc 85mg

BREAD SALAD WITH CHERRIES AND CHEESE

PointsPlus value per serving: 6

PREP: 7 minutes ■ COOK: 10 minutes

Use pitted fresh sour cherries when they're in season. Rubbing the salad bowl with cut garlic adds fresh garlic flavor without overpowering the salad. For another quick dressing option, combine 2 tablespoons of your favorite bottled balsamic vinaigrette with ¼ teaspoon freshly ground black pepper.

1 garlic clove, halved
2 cups (½-inch) cubed sourdough bread, toasted
    (about 2 [2-ounce] slices)
Olive oil–flavored cooking spray
4 cups gourmet salad greens
½ cup dried cherries
1 tablespoon water
2 teaspoons olive oil
2 teaspoons balsamic vinegar
¼ teaspoon freshly ground black pepper
½ cup (2 ounces) crumbled goat cheese

1. Rub salad bowl with cut sides of garlic; discard garlic. Place sourdough bread cubes in salad bowl. Coat bread cubes lightly with cooking spray; toss well.
2. Add salad greens and cherries to bowl. Combine 1 tablespoon water and next 3 ingredients in a small bowl; drizzle over greens. Add cheese; toss gently to coat. YIELD: 4 SERVINGS (SERVING SIZE: 1½ CUPS).

PER SERVING: Calories 223; Fat 5.8g (sat 2.5g, mono 2.4g, poly 0.5g); Protein 7.2g; Carb 34.9g; Fiber 4.1g; Chol 7mg; Iron 2.2mg; Sodium 260mg; Calc 54mg

FRUIT AND NUT TOSSED SALAD

PointsPlus value per serving: 5   *pictured on page 111*

PREP: 8 minutes ■ COOK: 4 minutes

Toasting brings out all the flavor of the pumpkinseeds, so it's best not to skip that step.

6 cups gourmet salad greens
1¼ cups chopped Braeburn apple (about ⅓ pound)
⅓ cup (1.3 ounces) crumbled feta cheese
¼ cup chopped walnuts, toasted
¼ cup unsalted pumpkinseed kernels, toasted
¼ cup sweetened dried cranberries
¼ cup golden raisins
¼ cup strawberry-balsamic dressing (such as Maple Grove Farms)

1. Combine all ingredients in a large bowl; toss gently. Divide salad evenly among 6 plates. YIELD: 6 SERVINGS (SERVING SIZE: 1 CUP).

PER SERVING: Calories 169; Fat 9.8g (sat 2g, mono 2.2g, poly 4.7g); Protein 3.3g; Carb 19g; Fiber 3.1g; Chol 7mg; Iron 1mg; Sodium 148mg; Calc 55mg

TOASTING PUMPKINSEEDS

To toast pumpkinseeds, spread the seeds on a baking sheet coated with cooking spray. Roast at 325° for 15 to 25 minutes or until the seeds are dry and crunchy.

PAN-GRILLED POTATO AND ARUGULA SALAD

PointsPlus value per serving: 3

PREP: 2 minutes ■ COOK: 18 minutes

Grilling the potato adds nice flavor and texture to this warm salad.

Cooking spray
2 pounds Yukon Gold potatoes, cut into ¼-inch slices
1 small red onion, cut into ¼-inch slices
¼ cup creamy mustard blend (such as Dijonnaise)
3 tablespoons white wine vinegar
¼ teaspoon freshly ground black pepper
1 (5-ounce) package arugula

1. Heat a nonstick grill pan over medium-high heat. Coat pan with cooking spray.
2. Place one-third of potato and onion in pan, and cook 3 minutes on each side or until tender. Repeat procedure twice with remaining potato and onion.
3. Combine mustard blend, vinegar, and pepper in a large bowl, stirring with a whisk. Add grilled vegetables and arugula to dressing; toss gently to coat. YIELD: 6 SERVINGS (SERVING SIZE: 1 CUP).

PER SERVING: Calories 140; Fat 0.3g (sat 0.1g, mono 0g, poly 0.1g); Protein 3.9g; Carb 31.1g; Fiber 4.1g; Chol 0mg; Iron 1.6mg; Sodium 156mg; Calc 61mg

MEDITERRANEAN SALAD

PointsPlus value per serving: 2

PREP: 4 minutes

Add grilled chicken or shrimp to make this salad a main dish.

1 (2½-inch) piece English cucumber
⅓ cup (1.3 ounces) crumbled feta cheese
¼ cup light red wine vinegar and olive oil salad dressing
2 plum tomatoes, sliced
2 thin slices small red onion, separated into rings
1 (6-ounce) package 5-lettuce blend salad greens

1. Cut cucumber in half lengthwise; cut halves into thin slices to measure ¾ cup. Combine cucumber and remaining ingredients in a large salad bowl; toss well. Serve immediately. **YIELD: 4 SERVINGS (SERVING SIZE: 1½ CUPS).**

PER SERVING: Calories 76; Fat 5g (sat 2.1g, mono 1.4g, poly 1.2g); Protein 2.2g; Carb 4.9g; Fiber 0.6g; Chol 11mg; Iron 0.6mg; Sodium 347mg; Calc 79mg

WARM ORZO SALAD WITH ZUCCHINI AND FETA

PointsPlus value per serving: 6

PREP: 3 minutes ■ COOK: 18 minutes

Using a vegetable peeler to slice the zucchini creates beautiful ribbons of green throughout the orzo.

1 cup uncooked orzo (rice-shaped pasta)
1 medium zucchini
Cooking spray
2 garlic cloves, minced
¼ teaspoon salt
¼ teaspoon freshly ground black pepper
1 cup grape tomatoes, halved
2 tablespoons chopped fresh basil
¼ cup (1 ounce) crumbled feta cheese

1. Cook orzo according to package directions, omitting salt and fat. Drain.
2. While orzo cooks, slice zucchini lengthwise into ribbons using a vegetable peeler. Heat a medium skillet over medium-high heat. Coat pan with cooking spray. Add zucchini and garlic to pan. Sprinkle with salt and pepper. Cook 5 minutes, stirring often. Add tomatoes. Sauté 2 minutes or until tomatoes soften.

3. Stir orzo and basil into zucchini mixture. Transfer pasta mixture to a serving platter; sprinkle with cheese. **YIELD: 4 SERVINGS (SERVING SIZE: ABOUT ¾ CUP).**

PER SERVING: Calories 221; Fat 2.8g (sat 1.6g, mono 0.4g, poly 0.1g); Protein 9g; Carb 40.8g; Fiber 3g; Chol 8mg; Iron 1.9mg; Sodium 263mg; Calc 78mg

SEVEN-LAYER SALAD

PointsPlus value per serving: 4

PREP: 6 minutes ■ COOK: 3 minutes

To show off the layers, serve this salad in a tall glass serving bowl.

1 (10-ounce) package Italian blend salad greens
1 (16-ounce) can chickpeas (garbanzo beans), rinsed and drained
2 cups broccoli florets, chopped
1 cup shredded carrot
1 cup frozen petite green peas, thawed and drained
1 cup light 3-cheese ranch dressing
1 cup (4 ounces) reduced-fat shredded extrasharp cheddar cheese
4 center-cut bacon slices, cooked and crumbled

1. Place salad greens in a salad bowl or large glass serving bowl. Layer chickpeas and next 3 ingredients over greens. Drizzle dressing over salad; sprinkle with cheese and bacon. Cover and chill until ready to serve. **YIELD: 10 SERVINGS (SERVING SIZE: 1 CUP).**

PER SERVING: Calories 148; Fat 8.3g (sat 2.6g, mono 1.8g, poly 1.8g); Protein 6.3g; Carb 10.7g; Fiber 2.6g; Chol 11mg; Iron 0.9mg; Sodium 533mg; Calc 106mg

FROZEN PEAS

Green peas add fiber, color, and a slightly sweet snap to each bite of this salad. Buying the peas frozen saves time and allows you to enjoy them year-round. A quick rinse under cold running water is all that's needed to thaw the frozen peas. Of course, if you happen to find some freshly shelled peas, feel free to substitute them for the frozen peas.

TUSCAN WHITE BEAN SALAD WITH RICOTTA

PointsPlus value per serving: 5

PREP: 6 minutes ■ COOK: 2 minutes

Add some crusty bread to this meatless main-dish salad for a satisfying complete meal.

½ cup bottled roasted red bell peppers, cut into
   ¼-inch-thick strips
1 (15.5-ounce) can cannellini beans, rinsed and drained
1 (6-ounce) package fresh baby spinach
½ cup part-skim ricotta cheese
2 tablespoons pine nuts, toasted
⅓ cup light sun-dried tomato vinaigrette

1. Combine first 3 ingredients in a large bowl, tossing well. Divide salad mixture evenly among 4 plates. Dollop 2 tablespoons cheese onto each salad. Top each salad with 1½ teaspoons pine nuts. Drizzle vinaigrette evenly over salads. Serve immediately. YIELD: 4 SERVINGS (SERVING SIZE: 2¼ CUPS SALAD AND 4 TEASPOONS VINAIGRETTE).

PER SERVING: Calories 192; Fat 8g (sat 2.1g, mono 1.5g, poly 1.5g); Protein 9.5g; Carb 21.5g; Fiber 5.4g; Chol 10mg; Iron 2.7mg; Sodium 523mg; Calc 148mg

CANNELLINI BEANS

Quite popular in Italy, cannellini beans, also called white kidney or fazolia beans, are prized for their smooth texture and mellow nutty flavor. Because of their popularity, they're available year-round, either dried or canned. Dried cannellini beans must be soaked overnight and then boiled, but using canned beans can save time. Rinsing canned beans, as in this recipe, reduces the sodium by 40 percent.

SALMON BLT SALAD

PointsPlus value per serving: 6

PREP: 6 minutes ■ COOK: 12 minutes

This salmon salad is a take on the classic BLT sandwich. Be sure to add the dressing just before serving or the lettuce will become soggy.

2 (6-ounce) salmon fillets (about 1 inch thick)
1½ tablespoons brown sugar
¾ teaspoon chili powder
Cooking spray
3 tablespoons ranch dressing
3 tablespoons fat-free milk
5 cups chopped iceberg lettuce
2 cups chopped tomato (about 2 tomatoes)
4 center-cut bacon slices, cooked and crumbled

1. Preheat broiler.
2. Rub flesh sides of fillets with brown sugar and sprinkle with chili powder. Place fillets, skin sides down, on a broiler pan coated with cooking spray. Broil 12 minutes or until desired degree of doneness. Remove skin from fillets, and cut fish into chunks.
3. Combine dressing and milk in a small bowl, stirring with a whisk. Combine lettuce, tomato, fish, and bacon in a large bowl; toss gently. Place 2 cups salad mixture on each of 4 plates. Drizzle dressing mixture evenly over salads. YIELD: 4 SERVINGS (SERVING SIZE: 2 CUPS SALAD AND 4½ TEASPOONS DRESSING).

PER SERVING: Calories 230; Fat 10.8g (sat 2g, mono 2.5g, poly 1.7g); Protein 21.4g; Carb 11.5g; Fiber 1.9g; Chol 53mg; Iron 1.5mg; Sodium 333mg; Calc 57mg

GRILLED SALMON PANZANELLA

PointsPlus value per serving: 8

PREP: 6 minutes ■ **COOK:** 8 minutes

Tuscan bread salad gets pumped with healthy omega-3s.

2 (6-ounce) salmon fillets (about 1 inch thick)
Olive oil–flavored cooking spray
¼ teaspoon freshly ground black pepper
3 (3-ounce) slices ciabatta bread
1½ cups chopped English cucumber
1 cup grape tomatoes, halved
½ cup vertically sliced red onion
⅓ cup thinly sliced fresh basil
¼ cup light balsamic vinaigrette
Freshly ground black pepper (optional)

1. Preheat grill to medium-high heat.
2. Lightly coat fillets with cooking spray. Sprinkle fillets with ¼ teaspoon black pepper. Place fillets, skin sides up, on grill rack coated with cooking spray; grill 4 to 5 minutes on each side or until desired degree of doneness. Remove skin from fillets; break fish into bite-sized chunks.
3. While fish cooks, coat both sides of bread slices with cooking spray. Grill 1 minute on each side or until toasted.
4. Combine cucumber and next 4 ingredients in a large bowl; toss well. Cut bread into bite-sized pieces. Add bread and fish to salad; toss well. Sprinkle with additional pepper, if desired. **YIELD: 4 SERVINGS (SERVING SIZE: 2 CUPS).**

PER SERVING: Calories 320; Fat 7.8g (sat 1.1g, mono 2.9g, poly 1.5g); Protein 23.4g; Carb 40.3g; Fiber 2.2g; Chol 44mg; Iron 2.9mg; Sodium 732mg; Calc 34mg

GRILLED TUNA SALAD WITH AVOCADO WASABI DRESSING

PointsPlus value per serving: 6

PREP: 17 minutes ■ **COOK:** 4 minutes

3 (6-ounce) tuna steaks (1½ inches thick)
½ teaspoon freshly ground black pepper
¼ teaspoon salt
Cooking spray
⅓ cup ranch-flavored yogurt dressing
3 tablespoons water
2 teaspoons fresh lime juice
2 teaspoons wasabi paste (Japanese horseradish)
1 avocado, coarsely chopped
1 (6.5-ounce) package green and red butter lettuce blend
3 tablespoons thinly sliced green onions (2 onions)
2 tablespoons thinly sliced radishes (2 radishes)

1. Preheat grill to medium-high heat.
2. Sprinkle fish evenly with pepper and salt. Place fish on grill rack coated with cooking spray. Grill 2 to 3 minutes on each side or until desired degree of doneness. Break fish into chunks using 2 forks.
3. Place dressing and next 4 ingredients in a food processor; process until smooth.
4. Place about 1½ cups lettuce on each of 4 plates. Top evenly with grilled fish, green onions, and radishes. Drizzle dressing evenly over salads. **YIELD: 4 SERVINGS (SERVING SIZE: ABOUT 1½ CUPS LETTUCE, 3 OUNCES TUNA, ABOUT 2 TEASPOONS GREEN ONIONS, 1½ TEASPOONS RADISHES, AND 3 TABLESPOONS DRESSING).**

PER SERVING: Calories 268; Fat 10.6g (sat 2.1g, mono 4.2g, poly 1.8g); Protein 31.8g; Carb 7.8g; Fiber 3.2g; Chol 61mg; Iron 1.8mg; Sodium 438mg; Calc 58mg

Wasabi Paste

Wasabi, or "Japanese horseradish," is grated from a plant that's unrelated to horseradish. American wasabi is actually a blend of horseradish and mustard tinted green, but it still packs a strong, pungent punch of spiciness that goes great with fish.

GRILLED STEAK CAESAR SALAD

PointsPlus value per serving: 7

PREP: 8 minutes ■ COOK: 16 minutes
■ OTHER: 5 minutes

Mixing the seasoning with olive oil helps it adhere to the steaks while grilling. Don't be alarmed if some of the seasoning falls off—the steaks will still be very flavorful.

    2 tablespoons salt-free grilling blend steak seasoning (such as Mrs. Dash)
    2 teaspoons olive oil
    1 (1-pound) flank steak
    Cooking spray
    3 plum tomatoes
    8 cups fresh baby spinach
    ½ cup Caesar Parmigiano–flavored yogurt dressing (such as Bolthouse Farms)

1. Preheat grill to medium-high heat.
2. Combine steak seasoning and oil; rub over steak. Place steak on grill rack coated with cooking spray. Grill steak 8 minutes. Turn steak over; add tomatoes to grill. Grill steak and tomatoes 8 minutes, turning tomatoes after 4 minutes. Remove steak and tomatoes from grill. Cover steak with foil, and let stand 5 minutes. Cut each tomato into 4 slices. Cut steak diagonally across grain into thin slices.
3. Place 2 cups spinach on each of 4 plates. Arrange steak and tomato slices on top of spinach. Drizzle 2 tablespoons dressing over each salad. Serve immediately. **YIELD: 4 SERVINGS (SERVING SIZE: 2 CUPS SPINACH, 3 OUNCES STEAK, 3 TOMATO SLICES, AND 2 TABLESPOONS DRESSING).**

PER SERVING: Calories 290; Fat 15.3g (sat 4.2g, mono 4.8g, poly 1.8g); Protein 27g; Carb 10g; Fiber 2.8g; Chol 37mg; Iron 3.5mg; Sodium 342mg; Calc 126mg

SPICY THAI PORK SALAD

PointsPlus value per serving: 6

PREP: 16 minutes ■ COOK: 6 minutes

Serve each salad with a lime wedge—the freshly squeezed juice takes every bite over the top.

    1 pound lean ground pork
    ¼ cup chopped fresh cilantro
    2 tablespoons chile paste with garlic (such as sambal oelek)
    11 cups thinly sliced iceberg lettuce (about 1 head)
    1½ cups shredded carrot
    6 tablespoons thinly sliced radishes (about 4 medium)
    ¼ cup light sesame-ginger dressing (such as Newman's Own)

1. Heat a medium nonstick skillet over medium-high heat; add pork to pan, and cook 6 minutes or until browned, stirring to crumble. Remove pan from heat; drain pork well. Return pork to pan, and stir in cilantro and chile paste.
2. Combine lettuce and carrot in a large bowl. Place 3 cups lettuce mixture on each of 4 plates; top each with ¾ cup pork mixture, 1½ tablespoons radish slices, and 1 tablespoon dressing. **YIELD: 4 SERVINGS.**

PER SERVING: Calories 237; Fat 11.2g (sat 3.4g, mono 4.7g, poly 1.6g); Protein 23.9g; Carb 11.4g; Fiber 2.7g; Chol 85mg; Iron 1.7mg; Sodium 405mg; Calc 57mg

APPLE-PECAN CHICKEN SALAD

PointsPlus value per serving: 4

PREP: 9 minutes ■ COOK: 2 minutes

    8 cups chopped romaine lettuce (about 3 romaine hearts)
    2 cups coarsely chopped Fuji apple (2 apples)
    ¼ cup sweetened dried cranberries
    ¼ cup pecan pieces, toasted
    1 (6-ounce) package refrigerated grilled chicken strips
    ⅓ cup strawberry-balsamic vinaigrette
    ⅓ cup (1.3 ounces) crumbled blue cheese

1. Place first 5 ingredients in a large bowl. Add vinaigrette; toss well. Sprinkle salad with cheese. Serve immediately. **YIELD: 6 SERVINGS (SERVING SIZE: 2 CUPS).**

PER SERVING: Calories 151; Fat 6.5g (sat 2g, mono 2.8g, poly 1.3g); Protein 9.5g; Carb 15.5g; Fiber 3.3g; Chol 24mg; Iron 1.5mg; Sodium 374mg; Calc 87mg

CHOPPED BUFFALO CHICKEN SALAD

PointsPlus value per serving: 5

PREP: 8 minutes

For added convenience, purchase preshredded carrot. You can find it in the produce section of most grocery stores.

   6 cups chopped romaine lettuce (about 2 romaine hearts)
   1⅓ cups halved grape tomatoes
   1¼ cups grated carrot
   1 cup chopped celery
   2 cups chopped cooked chicken breast
   ¼ cup bottled buffalo sauce
   ½ cup light ranch dressing

1. Combine first 4 ingredients in a large bowl. Divide evenly among 5 plates.
2. Combine chicken and buffalo sauce, tossing to coat. Top salads evenly with chicken mixture; drizzle with dressing. **YIELD: 5 SERVINGS (SERVING SIZE: 2 CUPS SALAD MIXTURE AND ABOUT 1½ TABLESPOONS DRESSING).**

PER SERVING: Calories 196; Fat 7.8g (sat 1.1g, mono 1.9g, poly 2.4g); Protein 19.3g; Carb 11.5g; Fiber 3.4g; Chol 54mg; Iron 1.3mg; Sodium 724mg; Calc 64mg

BROCCOLI-SUNFLOWER SALAD

PointsPlus value per serving: 3

PREP: 10 minutes ■ **OTHER:** 10 minutes

Sunflower seeds give this salad an extra crunch, while the raisins add a punch of sweetness.

   1½ cups small cauliflower florets, chopped
   1 (12-ounce) package fresh broccoli florets, chopped
   ½ cup reduced-calorie salad dressing (such as Miracle Whip Light)
   1 tablespoon sugar
   3 tablespoons raisins
   2 tablespoons salted sunflower seed kernels

1. Place cauliflower and broccoli in a serving bowl. Combine salad dressing and sugar in a small bowl. Pour dressing mixture over florets; toss. Sprinkle with raisins and sunflower seed kernels. Chill 10 minutes or until ready to serve. **YIELD: 6 SERVINGS (SERVING SIZE: 1 CUP).**

PER SERVING: Calories 111; Fat 5.5g (sat 0.8g, mono 1.1g, poly 2.6g); Protein 3g; Carb 14.2g; Fiber 2.8g; Chol 6mg; Iron 0.8mg; Sodium 210mg; Calc 38mg

BROCCOLI PECAN SLAW WITH MUSTARD DRESSING

PointsPlus value per serving: 2

PREP: 14 minutes ■ **COOK:** 6 minutes

This is a cross between the old tried-and-true broccoli salad and a sweet and tangy cabbage slaw with a crunch. Store the remaining half of the ramen noodles in an airtight container or zip-top plastic bag to make this salad twice or for another use.

   ½ (3-ounce) package ramen noodles
   4 teaspoons chopped pecans
   1 tablespoon sugar
   3 tablespoons light mayonnaise
   2 tablespoons apple cider vinegar
   1 tablespoon stone-ground Dijon mustard
   ⅛ teaspoon freshly ground black pepper
   1 (12-ounce) package broccoli slaw
   1½ cups (1-inch) julienne-cut red bell pepper (about 1 small)

1. Preheat oven to 375°.
2. Remove and discard seasoning packet from noodles. Crumble noodles, and arrange in a single layer on half of a baking sheet; place pecans on other half of baking sheet.
3. Bake at 375° for 6 to 7 minutes or just until noodles are golden and pecans are toasted.
4. While noodles and pecans toast, combine sugar and next 4 ingredients in a large bowl, stirring with a whisk.
5. Add broccoli slaw, bell pepper, noodles, and pecans to dressing, tossing to coat. **YIELD: 7 SERVINGS (SERVING SIZE: 1 CUP).**

PER SERVING: Calories 80; Fat 3.4g (sat 0.4g, mono 0.5g, poly 0.3g); Protein 2.4g; Carb 10.6g; Fiber 2.5g; Chol 2mg; Iron 1.4mg; Sodium 120mg; Calc 28mg

APPLE AND ALMOND SLAW

PointsPlus value per serving: 4

PREP: 10 minutes ■ COOK: 2 minutes

This sweet-tart slaw is a refreshing alternative to mayonnaise-based coleslaw.

⅓ cup cider vinegar
2 tablespoons honey
1½ tablespoons olive oil
¼ teaspoon salt
4 cups packaged coleslaw
2 Fuji apples, quartered and cut into julienne strips
½ cup whole natural almonds, chopped and toasted

1. Combine first 4 ingredients in a large bowl, stirring with a whisk. Add coleslaw and apple strips; toss well. Sprinkle with almonds. YIELD: 6 SERVINGS (SERVING SIZE: ABOUT 1 CUP).

PER SERVING: Calories 165; Fat 9.4g (sat 0.9g, mono 6.2g, poly 1.8g); Protein 3.2g; Carb 19.1g; Fiber 3.8g; Chol 0mg; Iron 0.6mg; Sodium 109mg; Calc 54mg

WARM SOUR CREAM AND GREEN ONION POTATO SALAD

PointsPlus value per serving: 3   *pictured on page 134*

PREP: 3 minutes ■ COOK: 20 minutes

If you like sour cream and onion potato chips, you will love the familiar flavor in this potato salad.

3 pounds small red potatoes, cut into ¾-inch cubes (about 7 cups)
⅓ cup thinly sliced green onions
⅓ cup reduced-fat sour cream
2 tablespoons light mayonnaise
½ teaspoon salt
⅛ teaspoon freshly ground black pepper

1. Place potatoes in a large saucepan; cover with water. Bring to a boil; cook 12 to 13 minutes or until potatoes are tender. Drain.

2. While potatoes cook, combine green onions and next 4 ingredients in a large bowl. Add warm potatoes to sour cream mixture; toss well. Serve immediately, or chill until ready to serve, if desired. YIELD: 10 SERVINGS (SERVING SIZE: ½ CUP).

PER SERVING: Calories 113; Fat 2.7g (sat 0.8g, mono 0.7g, poly 0.5g); Protein 2.7g; Carb 21.4g; Fiber 2.3g; Chol 4mg; Iron 1mg; Sodium 154mg; Calc 24mg

GERMAN POTATO SALAD

PointsPlus value per serving: 4

PREP: 7 minutes ■ COOK: 18 minutes

German potato salad traditionally has a tart bacon dressing and is served warm or at room temperature. Stir in 2 teaspoons mustard seed for a twist.

1 pound small red potatoes (about 10 potatoes), cut into 1-inch pieces
4 center-cut bacon slices
½ cup finely chopped onion
¼ cup cider vinegar
2 tablespoons water
2 teaspoons sugar
¼ teaspoon salt
¼ teaspoon freshly ground black pepper

1. Place potatoes in a saucepan; cover with water. Bring to a boil; cook 10 minutes or until potatoes are very tender. Drain and keep warm.
2. Cook bacon in a large nonstick skillet over medium heat until crisp. Remove bacon from pan, reserving 2 teaspoons drippings in pan; crumble bacon. Add onion to drippings in pan; sauté 6 minutes. Remove from heat; stir in vinegar and next 4 ingredients. Pour dressing over potatoes; sprinkle with bacon and stir, mashing potatoes slightly. YIELD: 5 SERVINGS (SERVING SIZE: ½ CUP).

PER SERVING: Calories 161; Fat 8.3g (sat 2.8g, mono 3.6g, poly 1g); Protein 4g; Carb 17.5g; Fiber 1.8g; Chol 12mg; Iron 0.8mg; Sodium 276mg; Calc 14mg

Lobster Rolls, *page 125*

IRISH STOUT SLIDERS

PointsPlus value per serving: 10

PREP: 8 minutes ■ COOK: 8 minutes

Irish stout adds Celtic flavor to the ground beef in these sliders. Add a smear of whole-grain mustard for a spicy kick, if you like.

    1 pound extra lean ground beef
    ½ cup Irish stout
    ½ teaspoon freshly ground black pepper
    ¼ teaspoon salt
    Cooking spray
    ¾ cup (3 ounces) shredded Irish cheddar cheese
    1 cup packaged angel hair slaw
    8 (1-ounce) potato rolls, halved horizontally

1. Combine first 4 ingredients. Divide beef mixture into 8 equal portions, shaping each into a ½-inch patty.
2. Heat a large nonstick skillet over medium-high heat. Coat pan with cooking spray. Add patties to pan. Cook 4 minutes on each side or until done. Top patties evenly with cheese.
3. Place ⅛ cup slaw on bottom half of each roll. Top with patties and roll tops. Serve immediately. YIELD: **4 SERVINGS (SERVING SIZE: 2 SLIDERS).**

PER SERVING: Calories 376; Fat 13.5g (sat 6.7g, mono 4g, poly 0.7g); Protein 32.5g; Carb 30g; Fiber 1.8g; Chol 82mg; Iron 3.9mg; Sodium 646mg; Calc 203mg

GROUND BEEF BASICS

When buying ground beef, look to the percentages listed on the label. If the package is labeled "80% lean," that means it's 20% fat. In addition to ground chuck (20% fat), ground round (15% fat), ground sirloin (10% fat), and lean ground beef (7% fat), you may also find "extra lean" ground beef. At 5% fat, it's the leanest ground beef available. If the package just says "ground beef," that's an indication that it contains more than 20% fat.

THAI PORK BURGERS WITH MANGO-MINT MAYO

PointsPlus value per serving: 10   pictured on page 138

PREP: 13 minutes ■ COOK: 14 minutes

Every bite of these Thai-style burgers is full of flavor. The red pepper adds heat, but the mint in the mayo helps tame the fire.

    1 pound lean ground pork
    ¼ cup chopped fresh cilantro
    1 tablespoon grated peeled fresh ginger
    1 tablespoon lemongrass paste (such as Gourmet Garden)
    1½ teaspoons fish sauce
    ¼ teaspoon crushed red pepper
    2 garlic cloves, minced
    Cooking spray
    ¼ cup light mayonnaise
    2 tablespoons mango chutney
    1 tablespoon chopped fresh mint
    2 teaspoons fresh lime juice
    4 (1.8-ounce) white-wheat hamburger buns, toasted
    Cucumber slices (optional)

1. Preheat grill to medium-high heat.
2. Combine first 7 ingredients. Divide pork mixture into 4 equal portions, shaping each into a ½-inch-thick patty. Place on grill rack coated with cooking spray. Grill 7 to 8 minutes on each side or until done.
3. While burgers grill, combine mayonnaise and next 3 ingredients. Place 1 burger on bottom half of each bun; top each with about 1½ tablespoons mayonnaise mixture. Top evenly with cucumber slices, if desired, and place remaining bun halves on top. YIELD: **4 SERVINGS (SERVING SIZE: 1 BURGER).**

PER SERVING: Calories 382; Fat 18.4g (sat 5.3g, mono 6.2g, poly 4.7g); Protein 27.8g; Carb 32g; Fiber 5.3g; Chol 90mg; Iron 3mg; Sodium 775mg; Calc 263mg

SPICY KOREAN BURGERS WITH SRIRACHA KETCHUP

PointsPlus value per serving: 8   *pictured on page 140*

PREP: 10 minutes ■ COOK: 16 minutes

1 tablespoon Sriracha (hot chile sauce, such as Huy Fong)
¼ cup no-salt-added ketchup
1 pound ground chicken breast
1 cup refrigerated spicy kimchi, drained and chopped
¼ cup chopped green onions
1 tablespoon cornstarch
1 tablespoon lower-sodium soy sauce
1 teaspoon grated peeled fresh ginger
1 teaspoon minced garlic
¼ teaspoon dried red pepper
Cooking spray
4 (2.3-ounce) sesame sandwich rolls, toasted
4 romaine lettuce leaves

1. Combine Sriracha and ketchup; set aside.
2. Combine chicken and next 7 ingredients in a medium bowl. Divide chicken mixture into 4 equal portions, shaping each into a ½-inch-thick patty. (Mixture will be sticky.)
3. Heat a large nonstick skillet over medium-high heat. Coat pan with cooking spray. Add patties; cook 8 to 10 minutes on each side or until done.
4. Place a burger on bottom half of each sandwich roll; top each with 1 tablespoon Sriracha ketchup and a lettuce leaf. Top with roll tops. **YIELD: 4 SERVINGS (SERVING SIZE: 1 BURGER AND 1 TABLESPOON KETCHUP).**

PER SERVING: Calories 326; Fat 3.7g (sat 0.8g, mono 1.1g, poly 1.4g); Protein 31.8g; Carb 41.7g; Fiber 3g; Chol 66mg; Iron 2.6mg; Sodium 702mg; Calc 119mg

Kimchi

Kimchi, a staple side dish in Korean cuisine, is made of fermented cabbage (and sometimes radish) mixed with garlic, salt, vinegar, chile peppers, and other spices—there are many different varieties. You can find it in the refrigerated section of your grocery store or in an Asian market for around $4 for a 32-ounce jar.

TURKEY BURGERS WITH PIMIENTO CHEESE AND BACON

PointsPlus value per serving: 8

PREP: 5 minutes ■ COOK: 16 minutes

A quick, homemade pimiento cheese adds unique flavor beyond the traditional slice of cheddar. Add lettuce and tomato to each burger, if you like.

1 pound ground turkey breast
⅓ cup finely chopped Vidalia or other sweet onion
1 teaspoon freshly ground black pepper
⅛ teaspoon salt
1 large egg white, lightly beaten
Cooking spray
½ cup (2 ounces) reduced-fat shredded extrasharp cheddar cheese
2 tablespoons light mayonnaise
1 (2-ounce) jar diced pimiento, drained
4 (1.8-ounce) white-wheat hamburger buns, split and toasted
4 center-cut bacon slices, cooked

1. Preheat grill to medium-high heat.
2. Combine first 5 ingredients in a large bowl. Shape turkey mixture into 4 (½-inch-thick) patties. Place patties on grill rack coated with cooking spray; grill 8 minutes on each side or until a thermometer registers 165°.
3. While burgers cook, combine cheese, mayonnaise, and pimiento in a small bowl.
4. Place 1 burger on bottom half of each bun; top each with 2 tablespoons pimiento-cheese mixture and 1 bacon slice. Top with bun tops. **YIELD: 4 SERVINGS (SERVING SIZE: 1 BURGER).**

PER SERVING: Calories 328; Fat 10.8g (sat 4g, mono 1.5g, poly 2.5g); Protein 37.8g; Carb 24.2g; Fiber 5.6g; Chol 65mg; Iron 3.8mg; Sodium 672mg; Calc 358mg

CALIFORNIA TURKEY BURGERS

PointsPlus value per serving: 10

PREP: 5 minutes ■ **COOK:** 10 minutes

Ground turkey contains both the white and dark meat, which creates a moist, flavorful burger.

1 pound ground turkey
⅓ cup thinly sliced green onions (4 onions)
2 tablespoons Dijon mustard
¼ teaspoon freshly ground black pepper
1 garlic clove, minced
Cooking spray
4 (1.4-ounce) whole-wheat hamburger buns, toasted
4 (0.7-ounce) slices reduced-fat Monterey Jack cheese with jalapeño peppers
4 center-cut bacon slices, cooked and drained
½ peeled avocado, cut into 8 slices
4 small green leaf lettuce leaves

1. Combine first 5 ingredients in a large bowl. Divide turkey mixture into 4 equal portions, shaping each into a ½-inch-thick patty.
2. Heat a large nonstick skillet over medium-high heat. Coat pan with cooking spray. Add patties to pan; cook 5 minutes on each side or until a thermometer registers 165°.
3. Place 1 patty on bottom half of each bun. Top each patty with 1 cheese slice, 1 bacon slice, 2 avocado slices, 1 lettuce leaf, and top half of bun. **YIELD: 4 SERVINGS (SERVING SIZE: 1 BURGER).**

PER SERVING: Calories 372; Fat 18.6g (sat 5.9g, mono 7.5g, poly 3.7g); Protein 32.9g; Carb 25.1g; Fiber 6.2g; Chol 115mg; Iron 3.3mg; Sodium 695mg; Calc 94mg

POT ROAST SLIDERS WITH ROSEMARY MAYONNAISE

PointsPlus value per serving: 6

PREP: 8 minutes ■ **COOK:** 4 minutes

You can use whatever fresh herbs you like. Basil, oregano, or thyme make great substitutes for rosemary in the mayo.

1 (17-ounce) Italian beef roast au jus (such as Hormel)
½ cup light mayonnaise
1 tablespoon chopped fresh rosemary
¼ teaspoon freshly ground black pepper
8 (1.3-ounce) whole-wheat slider buns, halved horizontally

1. Microwave roast according to package directions. Drain roast, reserving jus for another use. Break roast into small chunks.
2. Combine mayonnaise, rosemary, and pepper in a small bowl. Spread mayonnaise mixture evenly on cut sides of buns. Place about ¼ cup roast on each bun bottom; top with bun tops. **YIELD: 8 SERVINGS (SERVING SIZE: 1 SLIDER).**

PER SERVING: Calories 243; Fat 11.5g (sat 3.5g, mono 3.2g, poly 3.6g); Protein 15.3g; Carb 20.8g; Fiber 2.8g; Chol 42mg; Iron 2.1mg; Sodium 447mg; Calc 40mg

ROAST BEEF SANDWICHES WITH LEMON-FETA SPREAD

PointsPlus value per serving: 8

PREP: 14 minutes

¼ cup (1 ounce) crumbled feta cheese
2 tablespoons chopped fresh parsley
3 tablespoons light mayonnaise
1 teaspoon grated lemon rind
8 (1-ounce) slices ciabatta bread
½ pound thinly sliced lower-sodium deli roast beef
2 cups arugula
4 thin red onion slices, cut crosswise in half (about ½ cup)

1. Combine first 4 ingredients in a small bowl. Spread cheese mixture evenly on 4 bread slices. Top each with 2 ounces roast beef, ½ cup arugula, 2 tablespoons onion, and 1 bread slice. **YIELD: 4 SERVINGS (SERVING SIZE: 1 SANDWICH).**

PER SERVING: Calories 306; Fat 10.3g (sat 3g, mono 3.2g, poly 0.3g); Protein 21.7g; Carb 34g; Fiber 1.5g; Chol 41mg; Iron 3.6mg; Sodium 642mg; Calc 58mg

LOBSTER ROLLS

PointsPlus value per serving: 6   *pictured on page 134*

PREP: 5 minutes ■ COOK: 1 minute

The ingredients are simple, yet lobster rolls are highbrow. Impress your friends when you serve this sandwich. Even though lobster is typically expensive, these rolls are almost always served on some sort of humble hot dog buns or New England–style hot dog buns. This recipe easily doubles.

5 tablespoons light mayonnaise
¼ cup refrigerated prechopped celery
4 teaspoons minced shallots
4 teaspoons chopped fresh parsley
2 teaspoons chopped fresh tarragon
¼ teaspoon salt
½ pound cooked lobster meat (about 2 [1¼-pound] Maine lobsters, coarsely chopped)
4 (1.6-ounce) white-wheat hot dog buns, toasted

1. Combine first 6 ingredients in a medium bowl, stirring well. Add lobster meat, tossing to coat. Spoon lobster mixture evenly into buns. YIELD: 4 SERVINGS (SERVING SIZE: 1 BUN AND ABOUT ⅓ CUP LOBSTER MIXTURE).

PER SERVING: Calories 209; Fat 7.1g (sat 1g, mono 2.4g, poly 2.2g); Protein 16.3g; Carb 24.8g; Fiber 5.6g; Chol 47mg; Iron 1.2mg; Sodium 767mg; Calc 86mg

EGG SALAD AND ASPARAGUS WRAPS

PointsPlus value per serving: 6

PREP: 7 minutes ■ COOK: 1 minute

12 asparagus spears (about 8 ounces)
1 tablespoon water
3 hard-cooked large eggs, chopped
⅓ cup light mayonnaise
¼ cup dill pickle relish
¼ teaspoon freshly ground black pepper
2 (2.5-ounce) spinach-herb wraps

1. Snap off tough ends of asparagus. Place asparagus and 1 tablespoon water in a zip-top steaming bag; seal bag. Spread asparagus into an even layer. Microwave according to package directions 1 to 2 minutes or until asparagus is tender. Carefully open bag (steam will escape). Plunge asparagus into ice water; drain and pat dry with paper towels.

2. Combine eggs and next 3 ingredients in a small bowl. Spread ¼ cup egg salad onto each wrap to within ½ inch of edges. Lay 3 asparagus spears crosswise on each wrap; roll up, and cut in half. YIELD: 4 SERVINGS (SERVING SIZE: 1 WRAP).

PER SERVING: Calories 238; Fat 12.7g (sat 3.5g, mono 3.8g, poly 4.4g); Protein 9g; Carb 21.6g; Fiber 1.7g; Chol 165mg; Iron 2.8mg; Sodium 702mg; Calc 34mg

HOW TO HARD-COOK EGGS

For perfect hard-cooked eggs, place the eggs in a large saucepan, and cover with cool water—you'll need enough water to cover to 1 inch above the eggs. Bring the water to a full boil. Immediately cover the pan, and remove it from the heat. Let the eggs stand 12 minutes. Transfer them to a bowl of ice water until they're completely cooled. Peel the shell from the eggs. Cooking the eggs slowly and then cooling them quickly creates whites that are firm but not rubbery, and solid, light yolks with no green ring around them.

PIMIENTO CHEESE BLTS

PointsPlus value per serving: 7

PREP: 10 minutes ■ COOK: 4 minutes

1 cup (4 ounces) reduced-fat shredded extrasharp cheddar cheese
¼ cup light mayonnaise
2 (2-ounce) jars diced pimiento, drained
8 (0.9-ounce) slices white-wheat bread, toasted
6 slices center-cut bacon, cooked and cut in half
8 (½-inch-thick) tomato slices
4 Bibb lettuce leaves

1. Combine first 3 ingredients in a small bowl. Spread pimiento cheese evenly on each of 4 bread slices. Top each with 3 half-slices of bacon, 2 tomato slices, 1 lettuce leaf, and 1 bread slice. YIELD: 4 SERVINGS (SERVING SIZE: 1 SANDWICH).

PER SERVING: Calories 300; Fat 14.3g (sat 5.8g, mono 3.1g, poly 3.5g); Protein 11.2g; Carb 29.2g; Fiber 5.5g; Chol 33mg; Iron 0.8mg; Sodium 727mg; Calc 217mg

HAM AND CHEESE STROMBOLI

PointsPlus value per serving: 7

PREP: 8 minutes ■ COOK: 17 minutes

This sandwich is open to endless interpretation, so feel free to experiment with your own fillings.

Cooking spray
1½ cups presliced green, yellow, and red bell pepper strips
¼ teaspoon freshly ground black pepper
1 (11-ounce) can refrigerated thin pizza crust dough
1 tablespoon country-style Dijon mustard
1 cup (4 ounces) shredded reduced-fat Jarlsberg cheese
6 ounces 33%-less-sodium ham, thinly sliced

1. Preheat oven to 375°.
2. Heat a large nonstick skillet over medium–high heat. Coat pan with cooking spray. Add bell pepper and black pepper to pan; cook, uncovered, 2 minutes, stirring occasionally.
3. Unroll pizza dough; press dough into a 14 x 10–inch rectangle on a large baking sheet. Spread mustard over dough to within ½ inch of edges. Sprinkle cheese over mustard; layer ham over cheese. Pat bell pepper strips with a paper towel to remove excess moisture; sprinkle over ham. Roll up dough, beginning at long end. Pinch dough to seal. Position roll on pan, seam side down. Coat stromboli with cooking spray.
4. Bake at 375° for 17 to 19 minutes or until crust is golden brown. Cut into 6 pieces. YIELD: 6 SERVING SIZE: 1 PIECE).

PER SERVING: Calories 252; Fat 9g (sat 3g, mono 3.2g, poly 1.1g); Protein 16.9g; Carb 25.8g; Fiber 1.1g; Chol 25mg; Iron 1.7mg; Sodium 726mg; Calc 181mg

CHICKEN CREMINI PANINIS

PointsPlus value per serving: 9

PREP: 8 minutes ■ COOK: 12 minutes

Mascarpone is a full-fat cheese, but using a small amount adds a lot of richness and flavor to this sandwich.

Cooking spray
1 pound cremini mushrooms, sliced
¼ teaspoon freshly ground black pepper
¼ teaspoon salt
2 tablespoons mascarpone cheese
8 (1.2-ounce) slices ciabatta bread
1⅓ cups thinly sliced deli chicken breast
2 cups packed arugula

1. Preheat panini grill.
2. Heat a medium nonstick skillet over medium–high heat. Coat pan with cooking spray. Add mushrooms and pepper. Cook 6 minutes or until mushrooms are lightly browned and tender; drain and return to pan. Stir in salt.
3. Spread ½ tablespoon mascarpone cheese on each of 4 bread slices; top each evenly with chicken, mushrooms, arugula, and another bread slice.
4. Coat both sides of sandwiches with cooking spray. Place sandwiches on panini grill. Grill 3 minutes or until golden brown. Serve immediately. YIELD: 4 SERVINGS (SERVING SIZE: 1 SANDWICH).

PER SERVING: Calories 331; Fat 11g (sat 4.3g, mono 2.5g, poly 0.7g); Protein 23.4g; Carb 36g; Fiber 1.9g; Chol 57mg; Iron 2.9mg; Sodium 587mg; Calc 64mg

MAKING PANINIS WITHOUT A PRESS

You don't need a panini press to make pressed sandwiches. Use a cast-iron skillet or any heavy skillet to weigh down a sandwich in a nonstick skillet or grill pan. Place the skillet on top of the filled sandwich; press gently to flatten. Cook until the bread is toasted, leaving the skillet on the sandwich while it cooks.

CHICKEN REUBENS

PointsPlus value per serving: 9

PREP: 7 minutes ■ COOK: 10 minutes

A classic Reuben could have a *PointsPlus* value per serving of 17 or more and contain more than 2,000 milligrams of sodium. This lightened Reuben provides those same classic flavors in a healthier package.

 4 (4-ounce) chicken cutlets
 ¼ teaspoon freshly ground black pepper
 Cooking spray
 ¼ cup light Thousand Island dressing
 8 (1-ounce) slices rye bread
 ½ cup drained refrigerated sauerkraut
 4 (0.75-ounce) slices reduced-fat Swiss cheese

1. Sprinkle chicken evenly with pepper. Heat a large nonstick skillet over medium-high heat. Coat pan with cooking spray. Add chicken to pan; cook 3 minutes on each side or until done. Remove chicken from pan, and keep warm. Wipe pan with a paper towel.
2. Spread 1 tablespoon dressing on 1 side of each of 4 bread slices. Top each with 2 tablespoons sauerkraut, 1 chicken cutlet, 1 cheese slice, and 1 bread slice.
3. Heat a large skillet over medium heat. Coat both sides of sandwiches with cooking spray. Add sandwiches to pan; cook 2 minutes on each side or until bread is browned and cheese melts. Remove sandwiches from pan and cut in half. Serve immediately. **YIELD: 4 SERVINGS (SERVING SIZE: 1 SANDWICH).**

PER SERVING: Calories 369; Fat 8.5g (sat 2.8g, mono 2.1g, poly 1.1g); Protein 38.1g; Carb 34g; Fiber 3.9g; Chol 81mg; Iron 2.4mg; Sodium 823mg; Calc 257mg

TARRAGON CHICKEN SALAD MELTS

PointsPlus value per serving: 8

PREP: 10 minutes ■ COOK: 5 minutes

Substitute your favorite herb for the tarragon to change the flavor of this mini grinder.

 3 cups chopped cooked chicken breast
 ½ cup chopped celery
 ⅓ cup light mayonnaise
 1 tablespoon Dijon mustard
 2 teaspoons chopped fresh tarragon
 ¼ teaspoon salt
 ¼ teaspoon freshly ground black pepper
 1 (8.5-ounce) French bread baguette, cut crosswise into
     6 equal pieces
 ¾ cup (3 ounces) shredded reduced-fat Jarlsberg cheese

1. Preheat oven to 450°.
2. Combine first 7 ingredients. Cut each piece of bread in half lengthwise, cutting to but not through other side.
3. Open each piece of bread and place, hinged side down, on a baking sheet. Spoon ½ cup chicken mixture into each opened bread piece; top each with 2 tablespoons cheese.
4. Bake at 450° for 5 minutes or until cheese melts. Serve immediately. **YIELD: 6 SERVINGS (SERVING SIZE: 1 SANDWICH).**

PER SERVING: Calories 316; Fat 9.1g (sat 2.6g, mono 2.5g, poly 3.3g); Protein 31.2g; Carb 25.7g; Fiber 1.6g; Chol 69mg; Iron 2.2mg; Sodium 658mg; Calc 160mg

TURKEY CLUB SANDWICHES

PointsPlus value per serving: 8   *pictured on page 137*

PREP: 7 minutes ■ COOK: 5 minutes

This club offers whole grains and fiber from the bread and healthy monounsaturated fats from the avocado.

> 8 teaspoons creamy mustard blend (such as Dijonnaise)
> 8 (1-ounce) slices whole-wheat bread, toasted
> ½ pound shaved lower-sodium deli turkey breast (such as Boar's Head)
> 4 lettuce leaves
> 4 (¼-inch-thick) slices red onion
> 1 cup sliced peeled avocado (about 1 small)
> 1 large ripe tomato (about ¾ pound), sliced
> 4 center-cut bacon slices, cooked and drained

1. Spread 2 teaspoons creamy mustard blend on 1 side of each of 4 bread slices. Top each evenly with turkey, lettuce, onion, avocado, tomato, and bacon. Top with remaining 4 bread slices. Secure sandwiches with wooden picks. **YIELD: 4 SERVINGS (SERVING SIZE: 1 SANDWICH).**

PER SERVING: Calories 345; Fat 11.6g (sat 1.6g, mono 5.9g, poly 1.9g); Protein 22.7g; Carb 34.4g; Fiber 8.8g; Chol 25mg; Iron 2.6mg; Sodium 799mg; Calc 66mg

HOT BROWN SANDWICHES

PointsPlus value per serving: 7

PREP: 8 minutes ■ COOK: 7 minutes

Toasting helps keep the bread from getting soggy. You can toast the bread slices while you prepare the Mornay Sauce.

> Mornay Sauce
> 4 (1.5-ounce) slices 100% whole-wheat bread, toasted
> Cooking spray
> 8 ounces shaved lower-sodium oven-roasted turkey breast
> 8 center-cut bacon slices, cooked and drained
> 8 (¼-inch-thick) tomato slices

1. Preheat broiler.

2. Prepare Mornay Sauce.

3. Place bread on a large baking sheet coated with cooking spray. Coat bread with cooking spray. Top each bread slice with 2 ounces turkey and about ¼ cup Mornay Sauce. Broil 2 minutes or until hot and bubbly. Top each serving with 2 bacon slices and 2 tomato slices. **YIELD: 4 SERVINGS (SERVING SIZE: 1 OPEN-FACED SANDWICH).**

PER SERVING: Calories 299; Fat 9g (sat 3.6g, mono 1.9g, poly 0.5g); Protein 25.9g; Carb 27.2g; Fiber 3.1g; Chol 44mg; Iron 2mg; Sodium 834mg; Calc 196mg

Mornay Sauce

PointsPlus value per serving: 1

PREP: 2 minutes ■ COOK: 5 minutes

> 1 tablespoon light butter
> 1½ tablespoons all-purpose flour
> ⅛ teaspoon salt
> ⅛ teaspoon freshly ground black pepper
> 1 cup 1% low-fat milk
> ¼ cup (1 ounce) shredded Gruyère cheese

1. Melt butter in a medium saucepan over medium-high heat. Add flour, salt, and pepper; cook, stirring constantly with a whisk, 1 minute. Gradually stir in milk; cook, stirring constantly, 3 minutes or until thick. Stir in cheese. **YIELD: ABOUT 1 CUP (SERVING SIZE: 1 TABLESPOON).**

PER SERVING: Calories 19; Fat 1.1g (sat 0.6g, mono 0.2g, poly 0g); Protein 1.1g; Carb 1.4g; Fiber 0g; Chol 4mg; Iron 0mg; Sodium 37mg; Calc 35mg

Smoked BBQ Tofu Pizza,
page 82

Grilled Rosemary Lamb Chops with
Ruby Port-Fig Chutney, *page 92*

Baked Spaghetti,
page 96

Chicken Broccoli
Stir-Fry, *page 103*

Japanese Teriyaki
Chicken Cakes,
page 106

Chicken Cutlets with Warm Lemon-
Artichoke Relish, *page 102*

Chicken Curry, *page 98*

Warm Sour Cream and
Green Onion Potato
Salad, *page 120*

Lobster Rolls, *page 125*

Watermelon-Tomato
Salad, *page 113*

Pear-Walnut Salad with Gorgonzola Buttermilk Dressing, *page 113*

Cast-Iron Broccoli with
Goat Cheese, *page 147*

Turkey Club Sandwiches,
page 128

Thai Pork Burgers with Mango-Mint
Mayo, *page 122*

Sautéed Spinach with Almonds and Golden Raisins, *page 153*

Roasted Brussels Sprouts with Browned Butter Walnuts, *page 148*

Spicy Korean Burgers with Sriracha
Ketchup, *page 123*

Mexican Chicken Stew, *page 162*

Ropa Vieja,
page 161

Kentucky Burgoo, *page 161*

Aztec Hot Chocolate Cupcakes,
page 166

Roasted Brussels Sprouts with Browned Butter Walnuts, *page 148*

SAVORY ROASTED APPLES

PointsPlus value per serving: 1

PREP: 25 minutes ■ **COOK**: 30 minutes

Using a combination of naturally sweet apples yields the best flavor and eliminates the need for added sugar in this unique recipe.

> 6 medium apples (such as Gala, Pink Lady, or Golden Delicious), peeled and coarsely chopped
> Cooking spray
> 1 tablespoon chopped fresh rosemary
> 1 tablespoon chopped fresh thyme
> ¼ teaspoon salt
> ¼ teaspoon freshly ground black pepper
> 1 tablespoon butter, melted

1. Preheat oven to 450°.
2. Place apples on a large jelly-roll pan coated with cooking spray. Sprinkle apples with rosemary and next 3 ingredients; coat with cooking spray, and toss well.
3. Bake at 450° for 30 minutes or until apples are tender and lightly browned. Transfer apple mixture to a serving dish; stir in butter. **YIELD: 8 SERVINGS (SERVING SIZE: ½ CUP).**

PER SERVING: Calories 48; Fat 1.7g (sat 0.9g, mono 0.4g, poly 0.1g); Protein 0.2g; Carb 9g; Fiber 1g; Chol 4mg; Iron 0.1mg; Sodium 84mg; Calc 6mg

SMOKY-SPICY ROASTED ASPARAGUS

PointsPlus value per serving: 1

PREP: 4 minutes ■ **COOK**: 12 minutes

Chipotle chile powder gives this asparagus a spicy kick of flavor. To tame the heat, you can use half the amount called for in the recipe.

> 1 pound asparagus spears, trimmed
> 1 tablespoon olive oil
> ½ teaspoon chipotle chile powder
> ¼ teaspoon salt
> ⅛ teaspoon crushed red pepper
> 1 garlic clove, minced

1. Preheat oven to 425°.
2. Combine all ingredients in a large bowl, tossing well to coat. Arrange asparagus mixture in a single layer on a baking sheet.

3. Bake at 425° for 12 minutes or until crisp-tender. **YIELD: 4 SERVINGS (SERVING SIZE: ¼ OF ASPARAGUS).**

PER SERVING: Calories 54; Fat 3.5g (sat 0.5g, mono 2.5g, poly 0.4g); Protein 2.6g; Carb 4.7g; Fiber 2.4g; Chol 0mg; Iron 2.5mg; Sodium 160mg; Calc 29mg

ROASTED GREEN BEANS AND CASHEWS

PointsPlus value per serving: 3

PREP: 5 minutes ■ **COOK**: 20 minutes

Roasting green beans rather than blanching them produces an entirely different texture and sweetness. Salty nuts and cheese make this side dish delectable.

> 1½ pounds green beans, trimmed
> ½ cup cashews with sea salt
> ½ cup finely chopped onion
> 2 teaspoons olive oil
> ¼ teaspoon freshly ground black pepper
> ⅛ teaspoon fine sea salt
> Cooking spray
> 2 tablespoons grated fresh Parmesan cheese

1. Preheat oven to 500°.
2. Combine first 6 ingredients in a shallow roasting pan coated with cooking spray.
3. Bake at 500° for 20 minutes, stirring every 5 minutes. Remove from oven, and sprinkle with Parmesan cheese. **YIELD: 6 SERVINGS (SERVING SIZE: ⅙ OF BEAN MIXTURE).**

PER SERVING: Calories 120; Fat 7.4g (sat 1.6g, mono 4.4g, poly 1.1g); Protein 3.9g; Carb 11.9g; Fiber 4.7g; Chol 1mg; Iron 1.2mg; Sodium 139mg; Calc 82mg

Sea Salt

These salts come from all over the world in a variety of textures and colors. Sea salt doesn't contain additives, but it does contain more minerals than table salt. Because their taste nuances become almost untraceable once absorbed in food and they tend to be pricier, sea salts are often used in simple dishes to let their flavor shine or as finishing touches.

ROASTED BEETS AND RED ONIONS

PointsPlus value per serving: 3

PREP: 9 minutes ■ COOK: 45 minutes

A squeeze of lemon intensifies the flavor and ruby color of these beets and onions, which are sweetened by roasting and complemented by creamy blue cheese.

1½ pounds beets, peeled and cut into ½-inch-thick wedges
1 medium-sized red onion, cut into ½-inch-thick wedges
Cooking spray
1 tablespoon olive oil
½ teaspoon freshly ground black pepper
¼ teaspoon kosher salt
2 tablespoons fresh lemon juice
¼ cup (1 ounce) crumbled blue cheese

1. Preheat oven to 425°.
2. Place beets and onion on a large jelly-roll pan coated with cooking spray; drizzle vegetables with oil. Sprinkle with pepper and salt, and toss to coat.
3. Bake at 425° for 45 minutes, stirring after 25 minutes. Transfer vegetables to a bowl.
4. Drizzle vegetables with lemon juice; toss well. Sprinkle with cheese. Serve immediately. YIELD: 4 SERVINGS (SERVING SIZE: ¾ CUP).

PER SERVING: Calories 124; Fat 6.2g (sat 2.1g, mono 3.2g, poly 0.5g); Protein 4g; Carb 14.4g; Fiber 3.7g; Chol 6mg; Iron 1mg; Sodium 327mg; Calc 71mg

BUYING AND HANDLING BEETS

 When buying beets, look for small to medium ones with firm, smooth skin and no soft spots. The ones with stems and leaves attached are best. Because the juice can stain your hands and countertops, wear disposable latex gloves, which you can pick up at drugstores. They're thin enough to allow dexterity while protecting your hands from stains. The leafy green tops leach nutrients from the beets, so immediately trim the tops to about an inch.

CAST-IRON BROCCOLI WITH GOAT CHEESE

PointsPlus value per serving: 2   *pictured on page 137*

PREP: 3 minutes ■ COOK: 20 minutes

High-heat roasting and a cast-iron skillet bring out the best in this broccoli side. Creamy goat cheese and toasted pine nuts add deeper layers of flavor.

1 (12-ounce) package broccoli florets
1 teaspoon olive oil
¼ teaspoon salt
¼ teaspoon black pepper
Cooking spray
2 tablespoons crumbled goat cheese
1 tablespoon pine nuts, toasted

1. Preheat oven to 450°.
2. Combine first 4 ingredients in a medium bowl; toss well. Arrange broccoli mixture in a single layer in a large cast-iron skillet coated with cooking spray.
3. Bake at 450° for 20 minutes, without stirring. Sprinkle with goat cheese and pine nuts before serving. YIELD: 5 SERVINGS (SERVING SIZE: ½ CUP).

PER SERVING: Calories 55; Fat 3.7g (sat 1.1g, mono 1.3g, poly 0.8g); Protein 3.3g; Carb 3.9g; Fiber 2.1g; Chol 3mg; Iron 0.8mg; Sodium 157mg; Calc 41mg

ROASTED BRUSSELS SPROUTS WITH BROWNED BUTTER WALNUTS

PointsPlus value per serving: 3   *pictured on page 139*

PREP: 8 minutes ■ **COOK:** 17 minutes

5¼ cups trimmed Brussels sprouts (about
    1 pound), halved
Cooking spray
¼ teaspoon salt
¼ teaspoon freshly ground black pepper
2 tablespoons butter
6 tablespoons chopped walnuts

1. Preheat oven to 425°.
2. Place Brussels sprouts on a large baking sheet coated with cooking spray. Heavily coat sprouts with cooking spray; sprinkle with salt and pepper, tossing well. Bake at 425° for 8 minutes. Turn Brussels sprouts over, using a wide spatula. Bake an additional 7 minutes or until tender and browned.
3. Melt butter in a small saucepan over medium heat; add walnuts, and cook until butter browns and walnuts are toasted, stirring frequently.
4. Spoon roasted sprouts into a serving dish; add walnut mixture, tossing well to coat. **YIELD: 6 SERVINGS (SERVING SIZE: ABOUT ½ CUP).**

PER SERVING: Calories 116; Fat 9g (sat 2.9g, mono 1.7g, poly 3.7g); Protein 3.7g; Carb 7.8g; Fiber 3.4g; Chol 10mg; Iron 1.3mg; Sodium 145mg; Calc 40mg

---

BUYING BRUSSELS SPROUTS

When choosing Brussels sprouts, look for small bright green sprouts with a compact head. The smaller the sprouts, the sweeter the flavor. Avoid soft, wilted, puffy, or dull-colored sprouts, as well as those with loose or yellowish leaves. They're available year-round, but the peak season is from September to mid-February.

CREOLE CABBAGE

PointsPlus value per serving: 1

PREP: 5 minutes ■ **COOK:** 13 minutes

To kick up this side dish a little more, add hot sauce or ground red pepper. Use organic diced tomatoes for a lower-sodium option.

2 center-cut bacon slices, cut crosswise into thin strips
5 cups (2 x 1–inch) strips green cabbage (1 small head)
1 cup frozen seasoning blend
1 (14.5-ounce) can diced tomatoes with zesty green chiles,
    undrained
½ teaspoon Creole seasoning

1. Cook bacon in a large nonstick skillet over medium heat 5 minutes or until crisp. Remove bacon from pan with a slotted spoon, and drain on paper towels, reserving drippings in pan. Add cabbage to drippings in pan. Cook over medium–high heat 2 minutes or until cabbage is browned, stirring often.
2. Stir in seasoning blend, tomatoes, and Creole seasoning. Bring to a boil; cover, reduce heat, and simmer 5 minutes or until cabbage is tender. Stir in bacon. **YIELD: 6 SERVINGS (SERVING SIZE: ¾ CUP).**

PER SERVING: Calories 58; Fat 0.8g (sat 0.4g, mono 0g, poly 0g); Protein 2.7g; Carb 10.8g; Fiber 3.5g; Chol 3mg; Iron 0.9mg; Sodium 364mg; Calc 61mg

---

ROASTED CARROTS WITH RED WINE SAUCE

PointsPlus value per serving: 4

PREP: 5 minutes ■ **COOK:** 30 minutes

Roasting is a great way to bring out the natural sweetness in root vegetables. Pairing roasted carrots with maple-infused red wine sauce creates an anything-but-ordinary side dish.

4¼ cups (¾-inch) pieces carrot (about 1¾ pounds)
Cooking spray
¼ teaspoon freshly ground black pepper
⅛ teaspoon salt
½ cup coarsely chopped shallots
1 cup dry red wine
⅓ cup maple syrup
2 teaspoons cider vinegar

1. Preheat oven to 425°.

2. Place carrot on a large jelly-roll pan coated with cooking spray. Coat carrot with cooking spray; sprinkle with pepper and salt. Bake, uncovered, at 425° for 20 minutes. Add shallots, and bake an additional 10 minutes or until carrot is tender.

3. While vegetables bake, combine wine, maple syrup, and vinegar in a small saucepan. Cook, uncovered, over medium heat 18 minutes or until sauce is reduced to ⅓ cup, stirring occasionally. Transfer carrot mixture to a bowl. Drizzle sauce over carrot. **YIELD: 4 SERVINGS (SERVING SIZE: ABOUT ½ CUP).**

PER SERVING: Calories 176; Fat 0.5g (sat 0.1g, mono 0g, poly 0.2g); Protein 1.8g; Carb 38.3g; Fiber 5.8g; Chol 0mg; Iron 2.5mg; Sodium 234mg; Calc 91mg

CARROT-PARSNIP FRITTERS

PointsPlus value per serving: 2

PREP: 6 minutes ■ **COOK:** 10 minutes

This combination of roasted carrots and parsnips makes an elegant side dish.

1 large egg
¾ cup shredded carrot
¾ cup shredded parsnips
3 tablespoons panko (Japanese breadcrumbs)
2 teaspoons chopped fresh thyme leaves
¼ teaspoon salt
⅛ teaspoon freshly ground pepper
1 tablespoon vegetable oil

1. Place egg in a medium bowl; stir with a whisk. Add carrot and remaining ingredients except oil, stirring with a wooden spoon.

2. Heat oil in a large nonstick skillet over medium heat. Spoon 2 tablespoons vegetable mixture per fritter into hot pan. Cook 5 minutes. Reduce heat to medium-low; turn fritters over, and cook 5 minutes or until golden brown and vegetables are tender. Serve immediately. **YIELD: 4 SERVINGS (SERVING SIZE: 2 FRITTERS).**

PER SERVING: Calories 83; Fat 5g (sat 0.9g, mono 1.3g, poly 2.5g); Protein 2.4g; Carb 7.8g; Fiber 1.8g; Chol 53mg; Iron 0.5mg; Sodium 189mg; Calc 23mg

CURRIED CAULIFLOWER WITH GOLDEN RAISINS

PointsPlus value per serving: 3

PREP: 3 minutes ■ **COOK:** 10 minutes

Using full-fat coconut milk makes a significant difference in this dish—it's much more flavorful and satisfying. Light coconut milk works fine in this recipe, too, but you'll need to add ¼ teaspoon salt. The *PointsPlus* value per serving will be 2, and the sodium will increase to 176 milligrams per serving.

1 (10-ounce) package cauliflower florets
½ cup coconut milk
1 teaspoon curry powder
¼ cup golden raisins
2 tablespoons chopped fresh cilantro

1. Cut larger cauliflower florets in half, if needed. Heat a medium skillet over medium heat. Add cauliflower, coconut milk, and curry powder; bring to a simmer. Cover and simmer 5 minutes, stirring once. Uncover; cook 1 minute or until liquid almost evaporates.

2. Remove from heat; stir in raisins and cilantro. **YIELD: 4 SERVINGS (SERVING SIZE: ABOUT ½ CUP).**

PER SERVING: Calories 106; Fat 6.2g (sat 5.4g, mono 0.3g, poly 0.1g); Protein 2.4g; Carb 13g; Fiber 2.4g; Chol 0mg; Iron 1.6mg; Sodium 26mg; Calc 29mg

ASIAN PICKLED CUCUMBERS

PointsPlus value per serving: 1

PREP: 8 minutes ■ **OTHER:** 3 hours

These are delicious with grilled salmon or tuna. Spoon the cucumbers with their juices over the cooked fish for a simple and flavorful entrée.

2 tablespoons rice vinegar
1 tablespoon lower-sodium soy sauce
2 teaspoons sugar
1 teaspoon dark sesame oil
½ teaspoon crushed red pepper
1 English cucumber, halved lengthwise and thinly sliced (about 2¼ cups)

1. Combine first 5 ingredients in a medium bowl. Add cucumber, and toss to coat. Cover and chill at least 3 hours. **YIELD: 4 SERVINGS (SERVING SIZE: ABOUT ½ CUP).**

PER SERVING: Calories 29; Fat 1.2g (sat 0.2g, mono 0.5g, poly 0.5g); Protein 1g; Carb 4.1g; Fiber 0.9g; Chol 0mg; Iron 0.4mg; Sodium 134mg; Calc 16mg

EGGPLANT-BASIL STACKS

PointsPlus value per serving: 2

PREP: 12 minutes ■ COOK: 23 minutes

Serve these veggie stacks with grilled chicken and pasta.

2 medium eggplants (about 1¾ pounds), cut crosswise into
    12 (¾-inch) slices
Olive oil–flavored cooking spray
½ teaspoon freshly ground black pepper
¼ teaspoon salt
1 cup tomato-basil pasta sauce
½ cup (2 ounces) crumbled goat cheese
½ cup thinly sliced fresh basil leaves

1. Preheat oven to 450°.
2. Coat both sides of eggplant slices with cooking spray; sprinkle both sides evenly with pepper and salt. Place eggplant on a jelly-roll pan. Bake at 450° for 10 minutes. Turn eggplant over; bake an additional 5 minutes or until tender.
3. Turn eggplant over. Spoon pasta sauce evenly over eggplant. Sprinkle evenly with goat cheese.
4. Bake, uncovered, at 450° for 8 minutes. Sprinkle basil over cheese, and place 1 topped eggplant slice on top of each of 6 eggplant slices to create 6 stacks. Serve immediately. **YIELD: 6 SERVINGS (SERVING SIZE: 1 STACK).**

PER SERVING: Calories 69; Fat 2.6g (sat 1.4g, mono 0.5g, poly 0.1g); Protein 3.6g; Carb 9.4g; Fiber 4.4g; Chol 4mg; Iron 0.8mg; Sodium 265mg; Calc 56mg

BRAISED EGGPLANT WITH BASIL AND TOMATOES

PointsPlus value per serving: 2

PREP: 6 minutes ■ COOK: 17 minutes

1 tablespoon olive oil
1 cup chopped onion
2 teaspoons minced garlic
1¼ pounds eggplant (about 4 small), cut into 3 x ½–inch
    pieces
1 (28-ounce) can whole tomatoes, undrained
¾ cup water
¼ teaspoon salt
½ cup chopped fresh basil

1. Heat olive oil in a large nonstick skillet over medium-high heat. Add onion and garlic; cook 1 minute or until onion is slightly tender. Add eggplant and cook, stirring frequently, 5 minutes or until eggplant is slightly browned and tender.
2. Drain tomatoes, reserving ¼ cup juice. Chop tomatoes. Add tomatoes, reserved juice, ¾ cup water, and salt to eggplant mixture. Cook over medium-high heat 10 minutes or until eggplant is very tender, stirring occasionally. Remove from heat, and stir in basil.
YIELD: 6 SERVINGS (SERVING SIZE: ABOUT 1 CUP).

PER SERVING: Calories 73; Fat 2.8g (sat 0.4g, mono 1.7g, poly 0.4g); Protein 2g; Carb 11.6g; Fiber 4.4g; Chol 0mg; Iron 1.3mg; Sodium 228mg; Calc 48mg

EGGPLANT

The eggplant gets its name from the first varieties to reach the West, which were white, round, and egg-sized. While colors range from creamy white to green, the shiny, vivid purple eggplant is probably the most recognizable.
Shapes also vary. You'll find some that are small and spherical; others that are long, narrow, and curved like a banana; and still others that are large and bottle-shaped. Although available year-round, eggplants are best and most abundant from July to October. Look for firm eggplants that feel heavy for their size and have smooth, shiny skins. The stem should be bright green, and the skin should spring back when pressed.

SPICY GREENS AND BEANS

PointsPlus value per serving: 2

PREP: 5 minutes ■ COOK: 20 minutes

A package of preshredded collard greens shortens both prep and cook times.

    2 center-cut bacon slices
    2 garlic cloves, minced
    1 (32-ounce) package shredded fresh collard greens
    1 cup fat-free, lower-sodium chicken broth
    ¼ cup water
    ½ teaspoon crushed red pepper
    1 (15.5-ounce) can no-salt-added cannellini beans, rinsed
        and drained
    2 tablespoons grated fresh Parmesan cheese (optional)

1. Cook bacon in a 6-quart Dutch oven over medium heat until crisp. Remove bacon from pan; crumble. Add garlic to drippings in pan; sauté 1 minute. Add greens, broth, ¼ cup water, and red pepper. Bring to a boil, stirring often; cover, reduce heat to medium, and cook 12 minutes or just until greens are tender, stirring occasionally. Add beans; cook 1 minute or until beans are thoroughly heated. Sprinkle each serving with ½ teaspoon bacon and, if desired, 1 teaspoon cheese. YIELD: 6 SERVINGS (SERVING SIZE: 1⅓ CUPS GREENS MIXTURE AND ½ TEASPOON BACON).

PER SERVING: Calories 95; Fat 1.8g (sat 0.4g, mono 0.1g, poly 0.3g); Protein 6.8g; Carb 15.4g; Fiber 7.3g; Chol 3mg; Iron 0.9mg; Sodium 176mg; Calc 235mg

CRISP KALE

PointsPlus value per serving: 1

PREP: 5 minutes ■ COOK: 12 minutes

Scoot over, baked potato chips—these veggie chips offer a delicate crisp bite and plenty of vitamins. Look for basic kale with frilly leaves. The more exotic varieties of kale have thicker, flatter leaves and don't crisp up as well.

    9 cups cut prewashed kale (about ½ pound; such as Glory
        Foods)
    Olive oil–flavored cooking spray
    ½ teaspoon salt
    ½ teaspoon freshly ground black pepper
    ⅛ teaspoon sugar

1. Preheat oven to 350°.
2. Place kale in a very large bowl. Coat kale generously with cooking spray. Sprinkle with salt, pepper, and sugar; toss well. Arrange half of kale in each of 2 large jelly-roll pans.
3. Bake at 350° for 12 to 15 minutes or until crisp, tossing gently on pan after 8 minutes. YIELD: 6 SERVINGS (SERVING SIZE: 1 CUP).

PER SERVING: Calories 20; Fat 0.3g (sat 0g, mono 0g, poly 0.1g); Protein 1.3g; Carb 4g; Fiber 0.8g; Chol 0mg; Iron 0.7mg; Sodium 213mg; Calc 52mg

ROASTED OKRA AND TOMATOES

PointsPlus value per serving: 2

PREP: 9 minutes ■ COOK: 12 minutes

Separating the okra and tomatoes on the large baking sheet keeps the tomato juices away from the okra, allowing it to brown and roast.

    ½ pound okra pods, cut into ½-inch slices
    4 teaspoons olive oil, divided
    ½ teaspoon salt, divided
    ½ teaspoon freshly ground black pepper, divided
    2 cups grape tomatoes
    ¼ teaspoon hot sauce

1. Preheat oven to 450°.
2. Combine okra, 2 teaspoons oil, ¼ teaspoon salt, and ¼ teaspoon pepper; toss well. Arrange okra mixture in a single layer on half of a large jelly-roll pan. Combine tomatoes, remaining 2 teaspoons oil, remaining ¼ teaspoon salt, and remaining ¼ teaspoon pepper; toss well. Arrange tomatoes in a single layer on remaining half of pan.
3. Bake at 450° for 12 minutes or until okra is lightly browned and tomato skins burst and shrivel.
4. Scrape okra, tomatoes, and pan juices into a bowl with a rubber spatula; add hot sauce. Toss well, and serve immediately. YIELD: 5 SERVINGS (SERVING SIZE: ½ CUP).

PER SERVING: Calories 65; Fat 3.7g (sat 0.5g, mono 2.6g, poly 0.4g); Protein 1.6g; Carb 7.3g; Fiber 2.8g; Chol 0mg; Iron 0.4mg; Sodium 247mg; Calc 54mg

CARBONARA PEAS

PointsPlus value per serving: 2

PREP: 2 minutes ■ **COOK:** 7 minutes

This riff on the classic pasta carbonara dish gives you all the great flavor of the original in a side dish.

> 2 center-cut bacon slices
> ½ cup refrigerated prechopped onion
> 2 cups frozen petite green peas
> 2 tablespoons ⅓-less-fat chive and onion tub-style cream cheese
> 2 teaspoons chopped fresh parsley
> ¼ teaspoon freshly ground black pepper

1. Cook bacon in a medium nonstick skillet over medium heat until crisp. Remove bacon from pan; crumble. Add onion to drippings in pan; sauté 2 minutes.
2. Add peas, and cook 2 minutes or until thoroughly heated. Stir in cream cheese, parsley, and pepper. Sprinkle bacon over peas. **YIELD: 4 SERVINGS (SERVING SIZE: ½ CUP PEAS AND 1½ TEASPOONS CRUMBLED BACON).**

PER SERVING: Calories 85; Fat 2.1g (sat 1.1g, mono 0g, poly 0.2g); Protein 5.5g; Carb 11.6g; Fiber 3.4g; Chol 6mg; Iron 1.1mg; Sodium 159mg; Calc 31mg

SWEET POTATOES WITH PECAN STREUSEL

PointsPlus value per serving: 5

PREP: 7 minutes ■ **COOK:** 11 minutes
■ **OTHER:** 5 minutes

Washing the potatoes adds moisture, and wrapping them in wax paper holds it in while they cook in the microwave, yielding a moister potato. Be sure to use cold butter to create the streusel-like topping.

> 4 (8-ounce) sweet potatoes
> ¼ teaspoon salt
> ¼ teaspoon freshly ground black pepper
> 3 tablespoons all-purpose flour
> 3 tablespoons light brown sugar
> 2 tablespoons chilled light butter
> ¼ teaspoon ground cinnamon
> ½ cup chopped pecans, toasted
> ½ cup miniature marshmallows

1. Preheat broiler.
2. Scrub sweet potatoes; pat dry with paper towels, and wrap in wax paper. Microwave at HIGH 10 minutes or until tender. Cool 5 minutes. Cut each potato in half horizontally. Gently press ends of potato towards center to break up flesh. Sprinkle potatoes evenly with salt and pepper.
3. Combine flour and next 3 ingredients, stirring with a fork until crumbly. Stir in pecans and marshmallows. Sprinkle topping evenly over potato halves; place potatoes on a baking sheet. Broil 1 to 2 minutes or until topping is golden brown. **YIELD: 8 SERVINGS (SERVING SIZE: 1 POTATO HALF).**

PER SERVING: Calories 191; Fat 6.5g (sat 1.3g, mono 2.8g, poly 1.5g); Protein 2.8g; Carb 32.2g; Fiber 4.2g; Chol 4mg; Iron 1mg; Sodium 162mg; Calc 43mg

HERB ROASTED POTATOES

PointsPlus value per serving: 4

PREP: 6 minutes ■ **COOK:** 15 minutes

Fingerling potatoes grow smaller than a normal potato, but they're fully mature and come in colors ranging from yellow to red to purple.

> 1 pound fingerling potatoes, cut into 1-inch pieces
> 2 tablespoons chopped fresh parsley
> 2 tablespoons fresh thyme leaves
> 2 tablespoons olive oil
> ½ teaspoon kosher salt
> ½ teaspoon ground coriander
> ½ teaspoon freshly ground black pepper

1. Preheat oven to 450°.
2. Place potatoes on a large jelly-roll pan. Sprinkle with parsley and thyme. Drizzle with oil, and sprinkle with remaining ingredients. Toss to coat.
3. Bake at 450° for 15 to 18 minutes or until potatoes are tender and lightly browned, turning after 8 minutes. **YIELD: 4 SERVINGS (SERVING SIZE: ⅔ CUP).**

PER SERVING: Calories 141; Fat 6.9g (sat 1g, mono 4.9g, poly 0.8g); Protein 2.1g; Carb 18.4g; Fiber 3g; Chol 0mg; Iron 1mg; Sodium 248mg; Calc 19mg

LIGHT BUTTER VS. REGULAR BUTTER
Light butter has half the fat and calories of regular butter. It works well in a number of applications, but its lower fat content makes it a poor choice for baking or frying.

SAUTÉED SPINACH WITH ALMONDS AND GOLDEN RAISINS

PointsPlus value per serving: 3   *pictured on page 139*

PREP: 2 minutes ■ COOK: 6 minutes

Balsamic vinegar ties this side dish together by adding a tang that balances the sweetness of the raisins.

- 3 tablespoons sliced almonds
- 1 tablespoon olive oil
- 1 garlic clove, minced
- 2 (6-ounce) packages fresh baby spinach
- 3 tablespoons golden raisins
- 1 tablespoon balsamic vinegar
- ¼ teaspoon salt

1. Heat a large nonstick skillet over medium heat. Add almonds, and cook 2 minutes or until lightly toasted. Remove from pan, and set aside.
2. Heat oil in pan over medium heat. Add garlic; sauté 10 to 15 seconds. Add 1 package spinach; sauté 1 minute or until spinach wilts. Add remaining spinach; sauté 1 minute or until spinach wilts. Add raisins, vinegar, and salt, stirring well. Sprinkle with toasted almonds. YIELD: 4 SERVINGS (SERVING SIZE: ½ CUP).

PER SERVING: Calories 118; Fat 5.6g (sat 0.6g, mono 3.8g, poly 0.9g); Protein 3.3g; Carb 17g; Fiber 4.9g; Chol 0mg; Iron 3.1mg; Sodium 285mg; Calc 78mg

BASIL TOMATOES WITH OLIVES AND CHEESE

PointsPlus value per serving: 2

PREP: 6 minutes

Make this summer side dish ahead, and it will provide abundant flavor for your next cookout.

- 3 medium tomatoes, each cut into 5 slices
- ½ cup (2 ounces) crumbled reduced-fat feta cheese
- ¼ cup pitted kalamata olives, coarsely chopped
- 2 tablespoons fresh lemon juice
- ¼ cup chopped fresh basil
- ¼ teaspoon freshly ground black pepper

1. Arrange tomato slices on a serving platter. Sprinkle with cheese and olives; drizzle with lemon juice.

Sprinkle with basil and pepper. Cover and chill until ready to serve. YIELD: 5 SERVINGS (SERVING SIZE: 3 TOPPED TOMATO SLICES).

PER SERVING: Calories 66; Fat 4.1g (sat 1.5g, mono 1.6g, poly 0.3g); Protein 3.7g; Carb 4.7g; Fiber 1.2g; Chol 4mg; Iron 0.3mg; Sodium 321mg; Calc 55mg

ITALIAN CHEESE–BROILED TOMATOES

PointsPlus value per serving: 2

PREP: 6 minutes ■ COOK: 4 minutes

Any type of fresh herb can be used in the topping, so feel free to substitute your favorite for the oregano.

- ¼ cup preshredded reduced-fat 4-cheese Italian blend cheese
- 2 tablespoons light mayonnaise
- 2 tablespoons light butter, softened
- 1 teaspoon chopped fresh oregano
- ⅛ teaspoon salt
- ⅛ teaspoon freshly ground black pepper
- 1 garlic clove, pressed
- 2 medium tomatoes, cut horizontally in half

1. Preheat broiler.
2. Combine first 7 ingredients in a small bowl. Spread mayonnaise mixture evenly over tomato halves. Place halves on a broiler pan. Broil 4 minutes or until topping is golden brown. YIELD: 4 SERVINGS (SERVING SIZE: 1 TOMATO HALF).

PER SERVING: Calories 83; Fat 6.7g (sat 2.9g, mono 1.7g, poly 1.5g); Protein 2.7g; Carb 4.1g; Fiber 0.8g; Chol 14mg; Iron 0.2mg; Sodium 238mg; Calc 60mg

ZUCCHINI RIBBONS WITH GOAT CHEESE

PointsPlus value per serving: 2

PREP: 5 minutes ■ **COOK:** 7 minutes

By using a common vegetable peeler, you can create impressive-looking ribbons of zucchini. Serve this with grilled or roasted meats, poultry, or fish.

2 medium zucchini, trimmed
2 teaspoons olive oil
¼ teaspoon salt
¼ teaspoon freshly ground black pepper
1 teaspoon grated lemon rind
1 tablespoon fresh lemon juice
½ cup (2 ounces) crumbled goat cheese
1 tablespoon chopped fresh basil

1. Using a vegetable peeler, thinly slice zucchini lengthwise into ribbons.
2. Heat oil in a medium skillet over medium-high heat. Add zucchini, salt, and pepper; cook 5 minutes or until tender. Add lemon rind and juice to zucchini, tossing to coat. Cook 1 minute.
3. Sprinkle zucchini with goat cheese and basil; serve immediately. **YIELD: 4 SERVINGS (SERVING SIZE: ½ CUP).**

PER SERVING: Calories 75; Fat 5.4g (sat 2.4g, mono 2.3g, poly 0.4g); Protein 3.9g; Carb 3.9g; Fiber 1.2g; Chol 7mg; Iron 0.7mg; Sodium 210mg; Calc 37mg

ORZO WITH SPINACH AND TOMATOES

PointsPlus value per serving: 3

PREP: 2 minutes ■ **COOK:** 10 minutes

Enjoy this pasta-veggie side for dinner with grilled chicken or lamb, and then combine any leftover meat and pasta for lunch the next day.

1 cup uncooked orzo
½ cup chopped fresh baby spinach
½ cup grape tomatoes, halved
½ cup (2 ounces) crumbled feta cheese
½ teaspoon grated lemon rind
1 tablespoon fresh lemon juice
1 tablespoon extra-virgin olive oil
¼ teaspoon salt
¼ teaspoon freshly ground black pepper

1. Cook orzo according to package directions, omitting salt and fat. Drain.
2. Combine orzo, spinach, and remaining ingredients in a medium bowl, tossing well. **YIELD: 7 SERVINGS (SERVING SIZE: ½ CUP).**

PER SERVING: Calories 133; Fat 4.2g (sat 1.5g, mono 1.8g, poly 0.3g); Protein 4.3g; Carb 19.4g; Fiber 1.1g; Chol 7mg; Iron 0.1mg; Sodium 178mg; Calc 43mg

RED RICE WITH BACON AND OKRA

PointsPlus value per serving: 3

PREP: 1 minute ■ **COOK:** 9 minutes

Not to be confused with the type of rice called "red rice," this dish gets its color and flavor from diced tomatoes and bacon.

3 center-cut bacon slices
1 cup frozen cut okra, thawed
1 (14.5-ounce) can diced tomatoes with green pepper, celery, and onions, undrained
1 (8.8-ounce) package precooked basmati rice (such as Uncle Ben's Ready Rice)

1. Cook bacon in a medium nonstick skillet over medium heat 5 minutes or until crisp. Remove bacon from pan; drain and crumble. Add okra to drippings in pan; cook 2 minutes, stirring often. Stir in tomatoes; bring to a simmer.
2. Microwave rice according to package directions. Stir rice into okra mixture. Sprinkle servings evenly with crumbled bacon. **YIELD: 6 SERVINGS (SERVING SIZE: ABOUT ½ CUP).**

PER SERVING: Calories 97; Fat 1.6g (sat 0.3g, mono 0.4g, poly 0.2g); Protein 3.7g; Carb 17.9g; Fiber 0.8g; Chol 3mg; Iron 0.6mg; Sodium 239mg; Calc 55mg

soups & stews

Kentucky Burgoo, *page 161*

ROASTED BEET AND APPLE SOUP

PointsPlus value per serving: 4

PREP: 11 minutes ■ **COOK:** 22 minutes

Sweet tart apples are the perfect complement to earthy beets. Roasting brings out the natural sweetness in both. Garnish with toasted walnuts for a delicious crunch.

- **3 cups coarsely chopped peeled Granny Smith apple (about 1 pound)**
- **1½ cups chopped peeled beets (about 4 small)**
- **1 tablespoon chopped fresh thyme**
- **½ teaspoon salt**
- **½ teaspoon freshly ground black pepper**
- **3 cups organic vegetable broth**
- **½ cup crème fraîche**
- **Thyme sprigs (optional)**

1. Preheat oven to 425°.
2. Place apple and beets on a rimmed baking sheet. Sprinkle with 1 tablespoon thyme, salt, and pepper. Bake at 425° for 20 minutes or until beets are tender.
3. Place beet mixture and vegetable broth in a blender. Remove center piece of blender lid (to allow steam to escape); secure blender lid on blender. Place a clean towel over opening in blender lid (to avoid splatters). Blend until smooth. Pour into a large microwave-safe bowl. Cover with wax paper; microwave at HIGH 2 minutes or until very hot. Stir in crème fraîche. Garnish with thyme sprigs, if desired. **YIELD: 6 SERVINGS (SERVING SIZE: ABOUT ¾ CUP).**

PER SERVING: Calories 149; Fat 7.2g (sat 4.3g, mono 1g, poly 0.3g); Protein 2g; Carb 19.4g; Fiber 4g; Chol 19mg; Iron 0.8mg; Sodium 548mg; Calc 19mg

HOW TO PEEL A BUTTERNUT SQUASH

When peeling a butternut squash, a sturdy vegetable peeler works better than a paring knife.

1. For stability, use a sharp kitchen knife to cut 1 inch from the top and bottom of the squash, and discard.
2. Using a vegetable peeler, peel away the thick skin until you reach the deeper orange flesh of the squash.
3. Cut squash in half lengthwise. Using a spoon, scoop away the seeds and membranes; discard. Then cut the flesh according to your recipe directions.

BUTTERNUT SQUASH, APPLE, AND CELERY ROOT SOUP

PointsPlus value per serving: 3

PREP: 21 minutes ■ **COOK:** 35 minutes

If you can't find celeriac in your supermarket, parsnips make a good substitute.

- **1 tablespoon olive oil**
- **1 cup cubed peeled celeriac (celery root)**
- **¾ cup diced carrot**
- **½ cup diced onion**
- **1 garlic clove, chopped**
- **3 cups cubed peeled butternut squash**
- **1 cup cubed peeled apple (about 6 ounces)**
- **2 tablespoons chopped fresh sage**
- **3 cups fat-free, lower-sodium chicken broth**
- **¼ cup half-and-half**
- **¼ teaspoon salt**
- **¼ teaspoon ground red pepper**
- **Light sour cream or plain low-fat yogurt (optional)**
- **Chopped fresh sage (optional)**

1. Heat olive oil in a large saucepan over medium heat. Add celery root and next 3 ingredients; sauté 4 minutes or until tender but not browned. Add squash, apple, and 2 tablespoons sage to pan; sauté 5 minutes. Add chicken broth; bring to a boil. Reduce heat to medium-low, and simmer 15 minutes or until vegetables are very tender. Remove from heat; stir in half-and-half, salt, and red pepper.

2. Place half of butternut mixture in a blender. Remove center piece of blender lid (to allow steam to escape); secure blender lid on blender. Place a clean towel over opening in blender lid (to avoid splatters). Blend until smooth; transfer soup to a bowl. Repeat with remaining butternut mixture. Ladle soup into bowls. Top each serving with a dollop of light sour cream or yogurt, and garnish with fresh sage, if desired. YIELD: 6 SERVINGS (SERVING SIZE: ABOUT 1 CUP).

PER SERVING: Calories 104; Fat 3.7g (sat 1.1g, mono 2g, poly 0.4g); Protein 2.3g; Carb 17.5g; Fiber 2.9g; Chol 4mg; Iron 0.8mg; Sodium 367mg; Calc 70mg

CREAMY CAULIFLOWER SOUP

PointsPlus value per serving: 3

PREP: 3 minutes ■ COOK: 42 minutes

For an even creamier soup, reduce the chicken broth to 1½ cups.

1⅔ cups coarsely chopped onion
1 tablespoon olive oil
¼ teaspoon salt
¼ teaspoon freshly ground black pepper
1 (10-ounce) package fresh cauliflower florets
2 cups fat-free, lower-sodium chicken broth
1 cup 1% low-fat milk
½ cup fat-free half-and-half

1. Preheat oven to 400°.
2. Place first 5 ingredients in a large bowl; toss to coat. Spread cauliflower mixture in a single layer on a large jelly-roll pan. Bake, uncovered, at 400° for 25 minutes or until cauliflower begins to brown.
3. Combine chicken broth and milk in a Dutch oven; add cauliflower mixture. Bring to a boil; cover, reduce heat, and simmer 15 minutes or until cauliflower is very tender.
4. Place half of soup in a blender. Remove center piece of blender lid (to allow steam to escape); secure blender lid on blender. Place a clean towel over opening in blender lid (to avoid splatters). Blend until smooth. Pour into a large bowl. Repeat procedure with remaining soup.
5. Return soup to pan; stir in half-and-half. Cook over low heat 2 minutes or until thoroughly heated, stirring occasionally. YIELD: 4 SERVINGS (SERVING SIZE: 1 CUP).

PER SERVING: Calories 124; Fat 4.1g (sat 0.9g, mono 2.6g, poly 0.4g); Protein 5.6g; Carb 15.7g; Fiber 2.8g; Chol 3mg; Iron 0.5mg; Sodium 513mg; Calc 122mg

SPLIT PEA SOUP WITH DILL

PointsPlus value per serving: 6

PREP: 15 minutes ■ COOK: 1 hour and 2 minutes

This soup gets its creamy texture from pureeing a portion of it in the blender.

2 center-cut bacon slices
¾ cup chopped onion
½ cup chopped celery
½ cup chopped carrot
2 garlic cloves, minced
3½ cups fat-free, lower-sodium chicken broth
2 cups green split peas
2 cups water
3 tablespoons chopped fresh dill, divided

1. Cook bacon in a large saucepan over medium heat until crisp. Remove bacon from pan, reserving 2 teaspoons drippings in pan; crumble bacon. Add onion and next 3 ingredients to drippings in pan; sauté 4 minutes. Stir in broth, split peas, and 2 cups water. Bring to a boil; cover, reduce heat, and simmer 50 minutes or until peas are tender, stirring occasionally. Remove from heat.
2. Place 2 cups pea mixture and 2 tablespoons dill in a blender. Remove center piece of blender lid (to allow steam to escape); secure blender lid on blender. Place a clean towel over opening in blender lid (to avoid splatters). Blend until smooth; return to pan. Ladle soup into bowls, and sprinkle evenly with remaining 1 tablespoon dill and reserved bacon. YIELD: 6 SERVINGS (SERVING SIZE: ABOUT 1 CUP SOUP, ½ TEASPOON DILL, AND 1 TEASPOON CRUMBLED BACON).

PER SERVING: Calories 268; Fat 2.7g (sat 0.9g, mono 0.8g, poly 0.5g); Protein 19g; Carb 43.7g; Fiber 17.5g; Chol 3mg; Iron 3mg; Sodium 389mg; Calc 50mg

SPLIT PEAS

Split peas come from a variety of green and yellow peas that are specifically grown for drying. Once dried, the peas are steamed to loosen their skins. The skins are removed, and the peas are split along a natural seam. Both green and yellow varieties are as nutritious as dried beans, but unlike dried beans, they do not need a long soak before cooking, and they require a shorter cook time.

ROASTED TOMATO–BASIL SOUP WITH GOAT CHEESE

PointsPlus value per serving: 4

PREP: 10 minutes ■ COOK: 1 hour and 2 minutes

When tomatoes are out of season, balance the acidity by adding 1 tablespoon of sugar in step 2.

4 pounds tomatoes, halved vertically
6 garlic cloves, unpeeled
1 tablespoon olive oil
½ teaspoon fine sea salt
¼ teaspoon freshly ground black pepper
1 cup fat-free, lower-sodium chicken broth
¼ cup chopped fresh basil
1 cup (4 ounces) crumbled goat cheese

1. Preheat oven to 400°.
2. Place tomatoes, cut sides up, on a large baking sheet. Add garlic to pan. Drizzle vegetables with olive oil, and sprinkle with salt and pepper.
3. Bake, uncovered, at 400° for 1 hour or until edges of tomatoes are brown. Remove from oven. Let cool in pan on a wire rack until garlic is cool enough to handle. Peel garlic.
4. Place half of roasted tomato and garlic in a blender. Remove center piece of blender lid (to allow steam to escape); secure blender lid on blender. Place a clean towel over opening in blender lid (to avoid splatters). Blend until smooth; transfer to a Dutch oven. Repeat with remaining tomato and garlic.
5. Add broth and basil to tomato puree. Bring to a simmer over medium heat; simmer 2 minutes. Divide soup evenly among 6 bowls, and top each serving with about 2½ tablespoons goat cheese. YIELD: 6 SERVINGS (SERVING SIZE: ABOUT 1 CUP SOUP AND ABOUT 2½ TABLESPOONS GOAT CHEESE).

PER SERVING: Calories 133; Fat 6.9g (sat 3.2g, mono 2.7g, poly 0.6g); Protein 6.9g; Carb 13.3g; Fiber 3.7g; Chol 9mg; Iron 3.3mg; Sodium 347mg; Calc 66mg

CREAMY FISH CHOWDER

PointsPlus value per serving: 5

PREP: 5 minutes ■ COOK: 24 minutes

You can use orange roughy or halibut in place of grouper.

1 ounce very thinly sliced pancetta, cut into strips
1 (8-ounce) container refrigerated prechopped celery, onion, and bell pepper mix
3¼ cups frozen hash brown potatoes with onions and peppers (such as Ore-Ida Potatoes O'Brien)
1½ cups 1% low-fat milk
1 cup water
½ teaspoon dried thyme
¼ teaspoon freshly ground black pepper
1 (14-ounce) grouper fillet, cut into 1-inch pieces
1 (10.75-ounce) can condensed cream of potato soup, undiluted
Oyster crackers (optional)

1. Cook pancetta in a 3-quart saucepan over medium heat 3 minutes or until crisp, stirring often. Remove pancetta from pan with a slotted spoon, reserving drippings in pan. Add celery mix to drippings in pan; sauté 4 minutes. Stir in hash browns and next 6 ingredients; bring to a simmer. Cover and simmer 15 minutes or until vegetables are tender and fish is desired degree of doneness.
2. Flake fish into chunks, using 2 forks. Stir in pancetta. Ladle soup into bowls. Serve with oyster crackers, if desired. YIELD: 7 SERVINGS (SERVING SIZE: ABOUT 1 CUP).

PER SERVING: Calories 186; Fat 5.3g (sat 1.7g, mono 0.4g, poly 0.4g); Protein 15.6g; Carb 18g; Fiber 2.5g; Chol 28mg; Iron 0.9mg; Sodium 575mg; Calc 89mg

THAI COCONUT-LIME SOUP

PointsPlus value per serving: 5

PREP: 5 minutes ■ COOK: 13 minutes

Add some heat by stirring in crushed red pepper flakes or Asian chile sauce.

4¼ cups water
2 tablespoons lemongrass paste
1½ teaspoons grated lime rind
1 (14-ounce) can coconut milk
1 cup diced firm tofu
2½ tablespoons fish sauce
3 tablespoons fresh lime juice
2 tablespoons chopped fresh cilantro

1. Combine first 4 ingredients in a large saucepan. Bring to a boil; reduce heat to medium-low. Stir in tofu and fish sauce; cook, uncovered, 1 minute or until thoroughly heated. Remove from heat; stir in lime juice and cilantro. **YIELD: 7 SERVINGS (SERVING SIZE: 1 CUP).**

PER SERVING: Calories 179; Fat 15.8g (sat 11.2g, mono 1.2g, poly 1.9g); Protein 7.2g; Carb 5.1g; Fiber 0.9g; Chol 0mg; Iron 2.9mg; Sodium 623mg; Calc 260mg

BLACK BEAN AND CORN SOUP

PointsPlus value per serving: 4

PREP: 8 minutes ■ COOK: 25 minutes

Some salsas can carry a hefty load of sodium, so be sure to check the label and opt for the brand with the lowest amount of sodium.

> Cooking spray
> 1 cup chopped onion
> 3 garlic cloves, minced
> 2½ cups fat-free, lower-sodium chicken broth
> 1½ cups fresh salsa
> ½ cup water
> 2 (15-ounce) cans black beans, rinsed and drained
> 1 (15.25-ounce) can no-salt-added whole-kernel corn, drained
> 2 jalapeño peppers, seeded and finely chopped
> 1 tablespoon fresh lime juice
> 5 tablespoons light sour cream (optional)
> 5 teaspoons chopped fresh cilantro (optional)
> Baked tortilla chips (optional)

1. Heat a Dutch oven over medium-high heat. Coat pan with cooking spray. Add onion and garlic; cook 5 minutes or until tender. Add chicken broth and next 5 ingredients to pan. Bring to a boil; reduce heat and simmer, uncovered, 10 minutes, stirring occasionally.
2. Remove soup from heat; stir in lime juice. Ladle soup into bowls. Top evenly with sour cream and cilantro, and serve with chips, if desired. **YIELD: 5 SERVINGS (SERVING SIZE: ABOUT 1⅔ CUPS).**

PER SERVING: Calories 142; Fat 1.4g (sat 0g, mono 0.1g, poly 0.1g); Protein 6.7g; Carb 31.8g; Fiber 7.7g; Chol 0mg; Iron 1.5mg; Sodium 756mg; Calc 49mg

MINI CHICKEN MEATBALL SOUP

PointsPlus value per serving: 5

PREP: 11 minutes ■ COOK: 20 minutes

Tiny chicken meatballs, chewy barley, and tender vegetables are sure to make this version of chicken soup a favorite with your family.

> 4 cups fat-free, lower-sodium chicken broth
> ½ cup uncooked quick-cooking barley
> ½ cup thinly sliced baby carrots
> 1 (8-ounce) container refrigerated prechopped celery, onion, and bell pepper mix
> 2½ teaspoons salt-free garlic-and-herb seasoning blend (such as Mrs. Dash), divided
> ¾ pound ground chicken
> Cooking spray
> Unsalted saltine crackers (optional)

1. Combine first 4 ingredients and 1 teaspoon seasoning blend in a Dutch oven; cover and bring to a boil. Uncover and boil 12 minutes or until barley is tender.
2. Preheat oven to 450°.
3. While barley mixture cooks, combine chicken and remaining 1½ teaspoons seasoning blend; shape into 32 (¾-inch) balls. Place meatballs on a 15 x 10–inch foil-lined jelly-roll pan coated with cooking spray.
4. Bake at 450° for 8 minutes or just until lightly browned. Turn meatballs over. Bake an additional 2 minutes or just until lightly browned and done.
5. Add meatballs to soup. Cook 1 minute or until meatballs are slightly softened. Serve with unsalted saltine crackers, if desired. **YIELD: 5 SERVINGS (SERVING SIZE: ABOUT 1 CUP).**

PER SERVING: Calories 177; Fat 5.9g (sat 1.6g, mono 2.5g, poly 1.1g); Protein 16.4g; Carb 16.1g; Fiber 2.6g; Chol 59mg; Iron 0.9mg; Sodium 518mg; Calc 19mg

Barley
Barley has a neutral flavor and chewy texture, which makes it a great addition to soups. Barley also contains a type of fiber called beta-glucans (also found in oats), which may help lower levels of total cholesterol, including artery-clogging LDL cholesterol.

CURRIED LENTIL STEW

PointsPlus value per serving: 5

PREP: 9 minutes ■ **COOK:** 40 minutes ■ **OTHER:** 15 minutes

Lentils contain metabolism-boosting B vitamins, as well as magnesium for bone health and iron for healthy red blood cells. Plus, a cup of cooked lentils provides 90 percent of the recommended daily allowance of folic acid, a nutrient particularly important for women of childbearing age because it can guard against birth defects.

> **2 cups water, divided**
> **½ cup dried lentils**
> **Cooking spray**
> **1 cup thinly sliced onion**
> **1 cup diagonally sliced carrot**
> **1 tablespoon finely chopped garlic**
> **1 cup Thai coconut curry broth (such as College Inn)**
> **1 (13.5-ounce) can light coconut milk (such as Hokan)**
> **¼ cup chopped fresh cilantro**
> **1 tablespoon green curry paste**
> **1 tablespoon fresh lime juice**

1. Bring 1 cup water to a boil in a small saucepan. Stir in lentils; cover, remove from heat, and let stand 15 minutes. Drain.

2. Heat a Dutch oven over medium–high heat. Coat pan with cooking spray. Add onion, carrot, and garlic; sauté 3 minutes. Add remaining 1 cup water, cooked lentils, broth, and coconut milk. Bring to a boil; cover, reduce heat, and simmer 30 minutes or until lentils are tender, stirring occasionally.

3. Stir in cilantro, curry paste, and lime juice. **YIELD: 4 SERVINGS (SERVING SIZE: ABOUT 1 CUP).**

PER SERVING: Calories 171; Fat 6.1g (sat 4.8g, mono 0g, poly 0.1g); Protein 7.1g; Carb 25.8g; Fiber 5g; Chol 0mg; Iron 2mg; Sodium 368mg; Calc 39mg

---

LENTILS

Lentils have an advantage over other dried legumes—they are convenient. Dried beans and peas need to be soaked before cooking, and they often require more than an hour of simmering to become tender. But lentils are small and flat, which means that the cooking liquid doesn't have far to penetrate, so they cook relatively quickly with no need for presoaking.

BEEF AND LENTIL STEW

PointsPlus value per serving: 5

PREP: 4 minutes ■ **COOK:** 53 minutes

Loads of healthy vegetables and legumes take center stage in this fiber-rich soup.

> **1 (17-ounce) package cooked beef tips and gravy (such as Hormel)**
> **Cooking spray**
> **1 cup chopped carrot**
> **1 tablespoon bottled minced garlic**
> **1½ teaspoons dried Italian seasoning**
> **1 (8-ounce) container refrigerated prechopped celery, onion, and bell pepper mix**
> **2 cups dried lentils**
> **1 cup water**
> **½ teaspoon freshly ground black pepper**
> **3 (14.5-ounce) cans fat-free, lower-sodium beef broth**
> **1 (14.5-ounce) can no-salt-added diced tomatoes, undrained**
> **⅓ cup chopped fresh parsley**

1. Heat beef tips according to package directions; drain, discarding gravy.

2. Heat a 4-quart saucepan over medium–high heat. Coat pan with cooking spray. Add carrot, garlic, Italian seasoning, and celery mix; sauté 5 minutes or until vegetables are crisp–tender.

3. Add lentils and next 3 ingredients. Bring to a boil; cover, reduce heat, and simmer 25 minutes. Add beef tips and tomatoes to stew; cover and simmer 5 minutes or until thoroughly heated and lentils are tender. Remove from heat; stir in parsley. **YIELD: 11 SERVINGS (SERVING SIZE: 1 CUP).**

PER SERVING: Calories 212; Fat 2.8g (sat 0.8g, mono 0.1g, poly 0g); Protein 18.5g; Carb 29.4g; Fiber 6g; Chol 17mg; Iron 4.2mg; Sodium 761mg; Calc 30mg

ROPA VIEJA

PointsPlus value per serving: 3   *pictured on page 142*

PREP: 5 minutes ■ **COOK:** 16 minutes

Translated as "old clothes," this Cuban stew is cooked until the meat is so tender it shreds. We've taken a shortcut with a fully cooked roast and a vegetable blend, but no corners were cut on flavor.

> Cooking spray
> 3 garlic cloves, minced
> 1 (17-ounce) package refrigerated beef roast au jus (such as Hormel)
> 1 (16-ounce) package frozen bell pepper stir-fry (such as Birds Eye)
> 1 cup water
> 3 tablespoons sherry vinegar
> 1 tablespoon no-salt-added tomato paste
> ¼ cup sliced pimiento-stuffed olives
> 1 teaspoon ground cumin
> ½ teaspoon black pepper
> 3 cups hot cooked rice
> ¼ cup chopped fresh cilantro (optional)

1. Heat a large saucepan over medium heat. Coat pan with cooking spray. Add garlic; sauté 30 seconds. Increase heat to high; add beef roast with juices, pepper stir-fry, and 1 cup water. Bring to a boil; reduce heat, and simmer 5 minutes or until thoroughly heated. Shred roast with 2 forks.
2. Combine vinegar and tomato paste, stirring until blended. Add to roast. Add olives, cumin, and black pepper; bring to a simmer. Cook 5 minutes. Serve over rice, and sprinkle each serving with cilantro, if desired. **YIELD: 6 SERVINGS (SERVING SIZE: ¾ CUP STEW AND ½ CUP RICE).**

PER SERVING: Calories 138; Fat 2.7g (sat 0.8g, mono 0.5g, poly 0.3g); Protein 7g; Carb 20.6g; Fiber 1.3g; Chol 0mg; Iron 0.5mg; Sodium 203mg; Calc 11mg

KENTUCKY BURGOO

PointsPlus value per serving: 7   *pictured on page 143*

PREP: 13 minutes ■ **COOK:** 15 minutes

This recipe originated in Kentucky in the Civil War era. It was usually prepared in large quantities in huge kettles. When removing the beef and juices from the package, you may need to warm it slightly in the microwave for easier measuring.

> 1 (17-ounce) package refrigerated beef roast au jus (such as Hormel)
> Cooking spray
> 1 cup chopped onion
> 2 garlic cloves, minced
> 1 (14.5-ounce) can fat-free, lower-sodium chicken broth
> 2 cups frozen succotash vegetable blend
> ½ teaspoon dried Italian seasoning
> 1 (14.5-ounce) can no-salt-added diced tomatoes with basil, garlic, and oregano, undrained
> 1 cup shredded cooked chicken breast

1. Remove 1 cup beef and ¼ cup beef juices from beef roast package; reserve remaining meat for another use.
2. Heat a Dutch oven over medium-high heat until hot. Coat pan with cooking spray. Add onion and garlic; sauté 4 minutes or until onion is almost tender. Stir in chicken broth, scraping pan to loosen browned bits. Stir in roast beef, reserved beef juices, succotash, Italian seasoning, and tomatoes; bring to a boil over high heat. Cover, reduce heat, and simmer 7 minutes or just until vegetables are tender. Stir in chicken. **YIELD: 5 SERVINGS (SERVING SIZE: 1 CUP).**

PER SERVING: Calories 285; Fat 8.1g (sat 3.2g, mono 0.6g, poly 0.5g); Protein 33.9g; Carb 22.2g; Fiber 4.4g; Chol 78mg; Iron 2.5mg; Sodium 632mg; Calc 40mg

PORK AND PINTO BEAN STEW

PointsPlus value per serving: 5

PREP: 10 minutes ■ **COOK:** 12 minutes

Rather than adding broth as the liquid in this stew, dark beer was used to give it a rich flavor.

Cooking spray
2 cups chopped onion (about 1 large)
2 garlic cloves, minced
2 jalapeño peppers, seeded and chopped
2 cups (½ pound) pulled smoked pork
½ teaspoon salt
1 (28-ounce) can whole tomatoes, undrained and chopped
1 (16-ounce) can reduced-sodium pinto beans, rinsed and drained
1 (12-ounce) can dark beer
½ cup chopped fresh cilantro
Lime wedges (optional)

1. Heat a Dutch oven over medium-high heat; coat pan with cooking spray. Add onion, garlic, and jalapeño pepper; sauté 5 minutes or until tender.
2. Add pork and next 4 ingredients. Bring to a boil; reduce heat, and simmer, uncovered, 5 minutes. Stir in cilantro. Ladle into bowls, and serve with lime wedges, if desired. **YIELD: 6 SERVINGS (SERVING SIZE: 1 CUP).**

PER SERVING: Calories 176; Fat 5.8g (sat 2g, mono 2.4g, poly 0.6g); Protein 13.3g; Carb 18.6g; Fiber 5g; Chol 32mg; Iron 2.6mg; Sodium 472mg; Calc 84mg

MEXICAN CHICKEN STEW

PointsPlus value per serving: 5   *pictured on page 141*

PREP: 6 minutes ■ **COOK:** 14 minutes

Top with crumbled queso fresco and diced avocado to add even more Mexican flavor. Or pair the stew with baked tortilla chips for extra crunch.

2 ounces Mexican chorizo
1 cup chopped onion
2 garlic cloves, minced
3 cups shredded cooked chicken breast (about ¾ pound)
2 cups fat-free, lower-sodium chicken broth
1½ cups frozen whole-kernel corn
1 tablespoon chopped chipotle chile, canned in adobo sauce
1 (14.5-ounce) can stewed tomatoes, undrained and coarsely chopped
Lime wedges (optional)

1. Remove casings from chorizo. Cook chorizo in a Dutch oven over medium-high heat 5 minutes or until browned, stirring to crumble. Remove sausage from pan with a slotted spoon, and drain on paper towels, reserving 1 teaspoon drippings in pan. Add onion and garlic to drippings in pan; sauté 3 minutes or just until tender.
2. Add chorizo, chicken, and next 4 ingredients. Bring to a boil; reduce heat, and simmer, uncovered, 5 minutes. Ladle soup into bowls. Serve with lime wedges, if desired. **YIELD: 6 SERVINGS (SERVING SIZE: 1 CUP).**

PER SERVING: Calories 203; Fat 6.1g (sat 2g, mono 2.5g, poly 1g); Protein 22.9g; Carb 14.9g; Fiber 2.1g; Chol 57mg; Iron 1.9mg; Sodium 530mg; Calc 42mg

CHORIZO

This highly flavorful pork sausage is used in Mexican and Spanish cooking, and each cuisine has a unique blend of spices. You'll find versions made with fresh pork that need to be cooked and others that are dry-cured and ready to eat.

seasonal menus

Aztec Hot Chocolate Cupcakes, *page 166*

Fall Menu

Serves 4

Total **PointsPlus** value per serving: 17

Turkey Cutlets with Cranberry-Riesling Sauce

Celery Root and Yukon Gold Mash

Brussels Sprouts with Prosciutto

Aztec Hot Chocolate Cupcakes

GAME PLAN:

1. One day in advance:
- Trim and halve Brussels sprouts for **Brussels Sprouts with Prosciutto**; store in an airtight container in the refrigerator.

2. About 1½ hours before the meal:
- Prepare **Aztec Hot Chocolate Cupcakes.**

3. While cupcakes cool:
- Prepare **Celery Root and Yukon Gold Mash.**

4. While celery root and potatoes cook:
- Prepare **Brussels Sprouts with Prosciutto.**

5. While Brussels sprouts cook:
- Prepare **Turkey Cutlets with Cranberry-Riesling Sauce.**

TURKEY CUTLETS WITH CRANBERRY-RIESLING SAUCE

PointsPlus value per serving: 8

PREP: 4 minutes ▪ **COOK:** 24 minutes

This fall menu entrée pairs turkey cutlets with a sweeter-styled riesling wine as the base for a sauce, while sweetened dried cranberries provide a burst of flavor and added color.

¼ cup all-purpose flour
¼ teaspoon freshly ground black pepper
⅛ teaspoon salt
1¼ pounds turkey breast cutlets (about 12 cutlets)
2 tablespoons olive oil
1 cup riesling or other slightly sweet white wine
⅓ cup sweetened dried cranberries, chopped
¾ cup fat-free, lower-sodium chicken broth
2 teaspoons cornstarch
2 teaspoons sugar
1½ tablespoons cold butter, cut into small pieces

1. Combine first 3 ingredients in a shallow dish. Dredge turkey in flour mixture.

2. Heat 1 tablespoon oil in a large nonstick skillet over medium-high heat; add half of turkey. Reduce heat to medium; cook 5 minutes, turning after 3 minutes. Remove turkey from pan; keep warm. Repeat procedure with remaining 1 tablespoon oil and turkey. Stir in riesling and cranberries, scraping pan to loosen browned bits. Cook 5 minutes or until sauce is reduced by half and cranberries are soft, stirring occasionally.

3. Combine broth, cornstarch, and sugar, stirring with a whisk until smooth. Stir cornstarch mixture into cranberry mixture; cook 3 minutes or until sauce thickens slightly. Remove pan from heat; add butter, stirring until melted. Serve sauce with turkey cutlets.

YIELD: 4 SERVINGS (SERVING SIZE: 3 CUTLETS AND ¼ CUP SAUCE).

PER SERVING: Calories 314; Fat 11.8g (sat 3.7g, mono 6g, poly 0.9g); Protein 36.1g; Carb 11.3g; Fiber 0.6g; Chol 68mg; Iron 2.3mg; Sodium 313mg; Calc 4mg

CELERY ROOT AND YUKON GOLD MASH

PointsPlus value per serving: 4

PREP: 11 minutes ■ **COOK:** 28 minutes

Celery root, also known as celeriac, is a versatile root vegetable, widely used in French cooking. Here it is paired with potatoes in a mash, where it imparts a celery-like flavor to the dish. For ease in peeling celery root, use a serrated knife.

2½ cups (2-inch) cubed peeled Yukon Gold potato
2⅓ cups (1-inch) cubed celery root (1 medium)
¼ cup low-fat buttermilk
¼ cup reduced-fat sour cream
2 tablespoons butter
¼ teaspoon salt
¼ teaspoon freshly ground black pepper
1 tablespoon chopped fresh chives (optional)

1. Cook potato and celery root in boiling water in a large Dutch oven 25 minutes or until tender. Drain. Reduce heat to low. Return vegetables to Dutch oven.
2. Place buttermilk in a microwave-safe bowl. Microwave at HIGH 30 seconds or until thoroughly heated. Mash vegetables to desired consistency in pan with a potato masher. Add buttermilk and next 4 ingredients, stirring just until butter melts.
3. Remove pan from heat; transfer potato mixture to a serving dish. Garnish with chives, if desired. **YIELD:** **6 SERVINGS (SERVING SIZE: ABOUT ¾ CUP).**

PER SERVING: Calories 158; Fat 5.6g (sat 3.4g, mono 1.5g, poly 0.4g); Protein 3.8g; Carb 24.7g; Fiber 3.2g; Chol 16mg; Iron 1mg; Sodium 257mg; Calc 82mg

BRUSSELS SPROUTS WITH PROSCIUTTO

PointsPlus value per serving: 2

PREP: 5 minutes ■ **COOK:** 25 minutes

Roasting brings out the natural sweetness in vegetables, including fresh Brussels sprouts. The lemon provides balance with its bright acidity, and the pistachios round out the dish with added texture and a rich nutty flavor. Center-cut bacon or pancetta can be substituted for the prosciutto in this recipe.

4 cups trimmed Brussels sprouts (about 1 pound), halved lengthwise
1 tablespoon olive oil
¼ teaspoon freshly ground black pepper
Cooking spray
2 thin slices prosciutto, cut into ½-inch pieces
1 tablespoon butter
1 teaspoon grated lemon rind
1 tablespoon fresh lemon juice
2 tablespoons pistachios, coarsely chopped (optional)

1. Place a large jelly-roll pan on middle rack in oven. Preheat oven to 425°.
2. Place first 3 ingredients in a large bowl; toss to coat. Spread mixture on preheated pan coated with cooking spray. Bake at 425° for 20 minutes or until almost tender and browned, stirring twice.
3. Add prosciutto to pan. Bake an additional 5 minutes or until crisp.
4. Place Brussels sprouts mixture, butter, rind, juice, and, if desired, pistachios in a large bowl; toss gently. **YIELD: 6 SERVINGS (SERVING SIZE: ABOUT ⅔ CUP).**

PER SERVING: Calories 82; Fat 5g (sat 1.7g, mono 2.2g, poly 0.4g); Protein 3.9g; Carb 7.3g; Fiber 2.9g; Chol 9mg; Iron 1.2mg; Sodium 158mg; Calc 33mg

AZTEC HOT CHOCOLATE CUPCAKES

PointsPlus value per serving: 3   *pictured on page 144*

PREP: 13 minutes ■ COOK: 15 minutes

Chocolate, cinnamon, and ground red pepper are a classic flavor combination of Mexican cuisine. As they bake, the marshmallows toast and add crunch to the top.

Cooking spray
8 large marshmallows
4.5 ounces all-purpose flour (about 1 cup)
⅓ cup unsweetened dark cocoa (such as Hershey's Special Dark)
1 teaspoon baking soda
⅛ teaspoon salt
1 (0.52-ounce) packet ready brew cinnamon-flavored coffee (such as Starbucks VIA)
⅛ teaspoon ground red pepper (optional)
⅔ cup sugar
¼ cup butter, softened
½ cup egg substitute
1 teaspoon vanilla extract
½ cup 1% low-fat milk

1. Preheat oven to 350°.

2. Place 15 paper muffin cup liners in muffin cups; coat liners with cooking spray. Slice marshmallows in half horizontally.

3. Weigh or lightly spoon flour into a dry measuring cup; level with a knife. Combine flour and next 4 ingredients in a small bowl; stir well with a whisk. Stir in red pepper, if desired.

4. Place sugar and butter in a large bowl; beat with a mixer at medium speed until well blended. Add egg substitute and vanilla, beating well. Add flour mixture and milk alternately to sugar mixture, beginning and ending with flour mixture.

5. Spoon batter into prepared muffin cups, filling half full. Bake at 350° for 10 minutes. Place 1 marshmallow half on top of each cupcake; discard remaining marshmallow half. Bake an additional 5 to 8 minutes or until a wooden pick inserted to the side of the marshmallow comes out clean. Remove cupcakes from pan immediately; place on a wire rack. YIELD: 15 SERVINGS (SERVING SIZE: 1 CUPCAKE).

PER SERVING: Calories 120; Fat 3.6g (sat 2.1g, mono 0.9g, poly 0.3g); Protein 2.8g; Carb 20.3g; Fiber 0.2g; Chol 9mg; Iron 0.6mg; Sodium 151mg; Calc 17mg

CUPCAKE LINERS

Paper liners can be a fun way to add color and interest to your cupcakes, but their purpose is also functional—they keep these sweet treats from sticking to the pan and make cleanup easier and faster. If you're using liners, there's no need to coat the pan with cooking spray, but you will need to coat the liners to make it easier to peel them off without taking a lot of cupcake with them.

Winter Menu

Serves 4

Total **PointsPlus** value per serving: 14

Pork Chops with Maple-Mustard Pan Sauce

Cabbage with Pancetta

Rosemary Mashed Butternut Squash

Rum Raisin Apples

GAME PLAN:

1. One day in advance:
- Prepare onion and cabbage for **Cabbage with Pancetta**; store each separately in an airtight container in the refrigerator.
- Prepare **Rum Raisin Apples**.

2. About 1 hour before the meal:
- Prepare **Rosemary Mashed Butternut Squash**.

3. While squash cooks:
- Prepare **Cabbage with Pancetta**.
- Prepare **Pork Chops with Maple-Mustard Pan Sauce**.
- Reheat **Rum Raisin Apples**.

PORK CHOPS WITH MAPLE-MUSTARD PAN SAUCE

PointsPlus value per serving: 6

PREP: 3 minutes ■ COOK: 12 minutes

Thin, boneless pork chops make for a quick, inexpensive meal.

½ cup fat-free, lower-sodium chicken broth
3 tablespoons maple syrup
2 tablespoons Dijon mustard
Cooking spray
4 (4-ounce) boneless center-cut loin pork chops
   (½ inch thick)
¼ teaspoon freshly ground black pepper
⅛ teaspoon salt

1. Combine first 3 ingredients in a small bowl.

2. Heat a large nonstick skillet over medium-high heat. Coat pan with cooking spray. Sprinkle pork with pepper and salt; add to pan. Cook 3 to 4 minutes on each side or until done. Remove from pan, reserving drippings in pan; keep warm.

3. Stir in broth mixture, scraping pan to loosen browned bits. Bring to a boil; boil 3 minutes or until slightly syrupy. Pour sauce evenly over pork chops.

YIELD: 4 SERVINGS (SERVING SIZE: 1 PORK CHOP AND 1½ TABLESPOONS SAUCE).

PER SERVING: Calories 242; Fat 10.5g (sat 3.4g, mono 4g, poly 1.4g); Protein 23.6g; Carb 11.7g; Fiber 0g; Chol 78mg; Iron 0.9mg; Sodium 374mg; Calc 32mg

CABBAGE WITH PANCETTA

PointsPlus value per serving: 1

PREP: 5 minutes ■ COOK: 13 minutes

Pancetta lends a delicious saltiness to this cabbage, which contrasts nicely with the sweetness of Pork Chops with Maple-Mustard Pan Sauce.

    Cooking spray
    ¼ cup chopped pancetta (about 1 ounce)
    1 cup thinly sliced onion
    4 cups thinly sliced green cabbage
    ¼ teaspoon freshly ground black pepper
    ⅛ teaspoon salt

1. Heat a large nonstick skillet over medium heat. Coat pan with cooking spray. Add pancetta; cook 3 minutes or until crisp, stirring frequently. Remove pancetta from pan, reserving drippings in pan. Set pancetta aside. Add onion to drippings; sauté 3 minutes or until tender.
2. Add cabbage; sauté 6 minutes or until cabbage is tender and beginning to brown. Stir in pepper, salt, and pancetta. YIELD: 4 SERVINGS (SERVING SIZE: ⅔ CUP).

PER SERVING: Calories 57; Fat 2.6g (sat 1.1g, mono 0g, poly 0g); Protein 2.2g; Carb 6.8g; Fiber 2.3g; Chol 5mg; Iron 0.4mg; Sodium 204mg; Calc 35mg

ROSEMARY MASHED BUTTERNUT SQUASH

PointsPlus value per serving: 3

PREP: 6 minutes ■ COOK: 18 minutes

Steaming butternut squash in the microwave is the quickest and easiest way to ensure a smooth consistency in the final dish. Store leftovers in an airtight container in the refrigerator.

    1 (3-pound) butternut squash, quartered lengthwise
    2 tablespoons butter
    1 tablespoon chopped fresh rosemary
    ¼ teaspoon salt
    ¼ teaspoon ground allspice

1. Place squash in a 13 x 9–inch glass or ceramic baking dish. Add water to a depth of ½ inch. Cover dish with heavy-duty plastic wrap; vent. Microwave at HIGH 18 minutes or until very tender.

2. Discard seeds and membranes from squash. Scoop out pulp; place in a medium bowl. Add butter and remaining ingredients; mash with a potato masher until smooth. YIELD: 8 SERVINGS (SERVING SIZE: ½ CUP).

PER SERVING: Calories 93; Fat 3.1g (sat 1.9g, mono 0.8g, poly 0.2g); Protein 1.5g; Carb 17.5g; Fiber 3.1g; Chol 8mg; Iron 1.1mg; Sodium 80mg; Calc 74mg

RUM RAISIN APPLES

PointsPlus value per serving: 4

PREP: 11 minutes ■ COOK: 9 minutes

Jumbo raisins are very large dried grapes that are juicier and more plump than standard raisins. Serve over ice cream or as a topping for pancakes.

    ⅔ cup apple juice
    ⅓ cup dark rum
    ⅓ cup jumbo red raisins
    2 tablespoons dark brown sugar
    ¼ teaspoon ground cinnamon
    3 large Golden Delicious apples
    1 tablespoon cornstarch
    1 tablespoon water
    1 tablespoon butter

1. Combine first 5 ingredients in a large nonstick skillet. Let stand.
2. While apple juice mixture stands, peel and core apples. Slice each apple into 12 wedges. Add apples to juice mixture; bring to a boil. Cover and cook over medium-high heat 5 to 6 minutes or until apples are tender, stirring occasionally. Combine cornstarch and 1 tablespoon water; add to apples. Cook 1 minute or until slightly thick, stirring constantly. Add butter, stirring until butter melts. YIELD: 4 SERVINGS (SERVING SIZE: ¾ CUP).

PER SERVING: Calories 170; Fat 3g (sat 1.9g, mono 0.8g, poly 0.1g); Protein 0.7g; Carb 33.1g; Fiber 1.5g; Chol 8mg; Iron 0.4mg; Sodium 29mg; Calc 19mg

Spring Menu

Serves 4

Total **PointsPlus** value per serving: 13

Double Mustard–Apricot Chicken

Sugar Snap Peas with Pancetta and Thyme

Asparagus-Potato Salad with Creamy Asian Dressing

Baklava Strawberry Tartlets

GAME PLAN:

1. One day in advance:

- Prepare mini phyllo shells for **Baklava Strawberry Tartlets.** Store in a zip-top plastic bag at room temperature.
- Cook asparagus and potatoes, and prepare dressing for **Asparagus-Potato Salad with Creamy Asian Dressing;** store each separately in an airtight container in the refrigerator.

2. About 1 hour before the meal:

- Prepare **Double Mustard–Apricot Chicken.**
- Prepare **Sugar Snap Peas with Pancetta and Thyme.**

3. While chicken and peas cook:

- Prepare **Baklava Strawberry Tartlets.**
- Assemble **Asparagus-Potato Salad with Creamy Asian Dressing.**

DOUBLE MUSTARD–APRICOT CHICKEN

PointsPlus value per serving: 6

PREP: 1 minute ■ **COOK:** 14 minutes

Sweet apricot preserves combine deliciously with tangy and spicy mustards in this creamy sauce.

4 (6-ounce) skinless, boneless chicken breast halves
2 teaspoons Dijon mustard
½ teaspoon freshly ground black pepper
Cooking spray
¼ cup apricot preserves
2 tablespoons reduced-fat sour cream
1 tablespoon water
2 teaspoons stone-ground mustard

1. Brush chicken with Dijon mustard; sprinkle evenly with pepper.

2. Heat a large nonstick skillet over medium–high heat. Coat pan with cooking spray. Add chicken to pan. Cook 6 minutes on each side or until done. Remove chicken from pan; cover and keep warm.

3. Add preserves and next 3 ingredients to drippings in pan, scraping pan to loosen browned bits. Cook 1 minute or until thoroughly heated. Place chicken breast halves on plates; top evenly with sauce. YIELD: 4 SERVINGS (SERVING SIZE: 1 CHICKEN BREAST HALF AND 6 TABLESPOONS SAUCE).

PER SERVING: Calories 251; Fat 3.3g (sat 1.1g, mono 0.8g, poly 0.5g); Protein 39.7g; Carb 13.9g; Fiber 0.1g; Chol 102mg; Iron 1.4mg; Sodium 214mg; Calc 32mg

SUGAR SNAP PEAS WITH PANCETTA AND THYME

PointsPlus value per serving: 3

PREP: 2 minutes ■ COOK: 13 minutes

Pancetta makes this side dish extra special. If you can't find it, use center-cut bacon instead.

    Cooking spray
    2 ounces pancetta, chopped
    ½ cup refrigerated prechopped onion
    2 (8-ounce) packages trimmed sugar snap peas
    1 teaspoon chopped fresh thyme
    ¼ teaspoon freshly ground black pepper
    ⅛ teaspoon salt

1. Heat a large nonstick skillet over medium-high heat. Coat pan with cooking spray. Add pancetta to pan. Cook 4 minutes or until crisp, stirring frequently. Remove from pan with a slotted spoon, reserving drippings in pan. Drain pancetta on paper towels.

2. Add onion to drippings in pan; sauté 3 minutes or until tender. Stir in peas, pancetta, and remaining ingredients; sauté 5 minutes or until peas are crisp-tender. YIELD: 4 SERVINGS (SERVING SIZE: 1 CUP).

PER SERVING: Calories 128; Fat 5.8g (sat 3g, mono 0g, poly 0g); Protein 5.1g; Carb 15.4g; Fiber 3.3g; Chol 8mg; Iron 1.4mg; Sodium 230mg; Calc 63mg

ASPARAGUS-POTATO SALAD WITH CREAMY ASIAN DRESSING

PointsPlus value per serving: 3

PREP: 5 minutes ■ COOK: 25 minutes
■ OTHER: 10 minutes

Asparagus and red potatoes—two of spring's pleasures—are combined here with a creamy Asian dressing that gets a zing from pickled ginger.

    1½ cups (1½-inch) diagonally cut asparagus
    1½ cups (½-inch) cubed red potato
    Cooking spray
    ¼ cup light mayonnaise
    1 tablespoon finely minced pickled ginger
    1 teaspoon fresh lemon juice
    1 teaspoon lower-sodium soy sauce

1. Preheat oven to 425°.

2. Place asparagus and potato in 2 separate bowls. Coat asparagus and potato with cooking spray; toss. Spread potato in a single layer on a baking sheet. Bake at 425° for 15 minutes, turning after 8 minutes. Add asparagus in a single layer to pan; cook 10 minutes. Let cool to room temperature in pan on a wire rack.

3. Transfer asparagus and potato to a serving bowl. Combine mayonnaise and next 3 ingredients in a small bowl, stirring with a whisk. Pour dressing over asparagus mixture; toss well. Serve at room temperature, or cover and chill. YIELD: 4 SERVINGS (SERVING SIZE: ABOUT ⅔ CUP).

PER SERVING: Calories 113; Fat 5.4g (sat 1g, mono 1.3g, poly 2.1g); Protein 2.4g; Carb 14.3g; Fiber 2.2g; Chol 5mg; Iron 1.6mg; Sodium 182mg; Calc 20mg

BAKLAVA STRAWBERRY TARTLETS

PointsPlus value per serving: 1

PREP: 10 minutes ■ COOK: 12 minutes
■ OTHER: 10 minutes

There is nothing quite like the first strawberries of spring, especially when they're paired with creamy Greek yogurt, fresh mint, and balsamic glaze. Springtime never tasted so good.

    1 (1.9-ounce) package mini phyllo shells
    2 tablespoons honey
    1 tablespoon warm water
    1½ tablespoons turbinado sugar, divided
    1 cup coarsely chopped strawberries
    ¾ cup plain 2% reduced-fat Greek yogurt
    1 tablespoon chopped fresh mint
    1 tablespoon balsamic glaze

1. Preheat oven to 350°.

2. Place phyllo shells on a baking sheet lined with parchment paper. Combine honey and 1 tablespoon warm water; brush bottom and sides of phyllo shells with honey mixture. Sprinkle 1 tablespoon turbinado sugar evenly among shells.

3. Bake at 350° for 12 minutes or until lightly browned and sugar melts. Cool shells completely on a wire rack.

4. Combine strawberries and remaining 1½ teaspoons turbinado sugar in a small bowl. Combine yogurt and mint in another small bowl. Spoon about 2½ teaspoons yogurt mixture into each cooled shell. Spoon strawberries evenly over yogurt; drizzle shells evenly with balsamic glaze. YIELD: 15 SERVINGS (SERVING SIZE: 1 TARTLET).

PER SERVING: Calories 42; Fat 1.2g (sat 0.2g, mono 0.5g, poly 0.2g); Protein 1.2g; Carb 6.9g; Fiber 0.3g; Chol 1mg; Iron 0.3mg; Sodium 17mg; Calc 15mg

Vegetarian Spring Menu

Serves 6

Total **PointsPlus** value per serving: 14

Buddha's Delight

Simple Fried Rice

Hot and Sour Soup

Peach-Ginger Sorbet Sundaes

GAME PLAN:

1. One day in advance:
- Prepare strawberries for **Peach-Ginger Sorbet Sundaes.** Store in an airtight container in the refrigerator.
- Prepare rice for **Simple Fried Rice.** Store in an airtight container in the refrigerator.
- Prepare **Hot and Sour Soup** through step 2. Store in an airtight container in the refrigerator.

2. About 1 hour before the meal:
- Prepare marinade for **Buddha's Delight** and marinate tofu.

3. While tofu marinates:
- Reheat and finish preparing **Hot and Sour Soup.**
- Prepare **Simple Fried Rice.**

4. While soup heats:
- Prepare **Buddha's Delight.**
- Assemble **Peach-Ginger Sorbet Sundaes.**

BUDDHA'S DELIGHT

PointsPlus value per serving: 6

PREP: 9 minutes ■ COOK: 18 minutes ■ OTHER: 20 minutes

1 (14-ounce) package extra-firm tofu, drained
2 tablespoons lower-sodium soy sauce
2 tablespoons seasoned rice vinegar
1 tablespoon dark sesame oil
1 teaspoon dark brown sugar
1 tablespoon canola oil
2 cups red bell pepper strips (about 1 large)
1 tablespoon grated peeled fresh ginger
1 (12-ounce) package fresh vegetable stir-fry
3 garlic cloves, minced
½ cup water
1 teaspoon cornstarch
¾ cup unsalted peanuts, chopped

1. Press tofu between paper towels to remove excess moisture; cut into ½-inch cubes. Combine soy sauce and next 3 ingredients in a large heavy-duty zip-top plastic bag. Add tofu; seal bag. Marinate in refrigerator at least 20 minutes. Drain tofu, reserving marinade.

2. Heat oil in a large nonstick skillet over medium-high heat. Add tofu; cook 8 to 10 minutes or until browned, turning carefully with a spatula to keep cubes intact. Remove tofu; keep warm. Reduce heat to medium.

3. Add bell pepper strips and next 3 ingredients to pan. Stir-fry 4 to 5 minutes or until vegetables are crisp-tender. Return tofu to pan; stir-fry 1 minute.

4. Combine reserved marinade, ½ cup water, and cornstarch in a bowl; add to tofu mixture. Cook 30 seconds or until thick. Sprinkle with peanuts. YIELD: 6 SERVINGS (SERVING SIZE: 1 CUP TOFU MIXTURE AND 2 TABLESPOONS PEANUTS).

PER SERVING: Calories 223; Fat 15g (sat 2g, mono 7.1g, poly 5.2g); Protein 10.6g; Carb 13.3g; Fiber 2.9g; Chol 0mg; Iron 1.5mg; Sodium 328mg; Calc 36mg

SIMPLE FRIED RICE

PointsPlus value per serving: 4

PREP: 5 minutes ■ **COOK:** 8 minutes

You can turn this side into a main dish by adding cooked shrimp, chicken, or pork.

Cooking spray
1 large egg, beaten
1 tablespoon dark sesame oil
¼ teaspoon crushed red pepper
2 garlic cloves, minced
3 cups cooked brown rice
1 cup frozen peas and carrots, thawed
2 tablespoons lower-sodium soy sauce
2 tablespoons chopped green onions

1. Heat a large nonstick skillet over medium-high heat. Coat pan with cooking spray. Add egg; cook 1½ minutes, stirring occasionally until scrambled. Remove egg from pan.
2. Return pan to medium-high heat. Add oil, red pepper, and garlic. Cook 30 seconds or until garlic is tender. Add rice, and stir-fry 2 minutes. Stir in peas and carrots, soy sauce, and egg. Cook, stirring constantly, 1 minute or until thoroughly heated. Stir in green onions. YIELD: 6 SERVINGS (SERVING SIZE: ABOUT ¾ CUP).

PER SERVING: Calories 160; Fat 4.2g (sat 0.8g, mono 1.6g, poly 1.4g); Protein 4.8g; Carb 25.9g; Fiber 2.7g; Chol 35mg; Iron 0.9mg; Sodium 166mg; Calc 25mg

HOT AND SOUR SOUP

PointsPlus value per serving: 1

PREP: 9 minutes ■ **COOK:** 14 minutes

The chili garlic sauce gives this soup a definite kick. Decrease the amount if you'd prefer a milder soup.

2 (3.5-ounce) packages fresh shiitake mushrooms
2 cups organic vegetable broth
1½ cups water
1 tablespoon lower-sodium soy sauce
1 tablespoon chili garlic sauce
½ cup drained canned sliced bamboo shoots
2 tablespoons white vinegar
1 tablespoon cornstarch
2 tablespoons water
1 large egg, beaten
1 green onion, diagonally cut (optional)

1. Remove and discard stems from mushrooms; cut mushroom caps into slices.
2. Combine broth and next 3 ingredients in a 3-quart saucepan. Bring to a boil over high heat. Add mushroom slices and bamboo shoots. Cover, reduce heat, and cook 5 minutes or until mushrooms are tender. Stir in vinegar.
3. Combine cornstarch and 2 tablespoons water in a small bowl. Add cornstarch mixture to soup; bring to a boil. Cook 1 minute, stirring constantly. Remove pan from heat. Slowly stir in egg. Return to high heat. Cook 1 minute or until egg is cooked. Stir in green onions just before serving, if desired. YIELD: 6 SERVINGS (SERVING SIZE: ABOUT ¾ CUP).

PER SERVING: Calories 46; Fat 0.9g (sat 0.3g, mono 0.3g, poly 0.1g); Protein 2.1g; Carb 8.1g; Fiber 1g; Chol 35mg; Iron 0.4mg; Sodium 304mg; Calc 7mg

PEACH-GINGER SORBET SUNDAES

PointsPlus value per serving: 3

PREP: 8 minutes

2 cups peach-ginger sorbet (such as Ciao Bella)
1 cup chopped strawberries
6 tablespoons frozen reduced-calorie whipped topping, thawed
⅓ cup sesame sticks, crushed

1. Spoon ⅓ cup sorbet into each of 6 dessert cups. Top each with about 2½ tablespoons strawberries, 1 tablespoon whipped topping, and about 1 tablespoon crushed sesame sticks. YIELD: 6 SERVINGS (SERVING SIZE: 1 SUNDAE).

PER SERVING: Calories 118; Fat 2.8g (sat 0.8g, mono 0g, poly 0g); Protein 0.8g; Carb 23.6g; Fiber 0.8g; Chol 0mg; Iron 0.4mg; Sodium 82mg; Calc 16mg

Summer Menu

Serves 4

Total **PointsPlus** value per serving: 17

Sweet and Spicy Grilled Pepper Fillets

Grilled Sweet Peppers and Corn

Watermelon-Blueberry Salad

Blackberry Buttermilk Sherbet

GAME PLAN:

1. One day in advance:
- Cube watermelon, and prepare dressing, reserving mint for **Watermelon-Blueberry Salad;** store each in an airtight container in the refrigerator.
- Prepare **Blackberry Buttermilk Sherbet;** cover and freeze overnight.

2. About 1 hour before the meal:
- Prepare **Grilled Sweet Peppers and Corn.**
- Prepare **Sweet and Spicy Grilled Pepper Fillets.**

3. While beef stands:
- Assemble **Watermelon-Blueberry Salad.**
- Slightly thaw **Blackberry Buttermilk Sherbet** for easier serving.

SWEET AND SPICY GRILLED PEPPER FILLETS

PointsPlus value per serving: 6

PREP: 4 minutes ■ COOK: 14 minutes ■ OTHER: 5 minutes

Red pepper jelly makes a sweet-and-spicy glaze for grilled beef tenderloin steaks and fresh summer peaches at their juicy prime.

½ cup red pepper jelly
1 tablespoon balsamic vinegar
4 (4-ounce) beef tenderloin steaks, trimmed (1 inch thick)
¼ teaspoon salt
¼ teaspoon freshly ground black pepper
Cooking spray
4 small peaches, peeled and halved

1. Preheat grill to medium-high heat.
2. Combine jelly and vinegar in a small bowl. Sprinkle steaks evenly with salt and black pepper. Place steaks on grill rack coated with cooking spray. Grill 5 minutes; turn steaks over. Brush steaks with half of jelly mixture. Grill 5 minutes or until desired degree of doneness. Cover and let stand 5 minutes.
3. Brush peach halves with remaining jelly mixture. Grill 2 minutes on each side or until tender, basting once. Cut each peach half into thirds. Serve steaks with grilled peaches. YIELD: 4 SERVINGS (SERVING SIZE: 1 STEAK AND ½ CUP PEACHES).

PER SERVING: Calories 325; Fat 9.4g (sat 3.4g, mono 3.6g, poly 0.4g); Protein 33.3g; Carb 26.8g; Fiber 1.6g; Chol 90mg; Iron 2.4mg; Sodium 245mg; Calc 28mg

GRILLED SWEET PEPPERS AND CORN

PointsPlus value per serving: 3

PREP: 4 minutes ■ COOK: 12 minutes

2 ears shucked corn
1 red bell pepper, halved and seeded
1 small red onion, cut into ½-inch-thick slices
Cooking spray
¼ teaspoon salt
¼ teaspoon freshly ground black pepper
½ cup (2 ounces) crumbled goat cheese
2 tablespoons chopped fresh basil

1. Preheat grill to medium–high heat.

2. Coat corn, bell pepper halves, and onion slices with cooking spray. Sprinkle vegetables with salt and black pepper. Place vegetables on grill rack coated with cooking spray. Grill 12 minutes or until tender and beginning to char, turning after 6 minutes.

3. Cut kernels from ears of corn; place in a medium bowl. Chop bell pepper and onion; add to corn, tossing gently. Sprinkle with goat cheese and basil. Serve warm or at room temperature. **YIELD: 4 SERVINGS (SERVING SIZE: ¾ CUP).**

PER SERVING: Calories 98; Fat 3.9g (sat 2.2g, mono 0.8g, poly 0.4g); Protein 4.7g; Carb 12.8g; Fiber 2.4g; Chol 7mg; Iron 0.8mg; Sodium 209mg; Calc 30mg

HOW TO SHUCK AND DEKERNEL CORN

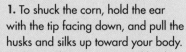
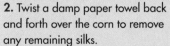

The husk helps retain the corn's natural moisture, which makes it taste fresher. Look for green husks that aren't dry, and then pull back an edge to check that the kernels are plump and have a vivid color.

1. To shuck the corn, hold the ear with the tip facing down, and pull the husks and silks up toward your body.
2. Twist a damp paper towel back and forth over the corn to remove any remaining silks.
3. To dekernel the corn, cut about ½ inch from the top of each ear to create a flat base on which to stand the cob while removing the kernels.
4. Stand the cob upright in a pie plate or bowl to catch the kernels, and use a sharp knife to slice away the kernels.

WATERMELON-BLUEBERRY SALAD

PointsPlus value per serving: 5

PREP: 11 minutes

Toss this salad just before serving so the fruit doesn't water out and dilute the dressing. To easily measure honey, coat the measuring spoon or cup with cooking spray to help prevent the honey from sticking.

>   4 cups cubed seeded watermelon
> ½ cup blueberries
> ¼ cup honey
> 1½ tablespoons fresh lemon juice
> 1½ tablespoons olive oil
> ¼ teaspoon salt
> ⅛ teaspoon freshly ground black pepper
> 2 tablespoons chopped fresh mint
> 4 to 8 Boston lettuce leaves (optional)

1. Place watermelon and blueberries in a medium bowl.
2. Combine honey and next 4 ingredients in a small bowl, stirring with a whisk. Stir in mint. Drizzle dressing over fruit, and toss gently. If desired, place 1 or 2 lettuce leaves on each of 4 plates, and spoon fruit mixture evenly over lettuce. **YIELD: 4 SERVINGS (SERVING SIZE: ABOUT 1 CUP).**

PER SERVING: Calories 168; Fat 5.6g (sat 0.8g, mono 3.8g, poly 0.9g); Protein 1.2g; Carb 32.2g; Fiber 1.2g; Chol 0mg; Iron 0.6mg; Sodium 151mg; Calc 17mg

BLACKBERRY BUTTERMILK SHERBET

PointsPlus value per serving: 3

PREP: 8 minutes ■ **COOK:** 5 minutes
■ **OTHER:** 3 hours and 30 minutes

This is a great base recipe to try with other fresh seasonal berries. You can substitute strawberries, blueberries, or raspberries for the blackberries in this sherbet, or try a combination of berries.

>   3 cups blackberries
> ¾ cup superfine sugar, divided
> 1 tablespoon water
> 2 cups low-fat buttermilk

1. Combine blackberries, ¼ cup sugar, and 1 tablespoon water in a medium saucepan. Bring to a boil; cook 4 minutes or until sugar dissolves, stirring occasionally. Pour blackberry mixture through a sieve into a bowl, pressing with the back of a spoon to remove as much liquid as possible; discard solids. Cool juice mixture completely. Cover and chill 2 hours.
2. Combine juice mixture, remaining ½ cup sugar, and buttermilk. Pour mixture into the freezer can of an ice-cream freezer; freeze according to manufacturer's instructions. Spoon ice cream into a freezer-safe container; cover and freeze 1 hour or until firm. **YIELD: 8 SERVINGS (SERVING SIZE: ½ CUP).**

PER SERVING: Calories 124; Fat 0.9g (sat 0.4g, mono 0.2g, poly 0.2g); Protein 3g; Carb 27.3g; Fiber 2.7g; Chol 4mg; Iron 0.3mg; Sodium 68mg; Calc 78mg

	MONDAY	TUESDAY	WEDNESDAY	THURSDAY
BREAKFAST	**grits,** 1 cup **egg,** 1 large scrambled **vanilla fat-free Greek yogurt,** 1 (6-ounce) carton **grapefruit sections,** 1 cup **light butter,** 2 teaspoons	**wheat bran flakes cereal with raisins,** ¾ cup **sliced strawberries,** 1 cup **fat-free milk,** 1 cup **light orange juice,** 1 cup	**Southwest Breakfast Wrap** (Whisk together 1 large egg, 1 large egg white, and 1 slice lean deli ham, cubed; scramble egg mixture in hot skillet. Spoon eggs down center of 1 warm [7-inch] whole-wheat tortilla; top with 2 tablespoons each of shredded reduced-fat Mexican blend cheese and salsa. Roll up burrito-style. - *PointsPlus* value per serving: 7) **banana,** 1 small **fat-free milk,** 1 cup	**Garlic Cheese Grits** (Stir 2 tablespoons reduced-fat shredded sharp cheddar cheese and a dash of garlic salt into 1 cup hot cooked grits. - *PointsPlus* value per serving: 6) **blueberries,** 1 cup **pomegranate fat-free Greek yogurt,** 1(6-ounce) carton
LUNCH	**Beef and Pepper Jack Sandwich** (Spread 1 teaspoon each of light mayonnaise and Dijon mustard over 1 slice toasted whole-wheat high-fiber bread. Top with 2 ounces lean deli roast beef and 1 ounce reduced-fat Monterey Jack cheese with jalapeño peppers. Broil until melted; top with tomato slice, lettuce, and additional toasted bread slice. - *PointsPlus* value per serving: 8) **baby carrots,** 10 **clementines,** 2	**Individual Broccoli-Cheddar Quiches,** 1 serving, page 85 **orange sections,** 1 cup **fat-free milk,** 1 cup	**chicken tortilla soup,** 2 cups canned **corn bread,** 1 (2-inch) square **coleslaw,** ½ cup **pear,** 1 medium	**chicken carbonara,** 1 low-fat frozen entrée **Fruit and Nut Tossed Salad,** 1 serving, page 114
DINNER	**Baked Honey Mustard Chicken Tenders,** 1 serving, page 103 **mashed potatoes,** ½ cup **steamed broccoli and carrots,** 1 cup **sliced strawberries,** 1 cup **fat-free milk,** 1 cup	**broiled flank steak, lean and trimmed,** 4 ounces **baked sweet potato,** 1 large **Sautéed Spinach with Almonds and Golden Raisins,** 1 serving, page 153	**grilled tuna steak,** 6 ounces **Goat Cheese Spinach Salad** (Combine 2 cups baby spinach leaves and 6 cherry tomatoes. Top with 2 tablespoons each of crumbled goat cheese and olive oil vinaigrette. - *PointsPlus* value per serving: 3) **whole-wheat French roll,** 1	**Smoked BBQ Tofu Pizza,** 1 serving, page 82 **mixed salad greens,** 2 cups **light balsamic vinaigrette,** 2 tablespoons **fruit salad,** 1 cup
SNACK	**Quick S'more Sandwich** (Spread 2 tablespoons marshmallow creme over 1 graham cracker sheet; sprinkle with 1 tablespoon semisweet chocolate minichips, and top with additional graham cracker sheet. - *PointsPlus* value per serving: 6)	**multigrain rice cakes,** 2 **light creamy cheese wedges,** 2	**fat-free cottage cheese,** 1 cup **pineapple chunks,** 1 cup	**Cinnamon Sugar Popovers,** 1 serving, page 32 **fat-free milk,** 1 cup
PointsPlus **VALUE**	**Total *PointsPlus* value for the day: 35**	**Total *PointsPlus* value for the day: 32**	**Total *PointsPlus* value for the day: 36**	**Total *PointsPlus* value for the day: 34**

One day's menu provides at least two servings of dairy and at least five servings of fruits and/or vegetables.

	FRIDAY	SATURDAY	SUNDAY
BREAKFAST	wheat bran flakes cereal with raisins, ¾ cup fat-free milk, 1 cup honeydew melon cubes, 1 cup light orange juice, 1 cup	Blueberry-Banana Smoothie (Combine 1 small banana, 1 [6-ounce] carton blueberry fat-free Greek yogurt, ½ cup blueberries, and ¼ cup light orange juice; process in blender until smooth. - *PointsPlus* value per serving: 4)	wheat bran flakes cereal with raisins, ¾ cup fat-free milk, 1 cup sliced strawberries, 1 cup
LUNCH	Open-Faced Naan Quesadillas, 2 servings, page 23 baby carrots, 10 strawberry fat-free Greek yogurt, 1 (6-ounce) carton	grilled chicken sandwich, 1 fast food with no mayonnaise lettuce leaf and tomato slice, 1 each French fries, 1 small fast food fruit cup, 1 fast food fat-free milk, 1 cup	Open-Faced Peanut Butter-Banana Sandwich (Spread 2 tablespoons reduced-fat peanut butter over 1 slice high-fiber bread. Top with ½ banana, sliced. Drizzle with 1 tablespoon honey. - *PointsPlus* value per serving: 8) fat-free milk, 1 cup grapes, 1 cup
DINNER	baked teriyaki turkey tenderloin, 4 ounces steamed brown rice, 1 cup Smoky-Spicy Roasted Asparagus, 1 serving, page 146	Spaghetti Sauce with Meat and Spinach (Add 2 ounces browned and drained lean ground beef and 1 cup torn spinach leaves to 1 cup tomato-basil pasta sauce; simmer until warm and spinach is slightly wilted. - *PointsPlus* value per serving: 4) whole-wheat spaghetti, 1 cup steamed green beans, 1 cup	Homestyle Fish Sticks, 1 serving, page 67 fresh tomato slices, 2 Broccoli Pecan Slaw with Mustard Dressing, 1 serving, page 119 corn bread, 1 (2-inch) square
SNACK	mixed raw vegetables (such as carrots, bell peppers, and cucumbers), 1 cup hummus, ⅓ cup pita round, 1 small, cut into wedges	"Fried" Cherry Pies, 1 serving, page 40	cookies and cream light ice cream, 1 cup
PointsPlus VALUE	Total *PointsPlus* value for the day: 34	Total *PointsPlus* value for the day: 31	Total *PointsPlus* value for the day: 33

WEEK 1

	MONDAY	TUESDAY	WEDNESDAY	THURSDAY
BREAKFAST	**poached egg,** 1 large **whole-wheat high-fiber toast,** 2 slices **all-fruit spread,** 1½ tablespoons	**Banana-Honey Oatmeal** (Stir 1 small banana, diced, and 1 tablespoon honey into 1 cup hot cooked oatmeal. - *PointsPlus* value per serving: 6) **fat-free milk,** 1 cup	**hard-cooked egg,** 1 large **whole-wheat high-fiber toast,** 1 slice **turkey bacon,** 3 slices **blueberries,** 1 cup	**Cranberry-Almond Oatmeal** (Stir 2 tablespoons dried cranberries and 1 tablespoon slivered almonds into 1 cup hot cooked oatmeal. - *PointsPlus* value per serving: 7) **light orange juice,** 1 cup
LUNCH	**spinach and mushroom pizza,** 1 low-fat frozen entrée **Berry Ginger Salad,** 1 serving, page 112 **fat-free milk,** 1 cup	**Ham and Spinach Frittata** (Sauté ¼ cup onion in 1 teaspoon olive oil in a small skillet; add 1 cup spinach, stirring until spinach wilts. Whisk together 1 large egg, 3 large egg whites, and a dash of salt; stir in 1 ounce chopped lean deli ham and 3 tablespoons reduced-fat shredded cheddar cheese. Pour egg mixture into pan; cook until set. - *PointsPlus* value per serving: 7) **tomato slices,** 4 **raspberries,** 1 cup	**BBQ Chicken Twice-Baked Potatoes,** 1 serving, page 106 **plums,** 2 small **fat-free milk,** 1 cup	**Turkey BLT** (Spread 2 teaspoons fat-free mayonnaise over 2 slices whole-wheat high-fiber bread. Place 2 ounces sliced deli turkey; 2 lettuce leaves; 2 tomato slices; and 2 slices cooked turkey bacon, halved, on 1 bread slice. Top with remaining bread slice. - *PointsPlus* value per serving: 6) **baked potato chips,** 1 ounce **cucumber slices,** 1 cup **pineapple fat-free Greek yogurt,** 1 (6-ounce) carton
DINNER	**Beef Stir-Fry Rice Bowl,** 1 serving, page 88 **pineapple chunks,** 1 cup **honey fat-free Greek yogurt,** 1 (6-ounce) carton	**rotisserie chicken breast,** 3 ounces with skin removed **New Potatoes with Basil** (Steam 2 to 3 small red potatoes [5 ounces]; toss with 2 teaspoons light butter, 1 teaspoon finely chopped fresh basil, and a dash of salt. - *PointsPlus* value per serving: 3) **Spicy Greens and Beans,** 1 serving, page 151	**Grilled Vegetable Tacos,** 1 serving, page 78 **Tropical Fruit Toss** (Combine ⅓ cup each of orange sections, grapefruit sections, grapes, and pineapple chunks with 1 tablespoon shredded coconut; toss to combine. - *PointsPlus* value per serving: 1)	**Grilled Salmon Panzanella,** 1 serving, page 117 **grapes,** 1 cup
SNACK	**gingersnaps,** 4 **unsweetened applesauce,** 1 cup	**fat-free cottage cheese,** 1 cup **sliced strawberries,** 1 cup **graham crackers,** 2 sheets	**Chocolate Milkshake** (Combine 1 cup chocolate light ice cream, ½ cup fat-free milk, 2 tablespoons sugar-free chocolate syrup, and ice cubes; process until smooth. - *PointsPlus* value per serving: 8)	**Caramel-Brickle Pie,** 1 serving, page 40 **fat-free milk,** 1 cup
PointsPlus VALUE	**Total *PointsPlus* value for the day: 31**	**Total *PointsPlus* value for the day: 30**	**Total *PointsPlus* value for the day: 33**	**Total *PointsPlus* value for the day: 36**

One day's menu provides at least two servings of dairy and at least five servings of fruits and/or vegetables.

	FRIDAY	SATURDAY	SUNDAY
BREAKFAST	**whole-wheat high-fiber toast,** 1 slice **peanut butter,** 1 tablespoon **fat-free milk,** 1 cup **blueberries,** 1 cup	**oatmeal,** 1 cup cooked **brown sugar,** 1 tablespoon **strawberry fat-free Greek yogurt,** 1 (6-ounce) carton **light orange juice,** 1 cup	**scrambled eggs,** 1 large egg and 2 large egg whites **turkey bacon,** 2 slices **light orange juice,** 1 cup
LUNCH	**beef soft taco,** 1 fast food with lettuce and tomato **apple,** 1 medium **fat-free milk,** 1 cup **carrot and celery sticks,** 1 cup	**Turkey-Cheese Melt** (Top 1 slice whole-wheat high-fiber bread with 2 ounces lean deli turkey, 1 [¾-ounce] slice reduced-fat Monterey Jack cheese with jalapeño peppers, and 1 bread slice. Spread 1 teaspoon light butter over each side of sandwich. Cook sandwich in a nonstick skillet over medium heat until browned on both sides and cheese melts. - **PointsPlus value per serving: 7)** **tomato slices,** 2 **baked potato chips,** 1 ounce **orange,** 1 medium	**chicken noodle soup,** 1½ cups canned **whole-wheat crackers,** 3 **coleslaw,** ½ cup **watermelon cubes,** 1 cup **fat-free milk,** 1 cup
DINNER	**Sesame-Honey Shrimp,** 1 serving, page 76 **steamed brown rice,** 1 cup **steamed sugar snap peas,** 1 cup	**Moroccan-Style Turkey Cutlets,** 1 serving, page 108 **couscous,** 1 cup **steamed carrots,** 1 cup	**Thai Pork Burgers with Mango-Mint Mayo,** 1 serving, page 122 **Roasted Potato Wedges** (Cut 2 [4-ounce] red potatoes into [1½-inch] cubes. Toss with 1 teaspoon olive oil and ⅛ teaspoon garlic salt. Roast potatoes at 450° for 40 minutes, stirring occasionally. - **PointsPlus value per serving: 5)** **steamed asparagus spears,** 12
SNACK	**whole-wheat pretzels,** 1 ounce **light creamy cheese wedges,** 2	**gingersnaps,** 2 **fat-free milk,** 1 cup	**light microwave popcorn,** 3 cups **cherries,** 1 cup **honey fat-free Greek yogurt,** 1 (6-ounce) carton
PointsPlus VALUE	**Total PointsPlus value for the day: 35**	**Total PointsPlus value for the day: 34**	**Total PointsPlus value for the day: 38**

WEEK 2

	MONDAY	TUESDAY	WEDNESDAY	THURSDAY
BREAKFAST	**low-fat whole-wheat waffles,** 2 frozen **light syrup,** 2 tablespoons **fat-free milk,** 1 cup **grapefruit,** 1 half	**bran flakes,** 1 cup **banana,** 1 small **fat-free milk,** 1 cup	**Strawberries and Cream Waffle** (Top 2 toasted low-fat whole-wheat waffles with ½ cup each of vanilla fat-free Greek yogurt and sliced strawberries. Drizzle with 1 tablespoon honey. - **PointsPlus** value per serving: 8) **fat-free milk,** 1 cup	**low-fat whole-wheat waffles,** 2 frozen **light syrup,** 2 tablespoons **fat-free milk,** 1 cup
LUNCH	**Hot Beef and Pepper Wrap** (Place 2 ounces lean deli roast beef in center of 1 [7-inch] whole-wheat tortilla. Top with ¼ cup roasted red bell pepper strips and 1 [0.75-ounce] slice reduced-fat provolone cheese. Heat 20 seconds in microwave until cheese melts; roll up tightly. - **PointsPlus** value per serving: 6) **apple,** 1 medium **peach fat-free Greek yogurt,** 1 (6-ounce) carton	**Greek Salad Pizza** (Toss together 1 cup salad greens, 2 tablespoons each of diced tomato, crumbled feta, and light Greek dressing. Spread 3 tablespoons hummus over 1 side of a pita round. Top hummus with lettuce mixture. - **PointsPlus** value per serving: 10) **orange,** 1 medium	**chicken and wild rice soup,** 1 cup canned **whole-wheat crackers,** 6 **deli coleslaw,** ½ cup **pear,** 1 medium	**Tex-Mex Fish Tacos,** 1 serving, page 70 **orange,** 1 medium **baked tortilla chips,** 12 **Grilled Corn, Tomatillo, and Avocado Salsa,** 1 serving, page 18
DINNER	**Pan-Seared Scallops with Succotash,** 1 serving, page 73 **steamed green beans,** 1 cup **grapes,** 1 cup **whole-wheat French roll,** 1 **light butter,** 2 teaspoons	**grilled sirloin steak, trimmed,** 3 ounces **Orzo with Spinach and Tomatoes,** 1 serving, page 154 **Zucchini Ribbons with Goat Cheese,** 1 serving, page 154	**Fettuccine Alfredo with Asparagus,** 1 serving, page 83 **steamed baby carrots,** 1 cup **whole-grain French bread,** 1 ounce **fat-free milk,** 1 cup	**Chicken Cordon Bleu Spirals,** 1 serving, page 99 **mashed potatoes,** ½ cup **steamed broccoli,** 1 cup **grapes,** 1 cup
SNACK	**mixed raw vegetables, such as** broccoli florets, carrots, and cucumbers, 1 cup **hummus,** ¼ cup	**Double Brownie Cheesecake Torte,** 1 serving, page 38 **fat-free milk,** 1 cup	**whole-wheat pretzels,** 1 ounce **part-skim mozzarella stick,** 1	**black cherry fat-free Greek yogurt,** 1 (6-ounce) carton **sliced strawberries,** 1 cup
PointsPlus VALUE	**Total PointsPlus value for the day: 32**	**Total PointsPlus value for the day: 34**	**Total PointsPlus value for the day: 36**	**Total PointsPlus value for the day: 35**

One day's menu provides at least two servings of dairy and at least five servings of fruits and/or vegetables.

	FRIDAY	SATURDAY	SUNDAY	
BREAKFAST	bran flakes, 1 cup sliced strawberries, 1 cup fat-free milk, 1 cup light orange juice, 1 cup	low-fat whole-wheat waffle, 1 frozen light syrup, 2 tablespoons turkey bacon, 2 slices light orange juice, 1 cup	Greek Yogurt Parfait (Top 1 cup vanilla fat-free Greek yogurt with ½ cup mixed berries and ¼ cup low-fat granola. Drizzle with 1 tablespoon honey. - *PointsPlus* value per serving: 7)	
LUNCH	Tuna Salad Wrap (Combine ½ cup drained canned tuna in water with 2 tablespoons chopped celery, 1 tablespoon reduced-fat mayonnaise, 1 teaspoon Dijon mustard, and a dash each of salt and pepper. Place lettuce leaves down center of 1 [7-inch] whole-wheat tortilla; top with tuna mixture and wrap tightly. - *PointsPlus* value per serving: 7) pear, 1 medium baby carrots, 10	hamburger, 1 small fast food lettuce leaf and tomato slice, 1 each French fries, 1 small fast food fat-free milk, 1 cup apple, 1 medium	Greek Tempeh Roll-Ups, 1 serving, page 81 watermelon cubes, 1 cup garlic-and-herb pita chips, 1 ounce fat-free milk, 1 cup	
DINNER	grilled or baked center-cut boneless pork chop, 3 ounces Red Rice with Bacon and Okra, 1 serving, page 154 Seven-Layer Salad, 1 serving, page 115	Black Bean and Corn Soup, 1 serving, page 159 Avocado, Orange, and Jicama Chopped Salad, 1 serving, page 112 honey fat-free Greek yogurt, 1 (6-ounce) carton	turkey burger, 1 (3-ounce) cooked patty made with 10%-fat ground beef lite wheat hamburger bun, 1 lettuce leaf and tomato slice, 1 each German Potato Salad, 1 serving, page 120	
SNACK	Caramel-Apple Crisp, 1 serving, page 36 fat-free milk, 1 cup	graham crackers, 2 sheets blueberries, 1 cup	raspberries, 1 cup hummus, ¼ cup baby carrots and cucumber slices, 1 cup	
***PointsPlus* VALUE**	Total *PointsPlus* value for the day: 32	Total *PointsPlus* value for the day: 36	Total *PointsPlus* value for the day: 32	

7-Day Menu Planner

WEEK 3

181

	MONDAY	TUESDAY	WEDNESDAY	THURSDAY
BREAKFAST	**light whole-wheat English muffin,** 1 toasted **peanut butter,** 1 tablespoon **mixed fruit salad,** 1 cup **fat-free milk,** 1 cup	**farina,** 1 cup cooked **peach,** 1 **black cherry fat-free Greek yogurt,** 1 (6-ounce) carton **light orange juice,** 1 cup	**Egg and Cheese Sandwich** (Split and toast 1 light whole-wheat English muffin. Place 1 large poached egg on bottom half of muffin; top with 1 [0.75-ounce] slice reduced-fat cheddar cheese and top half of muffin. - *PointsPlus* value per serving: 7) **grapefruit,** 1 half	**light whole-wheat English muffin,** 1 toasted **hard-cooked eggs,** 2 large **raspberries,** 1 cup **all-fruit spread,** 1½ tablespoons
LUNCH	**Loaded Chicken Nachos,** 1 serving, page 105 **pineapple chunks,** 1 cup **pomegranate fat-free Greek yogurt,** 1 (6-ounce) carton	**Turkey and Cheese Spud** (Cut a large [7-ounce] cooked baked potato in half; top with 2 ounces shredded lean deli turkey, ⅓ cup reduced-fat sharp cheddar cheese, 2 tablespoons diced tomato, and 1 tablespoon chopped green onions. Dollop with 2 tablespoons reduced-fat sour cream. - *PointsPlus* value per serving: 8) **cherries,** 1 cup **fat-free milk,** 1 cup	**macaroni and cheese,** 1 low-fat frozen entrée **cucumber slices,** ½ cup **unsweetened applesauce,** 1 cup **fat-free milk,** 1 cup	**Individual Supreme Pizza** (Spread 2 tablespoons tomato-basil pasta sauce over 1 side of a whole-wheat pita round, leaving a ½-inch border around edge. Top with 2 tablespoons each of chopped bell pepper and sliced mushrooms, 6 slices turkey pepperoni, and ⅓ cup shredded reduced-fat mozzarella cheese; broil until cheese melts. - *PointsPlus* value per serving: 6) **honeydew melon cubes,** 1 cup **fat-free milk,** 1 cup
DINNER	**grilled salmon fillet,** 5 ounces **Parmesan-Basil Squash** (Combine 1 cup spaghetti squash strands with 2 teaspoons each of light butter and finely chopped basil, and ¼ teaspoon salt. Toss well and sprinkle with 1 tablespoon grated Parmesan cheese. - *PointsPlus* value per serving: 2) **grilled asparagus spears,** 12	**Black Bean and Avocado Quesadillas,** 1 serving, page 79 **shredded lettuce and diced tomato,** 1 cup **Honey-Walnut Yogurt** (Top ½ cup plain fat-free Greek yogurt with 1 tablespoon each of honey and chopped walnuts. - *PointsPlus* value per serving: 5)	**Pork Medallions with Sautéed Apples,** 1 serving, page 93 **baked sweet potato,** 1 large **Roasted Brussels Sprouts with Browned Butter Walnuts,** 1 serving, page 148	**Easy Turkey Chili Mac,** 1 serving, page 109 **mixed salad greens,** 2 cups **reduced-fat Italian dressing,** 2 tablespoons **fat-free milk,** 1 cup
SNACK	**Lemon Cornmeal Biscotti,** 1 serving, page 48 **Mocha Coffee** (Combine 1 cup hot brewed coffee, 1 tablespoon unsweetened cocoa powder, 1 tablespoon sugar, and 2 tablespoons fat-free milk. - *PointsPlus* value per serving: 2)	**baby carrots,** 10 **hummus,** ¼ cup	**apple,** 1 medium **peanut butter,** 1 tablespoon **fat-free milk,** 1 cup	**Smoky Herbed Snack Mix,** 1 serving, page 24 **Fresh Peach Iced Tea,** 1 serving, page 26
PointsPlus VALUE	**Total *PointsPlus* value for the day: 32**	**Total *PointsPlus* value for the day: 33**	**Total *PointsPlus* value for the day: 35**	**Total *PointsPlus* value for the day: 31**

One day's menu provides at least two servings of dairy and at least five servings of fruits and/or vegetables.

	FRIDAY	**SATURDAY**	**SUNDAY**	
BREAKFAST	**Strawberry-Banana Smoothie** (Combine 1 small banana, 1 (6-ounce) container strawberry fat-free Greek yogurt, ½ cup sliced strawberries, and ¼ cup light orange juice in blender; process until smooth. - *PointsPlus* value per serving: 4)	**Breakfast PB&J** (Spread 1½ tablespoons each of peanut butter and strawberry all-fruit spread over cut side of 1 half of toasted whole-wheat English muffin; top with remaining muffin half. - *PointsPlus* value per serving: 7) **fat-free milk**, 1 cup	**farina**, 1 cup cooked **scrambled eggs**, 1 large egg and 2 large egg whites **light orange juice**, 1 cup **blueberry fat-free Greek yogurt**, 1 (6-ounce) carton	
LUNCH	**Minestrone soup**, 2 cups canned **garlic-and-herb pita chips**, 1 ounce **Blueberry Spinach Salad with Poppy Seed Dressing**, 1 serving, page 113 **fat-free milk**, 1 cup	**Apple-Pecan Chicken Salad**, 1 serving, page 118 **whole-wheat crackers**, 6 **baby carrots**, 10 **blueberry fat-free Greek yogurt**, 1 (6-ounce) carton	**Black Bean–Salsa Wrap** (Spread ½ cup fat-free refried black beans down center of 1 [7-inch] whole-wheat tortilla; top with 3 tablespoons reduced-fat shredded cheddar cheese. Microwave at HIGH 20 seconds; roll up and serve with salsa. - *PointsPlus* value per serving: 6) **watermelon cubes**, 1 cup **cucumber slices**, 1 cup **fat-free milk**, 1 cup	
DINNER	**Halibut with Herbs and Goat Cheese**, 1 serving, page 67 **Parmesan couscous**, 1 cup **steamed carrots and sugar snap peas**, 1 cup	**Oven-Baked Omelet with Arugula, Goat Cheese, and Mushrooms**, 1 serving, page 86 **salad greens**, 2 cups **light balsamic vinaigrette dressing**, 2 tablespoons **whole-wheat French bread**, 2 ounces **sliced strawberries**, 1 cup	**Lamb-Tabbouleh Meat Loaf**, 1 serving, page 92 **couscous**, 1 cup **Braised Eggplant with Basil and Tomatoes**, 1 serving, page 150	
SNACK	**light microwave popcorn**, 3 cups **pear**, 1 medium	**grapes**, 1 cup **dry-roasted almonds**, ¼ cup	**plums**, 2 small **light microwave popcorn**, 3 cups **part-skim mozzarella stick**, 1	
PointsPlus VALUE	Total *PointsPlus* value for the day: 33	Total *PointsPlus* value for the day: 34	Total *PointsPlus* value for the day: 34	

WEEK 4

GENERAL RECIPE INDEX

PointsPlus® Value Index

10 SIMPLE SIDE DISHES

Vegetable	Servings	Preparation	Cooking Instructions
Asparagus	3 to 4 per pound	Snap off tough ends. Remove scales, if desired.	To steam: Cook, covered, on a rack above boiling water 2 to 3 minutes. To boil: Cook, covered, in a small amount of boiling water 2 to 3 minutes or until crisp-tender.
Broccoli	3 to 4 per pound	Remove outer leaves and tough ends of lower stalks. Wash; cut into spears.	To steam: Cook, covered, on a rack above boiling water 5 to 7 minutes or until crisp-tender.
Carrots	4 per pound	Scrape; remove ends, and rinse. Leave tiny carrots whole; slice large carrots.	To steam: Cook, covered, on a rack above boiling water 8 to 10 minutes or until crisp-tender. To boil: Cook, covered, in a small amount of boiling water 8 to 10 minutes or until crisp-tender.
Cauliflower	4 per medium head	Remove outer leaves and stalk. Wash. Break into florets.	To steam: Cook, covered, on a rack above boiling water 5 to 7 minutes or until crisp-tender.
Corn	4 per 4 large ears	Remove husks and silks. Leave corn on the cob, or cut off kernels.	To boil: Cook, covered, in boiling water to cover 8 to 10 minutes (on cob) or in a small amount of boiling water 4 to 6 minutes (kernels).
Green beans	4 per pound	Wash; trim ends, and remove strings. Cut into 1½-inch pieces.	To steam: Cook, covered, on a rack above boiling water 5 to 7 minutes. To boil: Cook, covered, in a small amount of boiling water 5 to 7 minutes or until crisp-tender.
Potatoes	3 to 4 per pound	Scrub; peel, if desired. Leave whole, slice, or cut into chunks.	To boil: Cook, covered, in boiling water to cover 30 to 40 minutes (whole) or 15 to 20 minutes (slices or chunks). To bake: Bake at 400° for 1 hour or until done.
Snow peas	4 per pound	Wash; trim ends, and remove tough strings.	To steam: Cook, covered, on a rack above boiling water 2 to 3 minutes. Or sauté in cooking spray or 1 teaspoon oil over medium-high heat 3 to 4 minutes or until crisp-tender.
Squash, summer	3 to 4 per pound	Wash; trim ends, and slice or chop.	To steam: Cook, covered, on a rack above boiling water 6 to 8 minutes. To boil: Cook, covered, in a small amount of boiling water 6 to 8 minutes or until crisp-tender.
Squash, winter (including acorn, butternut, and buttercup)	2 per pound	Rinse; cut in half, and remove all seeds. Leave in halves to bake, or peel and cube to boil.	To boil: Cook cubes, covered, in boiling water 20 to 25 minutes. To bake: Place halves, cut sides down, in a shallow baking dish; add ½ inch water. Bake, uncovered, at 375° for 30 minutes. Turn and season, or fill; bake an additional 20 to 30 minutes or until tender.